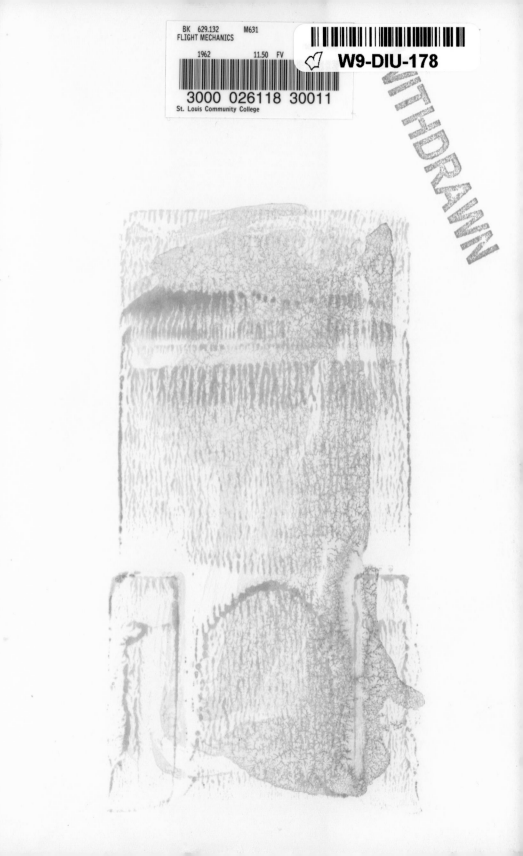

FLIGHT MECHANICS

Volume 1

THEORY OF FLIGHT PATHS

This book is in the

ADDISON-WESLEY SERIES IN THE
ENGINEERING SCIENCES

SPACE SCIENCE AND TECHNOLOGY

―――――――――

Consulting Editors

Howard W. Emmons   S. S. Penner
James C. Fletcher

FLIGHT MECHANICS

Volume 1

THEORY OF FLIGHT PATHS

---

by

ANGELO MIELE

Director of Astrodynamics and Flight Mechanics
Boeing Scientific Research Laboratories

and

Visiting Professor of Aeronautical Engineering
University of Washington

ADDISON-WESLEY PUBLISHING COMPANY, INC.

READING, MASSACHUSETTS · PALO ALTO · LONDON

CONTENTS

PREFACE ix

PART I. FOUNDATIONS

Introduction to Part I 3

CHAPTER 1. ELEMENTS OF KINEMATICS

1. Introduction 5
2. Elements of differential geometry 5
3. Motion of a point with respect to a reference frame 8
4. Angular motion of one reference frame with respect to another . 9
5. Rigid body 12
6. Relative motion 14

CHAPTER 2. ELEMENTS OF DYNAMICS

1. Introduction 18
2. Material point 18
3. Material system 19
4. Rigid body 21
5. Spinning rotor mounted on a rigid body 22
6. Variable mass systems 23

CHAPTER 3. EQUATIONS OF MOTION FOR ROCKET AND JET-POWERED
VEHICLES

1. Introduction 27
2. Rocket-powered vehicle 28
3. Rocket in flight 32
4. Stability and control analyses versus trajectory analyses. . . . 34
5. Simplified equation for trajectory analyses 35
6. Miscellaneous topics 36

CHAPTER 4. SCALAR EQUATIONS FOR FLIGHT OVER A FLAT EARTH

1. Introduction 42
2. Basic coordinate systems 42
3. Angular relationships 44
4. Evolutory velocity 46
5. Kinematic relationships 48
6. Dynamic relationships 49
7. Aircraft and engine characteristics 50
8. General discussion and particular cases 51

CHAPTER 5. SCALAR EQUATIONS FOR FLIGHT OVER A SPHERICAL EARTH

1. Introduction 58
2. Basic coordinate systems 58
3. Angular relationships 60
4. Angular velocities 62
5. Kinematic relationships 64
6. Dynamic relationships 64
7. Discussion 66

CHAPTER 6. AERODYNAMIC FORCES, BY K. E. VAN EVERY AND A. MIELE

1. Introduction 69
2. Continuum flow 72
3. Low subsonic aircraft 78
4. High subsonic–low transonic aircraft 80
5. Supersonic aircraft 83
6. Hypersonic vehicles 87
7. Free molecular flow 90
8. Aerodynamic components in a specified atmosphere 92

CHAPTER 7. PROPULSION SYSTEMS, BY J. W. CONNORS AND J. GREY

1. Introduction 95
2. Rocket 95
3. Single-flow, air-breathing propulsion systems 100
4. Multiflow propulsion systems 107
5. Hybrid propulsion systems 108
6. Performance in a specified atmosphere 109

PART II. QUASI-STEADY FLIGHT OVER A FLAT EARTH

Introduction to Part II 115

CHAPTER 8. INTRODUCTION TO THE PROBLEM OF AIRCRAFT
PERFORMANCE

1. Introduction 117
2. Flight in a vertical plane 118
3. Gliding flight 120
4. Level flight 124
5. Quasi-level flight 128
6. Climbing flight 132
7. Kinetic energy correction 137
8. Flight in a horizontal plane 139
9. Flight limitations 143
10. Conclusions and introduction to the following chapters 146

CHAPTER 9. PERFORMANCE OF AN AIRCRAFT WITH A PARABOLIC POLAR

1. Introduction 149

2. Flight in a vertical plane 149
3. Gliding flight 152
4. Level flight 157
5. Quasi-level flight 167
6. Climbing flight 171
7. Kinetic energy correction 177
8. Flight in a horizontal plane 179
9. Performance in a specified atmosphere 183
10. Comparison of constant thrust and constant power aircraft . . . 184

CHAPTER 10. PERFORMANCE OF AN AIRCRAFT WITH AN ARBITRARY POLAR

1. Introduction 190
2. Flight in a vertical plane 190
3. Gliding flight 192
4. Level flight 195
5. Quasi-level flight 198
6. Climbing flight 200
7. Flight in a horizontal plane 202
8. Performance in a specified atmosphere 206
9. Parabolic polar 207
10. Comparison of constant thrust and constant power aircraft . . . 207

CHAPTER 11. AIRCRAFT PERFORMANCE AT HIGH SUBSONIC,
TRANSONIC, AND SUPERSONIC SPEEDS

1. Introduction 213
2. Flight in a vertical plane 215
3. Gliding flight 219
4. Level flight 222
5. Quasi-level flight 227
6. Climbing flight 233
7. Flight in a horizontal plane 238
8. Performance for a given rotor speed in a specified atmosphere . . 240
9. Performance of an aircraft with an arbitrary polar 243
10. Supersonic aircraft performance 245

PART III. NONSTEADY FLIGHT OVER A FLAT EARTH

Introduction to Part III 255

CHAPTER 12. NONSTEADY AIRCRAFT PERFORMANCE

1. Introduction 257
2. Glide at constant altitude 258
3. Glide at constant angle of attack 262
4. Acceleration at constant altitude 264
5. Conservative paths 268
6. Take-off and landing 274

CHAPTER 13. PERFORMANCE OF HYPERVELOCITY VEHICLES

1. Introduction 284
2. Ascent of a sounding rocket 285
3. Reentry of a ballistic missile 288
4. Reentry of a glide vehicle 296
5. Reentry of a skip vehicle 297

CHAPTER 14. AERODYNAMIC HEATING OF HYPERVELOCITY VEHICLES,
BY M. BLOOM AND A. MIELE

1. Introduction 308
2. Mechanisms of heat flow into the vehicle 308
3. Vehicle protection and cooling 313
4. Reentry of a ballistic missile 315
5. Reentry of a glide vehicle 323
6. Reentry of a skip vehicle 325

CHAPTER 15. ROCKET PERFORMANCE IN A VACUUM

1. Introduction 335
2. Vertically ascending paths 336
3. Gravity turn trajectories 343
4. Trajectories flown with constant thrust inclination with respect to
the horizon 348

CHAPTER 16. MULTISTAGE ROCKETS IN A VACUUM

1. Introduction 358
2. Definitions pertinent to single-stage rockets 358
3. Performance limitations of single-stage rockets 359
4. Definitions pertinent to multistage rockets 361
5. Analysis of multistage rockets neglecting gravity 365
6. Analysis of multistage rockets including gravity 368

CHAPTER 17. ROCKET PERFORMANCE WITH AERODYNAMIC FORCES
INCLUDED

1. Introduction 382
2. Short range nonlifting missiles 383
3. Ascent of a sounding rocket 387
4. Some approximate performance of rocket-powered aircraft . . . 390

APPENDIX. PROPERTIES OF THE ATMOSPHERE

1. Introduction 399
2. Fundamental equations 399
3. Model atmosphere 400
4. Engineering approximations 402

AUTHOR INDEX 407

SUBJECT INDEX 409

PREFACE

This book, entitled *Flight Mechanics*, is an outgrowth of the lessons on the theory of flight taught by the author at the Polytechnic Institute of Brooklyn, Purdue University, and the University of Washington. Its principal topic is the analysis of trajectories of aircraft, missiles, satellites, and spaceships subjected to gravitational forces (uniform or central), aerodynamic forces, and thrust. Its main purpose is to illustrate the wealth of new problems in applied mathematics which have arisen in the last two decades and to show that the solution of these problems can be of considerable assistance in vehicle design.

Because of the extent and complexity of the subject matter, *Flight Mechanics* is divided into three volumes. Volume 1 is concerned with foundations plus flight in a uniform gravitational field and contains the following major parts: (a) general principles of kinematics, dynamics, aerodynamics, and propulsion which are necessary to the analytical development of the theory of the flight paths over either a flat or spherical Earth; (b) quasi-steady flight over a flat Earth with applications to aircraft powered by turbojet, turbofan, and ramjet engines flying at subsonic, transonic, and supersonic speeds; and (c) nonsteady flight over a flat Earth with applications to rocket vehicles operating in the hypervelocity domain. Volume 2, now in preparation, is concerned with the theory of the optimum flight paths and contains the following major divisions: method of Lagrange multipliers, extremization of linear integrals by Green's theorem, indirect methods of the Calculus of Variations, direct methods, and numerical methods. In each of these divisions, aircraft and rocket applications relative to flight in a uniform gravitational field are presented. Finally, Volume 3, also in preparation, deals with flight in a central gravitational field. The following classes of flight paths are investigated with both classical methods and variational methods: trajectories of hypervelocity vehicles, trajectories of space vehicles reentering the atmosphere at elliptic, parabolic, and hyperbolic velocities, and space trajectories.

A characteristic feature of this book is that it makes more extensive use of advanced mathematical techniques (vectors, differential equations, matrices, Lagrange multipliers, theory of linear integrals by Green's theorem, numerical methods, and indirect methods of the Calculus of Variations) than other books in the same area of problems published in the past. It is a fact that the most significant advance of the last ten years has been the utilization of variational methods; the vista is now beginning to widen on this promising application, and it seems possible that, with the progress of high-speed digital computing machines, the Calculus of Variations will become the standard, rather than the specialized, tool of optimum performance analyses of aircraft and missiles. In order to achieve the greatest economy of thought, extensive use is made of dimensionless variables in the representation of physical results. Finally, with regard to the two possible points of view in engineering, the *precision approach* and the *feasibility approach*, the following position is taken. Concerning precision studies, general equations are presented which can be solved only by digital computing equipment. Nevertheless, electronic computers can never replace mathematical and physical reasoning. Analytical solutions are of great interest to the engineer, provided that the range of applicability of these solutions is clearly understood. Since the greatest conceptual advances in the engineering applications of Flight Mechanics must be expected from feasibility studies, analytical solutions are emphasized.

Flight Mechanics is a textbook for engineering students as well as a reference book for engineers. As a textbook, it is designed for graduate courses in the general area of performance analysis. However, it is the experience of the author that the material covered in the first volume can be taught also at the senior level. The exercises at the end of each chapter are all of the analytical type and are conceived as an integral part of the text. While they are intended to demonstrate the use of the techniques outlined in the text, they are essentially employed as a means to include additional results and equations which would have made the basic text unwieldy. For the engineer who uses *Flight Mechanics* as a reference book, applications are presented in a general form, since, at the present rate of progress of the aeronautical and astronautical sciences, a handbook-type of volume would become obsolete in a relatively short time. Where possible, design considerations are included; however, as a general rule, basic understanding is emphasized while design is not. In fact, the design of aircraft, missile, satellite, and spaceship systems is partially a science and mostly an art; it is a compromise of so many contrasting requirements, that it is simply impossible to obtain clear-cut conclusions which are unrestrictedly valid for every case and subcase.

Acknowledgments. While the present work was initiated at Purdue University, its rapid completion has been possible because of the continuing support rendered by the Boeing Scientific Research Laboratories. Particular thanks are due to its director, Mr. Guilford L. Hollingsworth, as well as to Mr. George S. Schairer, Vice-President for Research and Development, The Boeing Company.

A continuous flow of constructive criticism as well as analytical and numerical assistance have been furnished by Dr. Mateo I. Abbona and by Messrs. David G. Hull, Arthur H. Lusty, Robert E. Pritchard, and Gary R. Saaris, members of the Astrodynamics and Flight Mechanics staff at the Boeing Scientific Research Laboratories.   For their efforts the author is deeply indebted.

Mr. Kermit E. Van Every (Douglas Aircraft Company) has co-authored the chapter on Aerodynamic Forces; Professors John W. Connors (Rensselaer Polytechnic Institute) and Jerry Grey (Princeton University) have contributed the chapter on Propulsion Systems; Professor Martin H. Bloom (Polytechnic Institute of Brooklyn) has co-authored the chapter on Thermal Problems; also, Professor Robert L. Halfman (Massachusetts Institute of Technology) has contributed a critical and constructive review of an early manuscript.   Finally, several authorities in aeronautical and astronautical engineering have been consulted for particular problems; the pertinent acknowledgments are to be found in the appropriate chapters. The preparation of the drawings and the typing have been in the competent hands of Mrs. Grace Boyd and Mrs. Geneva Mortimer, respectively.

A. M.

January, 1962
Seattle, Wash.

Part I

FOUNDATIONS

INTRODUCTION TO PART I

Before specific performance problems can be analyzed, it is necessary to build a foundation and derive general equations which are valid for every problem. In this connection, the basic elements of kinematics and dynamics are reviewed in Chapters 1 and 2 and then applied in Chapter 3 to derive the equations of motion for rocket-powered vehicles as well as vehicles propelled by air-breathing jet engines. Special effort is devoted to clarifying the basic concepts of thrust and aerodynamic force.

It is well known from Classical Mechanics that the translational motion of a body is described by the equation of linear momentum while the rotational motion is governed by the equation of angular momentum. Although stability and control analyses require that the translational and rotational motions be considered simultaneously, trajectory studies can be simplified by means of engineering hypotheses whose effect is to uncouple the equation of linear momentum from the equation of angular momentum. In this connection, after the vectorial equations governing the trajectory of a vehicle in both an inertial reference frame and a reference frame rigidly associated with the Earth are established, the corresponding scalar equations are derived in Chapter 4 with reference to a uniform gravitational field and in Chapter 5 with reference to a central gravitational field. Although Volume I is concerned with the flat Earth model only, the equations pertaining to flight over a spherical Earth are included in order to make the general discussion complete.

From the analysis of Chapters 4 and 5, it is apparent that, prior to solving any specific performance problem, a considerable amount of information on the characteristics of the vehicle and the engine is needed. Consequently, the aerodynamic forces acting on the vehicle (the drag, the side force, and the lift) in both continuous flow and free-molecular flow are discussed in Chapter 6. Analogously, the main characteristics of propulsion systems (the thrust and the specific fuel consumption) are presented in Chapter 7 with emphasis on rocket engines as well as air-breathing jet engines. It must be noted that these two chapters provide only the basic information needed for the analytical development of the theory of flight paths. Thus, no attempt is made to include the systematic data which are necessary for the estimation of the aerodynamic characteristics of arbitrary configurations or the propulsive characteristics of arbitrary powerplants.

3

CHAPTER 1

ELEMENTS OF KINEMATICS

1. INTRODUCTION

In this chapter, a survey of those kinematical properties which are essential to the analytical development of the theory of flight paths is presented. First, some elements of differential geometry are reviewed, and the concepts of velocity, acceleration, angular velocity, and angular acceleration are introduced. Then, the distribution of velocities and accelerations inside a rigid body is calculated. Finally, relative motion is considered, and the theorems of composition of velocities and accelerations are derived.

2. ELEMENTS OF DIFFERENTIAL GEOMETRY

In this section, a review of some elements of differential geometry is presented, and the tangent, principal normal, and binormal vectors are introduced. To do so, an arbitrary curve C referred to a Cartesian reference system $Oxyz$ is considered; its generic point P is characterized by the curvilinear abscissa or arc length s, which is measured from an arbitrary origin on the curve (Fig. 1). The geometric properties of such a curve can be described by the scalar, parametric equations

$$x = x(s), \qquad y = y(s), \qquad z = z(s) \tag{1}$$

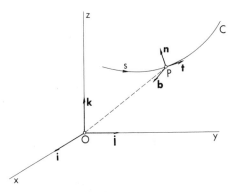

Fig. 1. Principal trihedral associated with a given curve.

where the curvilinear abscissa has been chosen to be the parameter. Consequently, if **i, j, k** are three unit vectors associated with the positive directions of the x, y, z-axes, respectively, and if the symbol

$$\mathbf{OP} = x\mathbf{i} + y\mathbf{j} + z\mathbf{k} \tag{2}$$

denotes the *position vector* (vector joining the origin of the reference frame with the point P), then the geometry of the curve can also be described by a vectorial equation having the form

$$\mathbf{OP} = \mathbf{OP}(s) \tag{3}$$

2.1 Tangent vector. By definition, the tangent vector **t** is a unit vector which is tangent to the curve C and positive when directed in the sense of the increasing curvilinear abscissa. If α, β, γ denote the three angles which this vector forms with the coordinate axes, the following relationship holds:

$$\mathbf{t} = \cos \alpha \mathbf{i} + \cos \beta \mathbf{j} + \cos \gamma \mathbf{k} \tag{4}$$

Since the direction cosines of the tangent vector can be written as

$$\cos \alpha = \frac{dx}{ds}, \qquad \cos \beta = \frac{dy}{ds}, \qquad \cos \gamma = \frac{dz}{ds} \tag{5}$$

the following result is obtained:

$$\mathbf{t} = \frac{d\mathbf{OP}}{ds} \tag{6}$$

Thus, the unit tangent vector is equal to the derivative of the position vector with respect to the curvilinear abscissa.

2.2 Osculating plane. Consider two points P and P' which are an infinitesimal distance ds apart on the curve C and the two unit vectors which are tangent to the curve at these points (Fig. 2), that is,

$$\mathbf{t}, \qquad \mathbf{t}' = \mathbf{t} + \frac{d\mathbf{t}}{ds} ds \tag{7}$$

If $\mathbf{t}''$ denotes another unit vector which is parallel to $\mathbf{t}'$ and has its origin at point P, then the two vectors $\mathbf{t}$ and $\mathbf{t}''$ determine a plane which is called the osculating plane. Therefore, the osculating plane is also the plane of the vectors

$$\mathbf{t}, \qquad \frac{d\mathbf{t}}{ds} \tag{8}$$

having a common origin at point P.

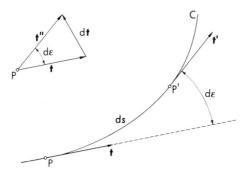

FIG. 2. Curvature of a planar curve.

Because the tangent vector is of unit modulus, the scalar product

$$\mathbf{t} \cdot \mathbf{t} = 1 \tag{9}$$

holds everywhere along the curve. Consequently, differentiation of Eq. (9) with respect to the curvilinear abscissa leads to

$$\mathbf{t} \cdot \frac{d\mathbf{t}}{ds} = 0 \tag{10}$$

which means that the unit tangent vector and its derivative are mutually perpendicular. Furthermore, the derivative $d\mathbf{t}/ds$ is always directed toward the center of curvature of C, as can be verified from simple geometric considerations.

2.3 Principal normal. The principal normal $\mathbf{n}$ is the unit vector which is perpendicular to the tangent vector, contained in the osculating plane, and positive when directed toward the center of curvature. Therefore, because of the previous results, the principal normal is parallel to $d\mathbf{t}/ds$ and can be written as

$$\mathbf{n} = \frac{d\mathbf{t}/ds}{|d\mathbf{t}/ds|} \tag{11}$$

Notice that associated with the infinitesimal increment ds of the curvilinear abscissa is an infinitesimal rotation $d\epsilon$ of the unit tangent vector (Fig. 2). The modulus of the rotation per unit increase of curvilinear abscissa is called the *curvature* and is given by

$$\frac{1}{r} = \left| \frac{d\epsilon}{ds} \right| \tag{12}$$

where r is the *radius of curvature*. Since $\mathbf{t}$ and $\mathbf{t}'$ are both unit vectors, the following relationship is valid:

$$|d\mathbf{t}| = |d\boldsymbol{\epsilon}| \tag{13}$$

Thus, after Eqs. (11) through (13) are combined, the principal normal can be expressed in the form

$$\mathbf{n} = r\frac{d\mathbf{t}}{ds} \tag{14}$$

2.4 Binormal. The binormal **b** is the unit vector perpendicular to the osculating plane and is such that **t, n, b** form a right-handed system (Fig. 1). Consequently, because of the properties of vectorial products, the following result is obtained:

$$\mathbf{b} = \mathbf{t} \times \mathbf{n} \tag{15}$$

The Cartesian system formed by the tangent, principal normal, and binormal vectors is called the *principal trihedral* and is of particular importance for aeronautical engineering applications. Its orientation in space depends on the curvilinear abscissa.

3. MOTION OF A POINT WITH RESPECT TO A REFERENCE FRAME

The object of this section is to introduce the concepts of velocity and acceleration. To do this, consider the motion of a point P with respect to a reference frame $Oxyz$. The position of this point can be specified by the scalar, parametric equations

$$x = x(t), \qquad y = y(t), \qquad z = z(t) \tag{16}$$

in which the time t is the parameter. Clearly, these scalar equations are equivalent to a single vectorial relationship having the form

$$\mathbf{OP} = \mathbf{OP}(t) \tag{17}$$

3.1 Velocity. By definition, the velocity of a point is the time derivative of its position vector, that is,

$$\mathbf{V} = \frac{d\mathbf{OP}}{dt} \tag{18}$$

If the vector **OP** is regarded as a function of a function, that is, as a function of the curvilinear abscissa which in turn is a function of the time, the following result is obtained:

$$\mathbf{V} = \frac{d\mathbf{OP}}{ds}\frac{ds}{dt} = \dot{s}\mathbf{t} \tag{19}$$

where the dot sign denotes a derivative with respect to time. Thus, the velocity is tangent to the path described by point P, and its modulus is equal to the absolute value of the time rate of change of the curvilinear abscissa.

3.2 Acceleration. By definition, the acceleration of a point is the time derivative of its velocity, that is,

$$\mathbf{a} = \frac{d\mathbf{V}}{dt} \tag{20}$$

After Eqs. (14) and (19) are accounted for and the unit tangent vector is regarded as being a function of the time through the intermediate coordinate s, the acceleration can be written as

$$\mathbf{a} = \frac{d}{dt}(\dot{s}\mathbf{t}) = \ddot{s}\mathbf{t} + \frac{\dot{s}^2}{r}\mathbf{n} \tag{21}$$

Thus, the acceleration possesses a *tangential component* and a *normal component*; the latter is directed toward the instantaneous center of curvature and is called the *centripetal acceleration*. There is no component of the acceleration along the binormal; this means that the acceleration is always contained in the osculating plane.

3.3 Remark. If the positive direction for the curvilinear abscissa is identical with that in which the point P is progressing, the time rate of change of the curvilinear abscissa becomes

$$\dot{s} = V \tag{22}$$

Consequently, Eqs. (19) and (21) can be rewritten in the form

$$\mathbf{V} = V\mathbf{t}, \qquad \mathbf{a} = \dot{V}\mathbf{t} + \frac{V^2}{r}\mathbf{n} \tag{23}$$

4. ANGULAR MOTION OF ONE REFERENCE FRAME WITH RESPECT TO ANOTHER

When one coordinate system rotates with respect to another, the associated unit vectors are functions of time. Their time derivatives are a measure of the rate of rotation and play an essential role in the subsequent determination of the angular velocity. In this connection, consider two reference frames $Oxyz$ and $\Omega\xi\eta\zeta$, and regard the former as moving and the latter as fixed (Fig. 3); furthermore, denote by $\mathbf{i}, \mathbf{j}, \mathbf{k}$ the unit vectors associated with the moving trihedral and by $\mathbf{i_*}, \mathbf{j_*}, \mathbf{k_*}$ the unit vectors associated with the fixed trihedral. The time derivatives of the

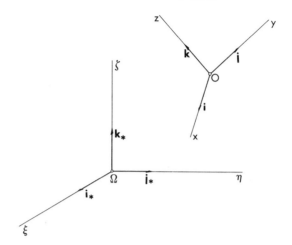

FIG. 3. Motion of one trihedral with respect to another.

moving unit vectors can be resolved into components on the moving axes and written as

$$\frac{d\mathbf{i}}{dt} = \left(\frac{d\mathbf{i}}{dt}\cdot\mathbf{i}\right)\mathbf{i} + \left(\frac{d\mathbf{i}}{dt}\cdot\mathbf{j}\right)\mathbf{j} + \left(\frac{d\mathbf{i}}{dt}\cdot\mathbf{k}\right)\mathbf{k}$$

$$\frac{d\mathbf{j}}{dt} = \left(\frac{d\mathbf{j}}{dt}\cdot\mathbf{i}\right)\mathbf{i} + \left(\frac{d\mathbf{j}}{dt}\cdot\mathbf{j}\right)\mathbf{j} + \left(\frac{d\mathbf{j}}{dt}\cdot\mathbf{k}\right)\mathbf{k} \qquad (24)$$

$$\frac{d\mathbf{k}}{dt} = \left(\frac{d\mathbf{k}}{dt}\cdot\mathbf{i}\right)\mathbf{i} + \left(\frac{d\mathbf{k}}{dt}\cdot\mathbf{j}\right)\mathbf{j} + \left(\frac{d\mathbf{k}}{dt}\cdot\mathbf{k}\right)\mathbf{k}$$

Since the unit vectors $\mathbf{i}$, $\mathbf{j}$, $\mathbf{k}$ have constant modulus and are mutually perpendicular, the following relationships hold:

$$\frac{d\mathbf{i}}{dt}\cdot\mathbf{i} = \frac{d\mathbf{j}}{dt}\cdot\mathbf{j} = \frac{d\mathbf{k}}{dt}\cdot\mathbf{k} = 0 \qquad (25)$$

$$\frac{d\mathbf{i}}{dt}\cdot\mathbf{j} + \frac{d\mathbf{j}}{dt}\cdot\mathbf{i} = \frac{d\mathbf{j}}{dt}\cdot\mathbf{k} + \frac{d\mathbf{k}}{dt}\cdot\mathbf{j} = \frac{d\mathbf{k}}{dt}\cdot\mathbf{i} + \frac{d\mathbf{i}}{dt}\cdot\mathbf{k} = 0 \qquad (26)$$

Consequently, Eqs. (24) can be transformed into the set

$$\frac{d\mathbf{i}}{dt} = r\mathbf{j} - q\mathbf{k}, \qquad \frac{d\mathbf{j}}{dt} = p\mathbf{k} - r\mathbf{i}, \qquad \frac{d\mathbf{k}}{dt} = q\mathbf{i} - p\mathbf{j} \qquad (27)$$

where, by definition,

$$p = \frac{d\mathbf{j}}{dt}\cdot\mathbf{k}, \qquad q = \frac{d\mathbf{k}}{dt}\cdot\mathbf{i}, \qquad r = \frac{d\mathbf{i}}{dt}\cdot\mathbf{j} \qquad (28)$$

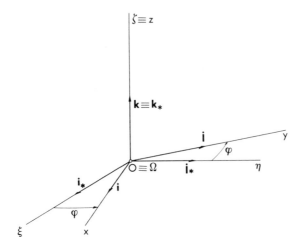

FIG. 4. Rotational motion of one trihedral with respect to another.

After introducing the new vector

$$\boldsymbol{\omega} = p\mathbf{i} + q\mathbf{j} + r\mathbf{k} \tag{29}$$

one obtains the important *Poisson's formulas*

$$\frac{d\mathbf{i}}{dt} = \boldsymbol{\omega} \times \mathbf{i}, \quad \frac{d\mathbf{j}}{dt} = \boldsymbol{\omega} \times \mathbf{j}, \quad \frac{d\mathbf{k}}{dt} = \boldsymbol{\omega} \times \mathbf{k} \tag{30}$$

which show that the derivatives of the moving unit vectors are perpendicular to $\boldsymbol{\omega}$. The physical significance of this vector, which is called the *angular velocity* of the moving reference frame with respect to the fixed reference frame, is illustrated in the next section.

4.1 Particular case. In this section, rotational motion around one fixed axis is considered; more specifically, it is assumed that the origin of the two reference frames coincide and that the z-axis is superimposed on the ζ-axis at all time instants (Fig. 4). If φ denotes the angle which the x-axis forms with the ξ-axis, then the function $\varphi(t)$ defines the motion of the rotating reference frame; its time derivative is customarily referred to as the *scalar angular velocity*. Since the moving unit vectors and the fixed unit vectors satisfy the relationships

$$\begin{aligned} \mathbf{i} &= \cos \varphi \mathbf{i}_* + \sin \varphi \mathbf{j}_* \\ \mathbf{j} &= -\sin \varphi \mathbf{i}_* + \cos \varphi \mathbf{j}_* \\ \mathbf{k} &= \mathbf{k}_* \end{aligned} \tag{31}$$

the time derivatives of the moving unit vectors can be written in the form

$$\frac{d\mathbf{i}}{dt} = \dot{\varphi}\mathbf{j}, \qquad \frac{d\mathbf{j}}{dt} = -\dot{\varphi}\mathbf{i}, \qquad \frac{d\mathbf{k}}{dt} = 0 \qquad (32)$$

Consequently, after the components of the angular velocity on the moving axes are evaluated as

$$p = q = 0, \qquad r = \dot{\varphi} \qquad (33)$$

the angular velocity becomes

$$\boldsymbol{\omega} = \dot{\varphi}\mathbf{k} \qquad (34)$$

Thus, its modulus is identical with the absolute value of $\dot{\varphi}$ and its direction is the same as the axis of rotation of the moving reference frame. Incidentally, if

$$d\boldsymbol{\Omega} = d\varphi\mathbf{k} \qquad (35)$$

denotes the vector corresponding to an infinitesimal rotation around the z-axis, the angular velocity can be rewritten in the form

$$\boldsymbol{\omega} = \frac{d\boldsymbol{\Omega}}{dt} \qquad (36)$$

4.2 Remark. The previous expression can be generalized to the case where the angular motion is arbitrary, that is, the case where three angular coordinates φ_i $(i = 1, 2, 3)$ are needed to describe the position of one system with respect to another (for instance, the Euler angles or the angles of yaw, pitch, and roll used in aerodynamics). If $\mathbf{u}_i(t)$ denotes the unit vector characterizing the infinitesimal partial rotation $d\varphi_i$ and if the vector corresponding to the infinitesimal total rotation is defined as

$$d\boldsymbol{\Omega} = \sum_{i=1}^{3} d\varphi_i \mathbf{u}_i \qquad (37)$$

then it can be shown that Eq. (36) is still valid (Ref. 6). Hence, the angular velocity is given by

$$\boldsymbol{\omega} = \sum_{i=1}^{3} \dot{\varphi}_i \mathbf{u}_i \qquad (38)$$

5. RIGID BODY

By definition, a rigid body is an assembly of points whose relative positions are invariant with respect to time. The kinematic properties of such a body can be investigated by introducing two reference systems:

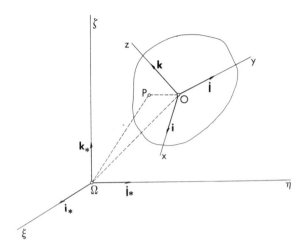

FIG. 5. Rigid body.

a fixed reference frame $\Omega\xi\eta\zeta$ and a reference frame $Oxyz$ which moves in such a way that the coordinates of each point of the body are constant with respect to time. Consequently, the position vector associated with the generic point is given by (Fig. 5)

$$\Omega P = \Omega O + OP = \Omega O + x\mathbf{i} + y\mathbf{j} + z\mathbf{k} \qquad (39)$$

where x, y, z are constant.

5.1 Distribution of velocities. To determine the distribution of velocities inside a rigid body, the time derivative of Eq. (39) must be calculated. After applying Poisson's formulas, one obtains the following result:

$$\mathbf{V} = \mathbf{V}_o + \boldsymbol{\omega} \times \mathbf{OP} \qquad (40)$$

where

$$\mathbf{V} = \frac{d\Omega P}{dt}, \qquad \mathbf{V}_o = \frac{d\Omega O}{dt} \qquad (41)$$

denote the velocities of points P and O with respect to the fixed trihedral. If a rigid body is subjected to translational motion only, the orientation of the moving trihedral is invariant with respect to time. Since $\boldsymbol{\omega} = 0$, Eq. (40) reduces to

$$\mathbf{V} = \mathbf{V}_o \qquad (42)$$

meaning that in translational motion all the points have equal velocities. On the other hand, if a rigid body is subjected to rotational motion only, around either a fixed point or a fixed axis, then $\mathbf{V}_o = 0$, so that the velocity distribution is supplied by

$$\mathbf{V} = \boldsymbol{\omega} \times \mathbf{OP} \tag{43}$$

In conclusion, it is possible to interpret Eq. (40) as follows: *The most general velocity field inside a rigid body is due to the superposition of two fields, one translational and the other rotational.*

5.2 Distribution of accelerations. To determine the distribution of accelerations inside a rigid body, it is necessary to calculate the time derivative of Eq. (40), which leads to

$$\mathbf{a} = \mathbf{a}_o + \boldsymbol{\omega} \times (\boldsymbol{\omega} \times \mathbf{OP}) + \dot{\boldsymbol{\omega}} \times \mathbf{OP} \tag{44}$$

where

$$\mathbf{a} = \frac{d\mathbf{V}}{dt}, \qquad \mathbf{a}_o = \frac{d\mathbf{V}_o}{dt} \tag{45}$$

denote the accelerations of points P and O with respect to the fixed trihedral. This means that *the acceleration field inside a rigid body is due to the superposition of three fields: one translational, one corresponding to a uniform rotation, and one due to the presence of angular acceleration.*

6. RELATIVE MOTION

In this section, the motion of a point P with respect to two reference systems, a fixed reference frame $\Omega\xi\eta\zeta$ and a moving reference frame $Oxyz$, is considered. After the *absolute motion* is defined as the motion of P with respect to $\Omega\xi\eta\zeta$, the *relative motion* (subscript r) as the motion of P with respect to $Oxyz$, and the *transport motion* (subscript t) as the ideal motion which P would have with respect to $\Omega\xi\eta\zeta$ if P were fixed with respect to $Oxyz$, the following question is posed: What relationships exist between the absolute and relative velocities and between the absolute and relative accelerations?

To answer this question, it is observed that, while the position of P with respect to the fixed trihedral is still defined by Eq. (39), a new element is introduced, namely, the time-dependence of the coordinates x, y, z. Consequently, the absolute velocity and the absolute acceleration are respectively given by

$$\mathbf{V} = \mathbf{V}_o + \boldsymbol{\omega} \times \mathbf{OP} + \dot{x}\mathbf{i} + \dot{y}\mathbf{j} + \dot{z}\mathbf{k}$$
$$\mathbf{a} = \mathbf{a}_o + \boldsymbol{\omega} \times (\boldsymbol{\omega} \times \mathbf{OP}) + \dot{\boldsymbol{\omega}} \times \mathbf{OP} \tag{46}$$
$$+ \ddot{x}\mathbf{i} + \ddot{y}\mathbf{j} + \ddot{z}\mathbf{k} + 2\boldsymbol{\omega} \times (\dot{x}\mathbf{i} + \dot{y}\mathbf{j} + \dot{z}\mathbf{k})$$

After the relative velocity, the relative acceleration, the transport velocity, the transport acceleration, and the Coriolis acceleration are defined as

$$\mathbf{V}_r = \dot{x}\mathbf{i} + \dot{y}\mathbf{j} + \dot{z}\mathbf{k}$$

$$\mathbf{a}_r = \ddot{x}\mathbf{i} + \ddot{y}\mathbf{j} + \ddot{z}\mathbf{k}$$

$$\mathbf{V}_t = \mathbf{V}_o + \boldsymbol{\omega} \times \mathbf{OP} \tag{47}$$

$$\mathbf{a}_t = \mathbf{a}_o + \boldsymbol{\omega} \times (\boldsymbol{\omega} \times \mathbf{OP}) + \dot{\boldsymbol{\omega}} \times \mathbf{OP}$$

$$\mathbf{a}_c = 2\boldsymbol{\omega} \times \mathbf{V}_r$$

the absolute velocity and the absolute acceleration can be rewritten in the form

$$\mathbf{V} = \mathbf{V}_r + \mathbf{V}_t$$

$$\mathbf{a} = \mathbf{a}_r + \mathbf{a}_t + \mathbf{a}_c \tag{48}$$

The first of these equations expresses the *theorem of composition of velocities: The absolute velocity is the vectorial sum of the relative velocity and the transport velocity.* Furthermore, the second of these equations expresses the *theorem of composition of accelerations: The absolute acceleration is the vectorial sum of the relative acceleration, the transport acceleration, and the Coriolis acceleration.*

EXERCISES

1. Consider a helix wrapped on a cylinder of radius R, and denote by α its constant inclination with respect to the xy-plane (Fig. 6). Show that the unit vectors associated with the principal trihedral are given by

$$\mathbf{t} = \cos\alpha\left[-\sin\left(\frac{s\cos\alpha}{R}\right)\mathbf{i} + \cos\left(\frac{s\cos\alpha}{R}\right)\mathbf{j}\right] + \sin\alpha\mathbf{k}$$

$$\mathbf{n} = -\left[\cos\left(\frac{s\cos\alpha}{R}\right)\mathbf{i} + \sin\left(\frac{s\cos\alpha}{R}\right)\mathbf{j}\right] \tag{49}$$

$$\mathbf{b} = \sin\alpha\left[\sin\left(\frac{s\cos\alpha}{R}\right)\mathbf{i} - \cos\left(\frac{s\cos\alpha}{R}\right)\mathbf{j}\right] + \cos\alpha\mathbf{k}$$

2. Consider a point P describing a planar trajectory, that is, a trajectory entirely contained in a reference plane Oxy (Fig. 7). Denote by ρ the modulus of the vector $\mathbf{OP}$ and by θ the angle which this vector forms with the x-axis. Indicate by $\mathbf{u}$ a unit vector radially directed and by $\boldsymbol{\tau}$ a unit vector transversally directed, that is, obtained from the

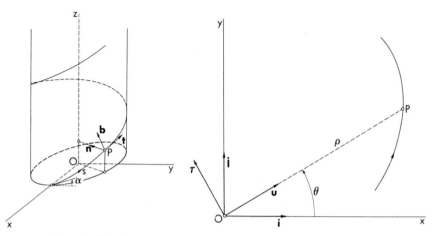

FIG. 6. Circular helix.   FIG. 7. Planar trajectory.

former by means of a 90° counterclockwise rotation. Using polar co-ordinates, show that the position vector, the velocity, and the acceleration are given by

$$\mathbf{OP} = \rho\mathbf{u}$$

$$\mathbf{V} = \dot{\rho}\mathbf{u} + \rho\dot{\theta}\boldsymbol{\tau} \tag{50}$$

$$\mathbf{a} = (\ddot{\rho} - \rho\dot{\theta}^2)\mathbf{u} + \frac{1}{\rho}\frac{d(\rho^2\dot{\theta})}{dt}\boldsymbol{\tau}$$

3. Starting with Poisson's formulas, show that the angular velocity can be written in the alternate form

$$\boldsymbol{\omega} = \frac{1}{2}\left(\mathbf{i} \times \frac{d\mathbf{i}}{dt} + \mathbf{j} \times \frac{d\mathbf{j}}{dt} + \mathbf{k} \times \frac{d\mathbf{k}}{dt}\right) \tag{51}$$

4. Show that the velocity of all the points of a rigid body have equal projections in the direction of the angular velocity. Furthermore, if the angular acceleration is zero, show that the projection of the acceleration in the direction of the angular velocity is a constant for all points of the body.

REFERENCES

1. LEVI-CIVITA, T. and AMALDI, U., *Lezioni di Meccanica Razionale*, Nicola Zanichelli Editore, Bologna, 1930.
2. SYNGE, J. L. and GRIFFITH, B. A., *Principles of Mechanics*, McGraw-Hill Book Company, Inc., New York, 1949.
3. HILDEBRAND, F. B., *Advanced Calculus for Engineers*, Prentice-Hall, Inc., New York, 1948.
4. PHILLIPS, H. B., *Vector Analysis*, John Wiley and Sons, Inc., New York, 1933.
5. LASS, H., *Vector and Tensor Analysis*, McGraw-Hill Book Company, Inc., New York, 1950.
6. GOLDSTEIN, H., *Classical Mechanics*, Addison-Wesley Publishing Company, Inc., Reading, Mass., 1950.

CHAPTER 2

ELEMENTS OF DYNAMICS

1. INTRODUCTION

In this chapter, a survey of those dynamical elements which are necessary for the analytical development of the theory of flight paths is
presented. First, Newton's law and the principle of action and reaction
are introduced. Then, the theorems of linear and angular momentum are
formulated and applied to a rigid body and to a spinning rotor mounted
on a rigid body. Finally, these theorems are extended to systems of
variable mass.

2. MATERIAL POINT

There are innumerable phenomena of motion in which the physical
dimensions of the body under consideration are small with respect to the
dimensions of the environment in which the motion takes place. Furthermore, depending on the nature of the forces applied to the body, the predominant interest of an observer may be focused on the translational
behavior of the body rather than on its rotational behavior. In such cases,
it is helpful to introduce the concept of a *material point*, or *particle*,
having the intrinsic properties of the body. This material point, which has
no physical dimensions, is only a mathematical abstraction, insofar as
there is a volume other than zero associated with each body of the
Universe. Nevertheless, this idealized scheme is useful and pertinent in
a wide variety of problems in Flight Mechanics.

The instantaneous dynamical behavior of the material point is described by *Newton's law*

$$\mathbf{F} = m\mathbf{a} \qquad (1)$$

which can be stated as follows: *At each time instant, the resultant
external force acting on a particle is proportional to the instantaneous
acceleration, the proportionality constant being the mass of the particle.*
A specific requirement of this law is that the mass be constant and that
the acceleration be calculated with respect to an *absolute reference frame,*
that is, a reference frame rigidly associated with the Fixed Stars (those
heavenly bodies which do not show any appreciable change in their
relative position from century to century).

3. MATERIAL SYSTEM

A material system is an assembly of particles which may be considered as either a *discrete set* or a *continuum*. The dynamical properties of such a system are now investigated with the assumption that the total mass is constant and with reference to the discrete case, that is, the case where the system is composed of n particles of mass m_j $(j = 1, \ldots, n)$ concentrated at points P_j. The properties of a continuum are then obtained from those of a discrete system by a limiting process in which the number of particles becomes infinitely large and the mass of each particle infinitely small, while the total mass remains constant.

In the following sections, two fundamental theorems are established, the theorem of linear momentum and the theorem of angular momentum. For this purpose, Newton's law must be combined with the *principle of action and reaction*, which can be stated as follows: *The internal force which a particle P_1 exerts on a particle P_2 belonging to the same system is equal in magnitude to, collinear with, and opposite in sense to the internal force which P_2 exerts on P_1.*

3.1 Theorem of linear momentum. In the analysis of a discrete system, it is convenient to divide the forces into *internal forces* (subscript i) and *external forces* (subscript e); the former are due to sources located inside the system, and the latter, to those outside the system. Since Newton's law holds for each of the particles of the system, the following n-equations can be written (the subscript j can take any value between 1 and n):

$$\mathbf{F}_{ij} + \mathbf{F}_{ej} = m_j \mathbf{a}_j \tag{2}$$

which, after summation, lead to

$$\sum_{j=1}^{n} \mathbf{F}_{ij} + \sum_{j=1}^{n} \mathbf{F}_{ej} = \sum_{j=1}^{n} m_j \mathbf{a}_j \tag{3}$$

Notice that, because of the principle of action and reaction, the resultant internal force is given by

$$\sum_{j=1}^{n} \mathbf{F}_{ij} = 0 \tag{4}$$

Thus, after the resultant external force is denoted by

$$\mathbf{F} = \sum_{j=1}^{n} \mathbf{F}_{ej} \tag{5}$$

Eq. (3) yields the *equation of forces*

$$\mathbf{F} = \sum_{j=1}^{n} m_j \mathbf{a}_j \tag{6}$$

This means that, if the *linear momentum*

$$Q = \sum_{j=1}^{n} m_j V_j \tag{7}$$

is introduced, the following relationship is obtained:

$$\mathbf{F} = \frac{d\mathbf{Q}}{dt} \tag{8}$$

This result, known as the *theorem of linear momentum,* can be stated as follows: *At each time instant, the resultant external force acting on a system is equal to the time rate of change of the linear momentum.*

3.2 Theorem of angular momentum. The theorem of angular momentum can be derived in much the same manner as was the theorem of linear momentum. As a first step, an arbitrary reference point R (either at rest or in motion) is introduced, and the moments due to the internal forces and the external forces with respect to point R are respectively defined as

$$\mathbf{M}_{ij} = \mathbf{RP}_j \times \mathbf{F}_{ij}, \qquad \mathbf{M}_{ej} = \mathbf{RP}_j \times \mathbf{F}_{ej} \tag{9}$$

Then, each of the n-equations (2) is multiplied vectorially by $\mathbf{RP}_j$, leading to

$$\mathbf{M}_{ij} + \mathbf{M}_{ej} = \mathbf{RP}_j \times m_j \mathbf{a}_j \tag{10}$$

which, after summation, becomes

$$\sum_{j=1}^{n} \mathbf{M}_{ij} + \sum_{j=1}^{n} \mathbf{M}_{ej} = \sum_{j=1}^{n} \mathbf{RP}_j \times m_j \mathbf{a}_j \tag{11}$$

Notice that, because of the principle of action and reaction, the resultant internal moment is given by

$$\sum_{j=1}^{n} \mathbf{M}_{ij} = 0 \tag{12}$$

Thus, after the resultant external moment is denoted by

$$\mathbf{M} = \sum_{j=1}^{n} \mathbf{M}_{ej} \tag{13}$$

Eq. (11) yields the *equation of moments*

$$\mathbf{M} = \sum_{j=1}^{n} \mathbf{RP}_j \times m_j \mathbf{a}_j \tag{14}$$

If the *angular momentum* is defined as

$$\mathbf{K} = \sum_{j=1}^{n} \mathbf{RP}_j \times m_j \mathbf{V}_j \tag{15}$$

and it is observed that

$$\frac{d\mathbf{K}}{dt} = -\mathbf{V}_R \times \sum_{j=1}^{n} m_j \mathbf{V}_j + \sum_{j=1}^{n} \mathbf{RP}_j \times m_j \mathbf{a}_j \tag{16}$$

the following relationship is obtained:

$$\mathbf{M} = \frac{d\mathbf{K}}{dt} + \mathbf{V}_R \times \mathbf{Q} \tag{17}$$

This result, known as the *theorem of angular momentum*, can be stated as follows: *At each time instant, the resultant external moment acting on a system is equal to the time rate of change of the angular momentum plus the vector product of the velocity of the reference point and the linear momentum.*

3.3 Continuous systems. According to the limiting process mentioned earlier, the dynamical properties of a continuum can be obtained from those of a discrete system by simply replacing the summation signs with integrals. In particular, the equations of forces and moments can be rewritten as

$$\mathbf{F} = \int_m \mathbf{a}\, dm$$
$$\mathbf{M} = \int_m \mathbf{RP} \times \mathbf{a}\, dm \tag{18}$$

where the subscript to the integral sign indicates that the integration is to be extended to the entire mass of the system. These equations lead once more to the theorems of linear and angular momentum, provided that the linear momentum and the angular momentum are defined as

$$\mathbf{Q} = \int_m \mathbf{V}\, dm, \qquad \mathbf{K} = \int_m \mathbf{RP} \times \mathbf{V}\, dm \tag{19}$$

Incidentally, the theorems of linear momentum and angular momentum have the same degree of generality as the equations of forces and moments. However, owing to the particular nature of the problems which follow, the use of Eqs. (18) is preferable.

4. RIGID BODY

To investigate the dynamical properties of a rigid body, two reference frames are necessary: an absolute reference frame $\Omega\xi\eta\zeta$ and a reference frame $Oxyz$ which is fixed with respect to the rigid body (*body axes system*). It is known from Chapter 1 that the distribution of accelerations inside a rigid body satisfies the relationship

$$\mathbf{a} = \mathbf{a}_o + \dot{\boldsymbol{\omega}} \times \mathbf{OP} + \boldsymbol{\omega} \times (\boldsymbol{\omega} \times \mathbf{OP}) \tag{20}$$

where $\mathbf{a}$ and $\mathbf{a}_o$ are the absolute accelerations of the generic point and the origin of the body axes system and where $\boldsymbol{\omega}$ is the absolute angular velocity of the rigid body. Consequently, the equations of forces and moments (18) lead to the relationships

$$\mathbf{F} = m\mathbf{a}_o + \dot{\boldsymbol{\omega}} \times \int_m \mathbf{OP}\, dm + \boldsymbol{\omega} \times \left(\boldsymbol{\omega} \times \int_m \mathbf{OP}\, dm \right)$$
$$\tag{21}$$
$$\mathbf{M} = \left(\int_m \mathbf{RP}\, dm \right) \times \mathbf{a}_o + \int_m \mathbf{RP} \times [\dot{\boldsymbol{\omega}} \times \mathbf{OP} + \boldsymbol{\omega} \times (\boldsymbol{\omega} \times \mathbf{OP})]\, dm$$

These equations can be simplified considerably if the center of mass* is chosen to be the origin of the body axes system as well as the reference point for the moments. In fact, after it is observed that

$$\int_m \mathbf{OP}\, dm = \int_m \mathbf{RP}\, dm = 0 \tag{22}$$

Eqs. (21) can be rewritten as

$$\mathbf{F} = m\mathbf{a}_o$$
$$\tag{23}$$
$$\mathbf{M} = \int_m \mathbf{OP} \times [\dot{\boldsymbol{\omega}} \times \mathbf{OP} + \boldsymbol{\omega} \times (\boldsymbol{\omega} \times \mathbf{OP})]\, dm$$

The corresponding scalar relationships on the body axes are called the *Euler equations* and are presented in Exercises 1 and 2.

5. SPINNING ROTOR MOUNTED ON A RIGID BODY

An extension of the previous problem consists of analyzing the motion of a spinning rotor mounted on a rigid body. If the total mass of the system (rotor plus rigid body) is denoted by m and its center of mass by O, the equation of forces can be shown to yield

$$\mathbf{F} = m\mathbf{a}_o \tag{24}$$

where $\mathbf{a}_o$ is the absolute acceleration of the center of mass. On the other hand, if the rotor has inertial symmetry with respect to its axis of

---

* By definition, the *center of mass* of any material system is the point G which satisfies the equation

$$\int_m \mathbf{GP}\, dm = 0$$

rotation, then the equation of moments leads to the relationship

$$\mathbf{M} + \mathbf{M}_G = \int_m \mathbf{OP} \times [\dot{\omega} \times \mathbf{OP} + \omega \times (\omega \times \mathbf{OP})] \, dm \qquad (25)$$

where

$$\mathbf{M}_G = I_R \omega_R \times \omega \qquad (26)$$

is the *gyroscopic moment,* ω the absolute angular velocity of the rigid body, I_R the moment of inertia of the rotor with respect to its axis of rotation, and ω_R the angular velocity of the rotor with respect to the rigid body (both its modulus and its orientation with respect to the rigid body are assumed to be constant). Incidentally, the gyroscopic moment is due to the Coriolis acceleration associated with the motion of the rotor relative to the rigid body and is always present in vehicles having rotating machinery (propellers, turbines, compressors, turbopumps, etc.).

It is of interest to note that the inertia terms appearing on the right-hand side of Eqs. (24) and (25) are identical with those which appear in the equations of motion of a totally rigid body. This observation leads to the *solidification principle: The equations governing the instantaneous motion of the system formed by a spinning rotor plus a rigid body are formally identical with those of a totally rigid body, provided that the following fictitious system of external forces is considered: the actual forces and the gyroscopic forces.*

6. VARIABLE MASS SYSTEMS

A variable mass system can be conceived as a system of particles whose total number varies with the time but whose individual mass is constant. Since Newton's law holds for each particle, the instantaneous motion of any discrete, variable mass system is still described by Eqs. (6) and (14), while the instantaneous motion of any continuous, variable mass system is still described by Eqs. (18). Furthermore, *the theorems of linear momentum and angular momentum are valid for variable mass systems, provided that the derivatives $d\mathbf{Q}/dt$, $d\mathbf{K}/dt$ are calculated as substantial derivatives.* This means that the same material particles, that is, the same total mass, must be considered at time instants t and $t + dt$.

6.1 Approximate derivation of the equation of motion of a rocket. A
simple, approximate derivation of the equation governing the translational motion of a rocket is possible, if the linear momentum theorem is employed in combination with the following idealized scheme (Fig. 1):

(a) At time instant t, all the particles located within the geometric boundary $ABCA$ of the rocket have the same absolute velocity $\mathbf{V}_o$, where O is any point of the solid walls of the rocket.

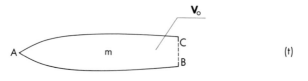

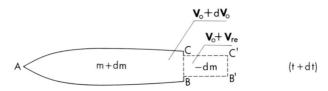

Fig. 1. Idealized scheme for an approximate derivation of the equation of motion of a rocket.

(b) At time instant $t + dt$, all the particles located within the rocket have the same absolute velocity $\mathbf{V}_o + d\mathbf{V}_o$. The mass $-dm$, which has been ejected across the exit section of the engine with a velocity $\mathbf{V}_{re}$ relative to the walls of the rocket, possesses the absolute velocity $\mathbf{V}_o + \mathbf{V}_{re}$.

Under these hypotheses, the linear momentum of the particles which are located within the geometric boundary of the rocket at time instant t is given by

$$\mathbf{Q} = m\mathbf{V}_o \qquad (27)$$

while the linear momentum of the same material particles at time instant $t + dt$ is written as

$$\mathbf{Q}' = (m + dm)(\mathbf{V}_o + d\mathbf{V}_o) - dm(\mathbf{V}_o + \mathbf{V}_{re}) \qquad (28)$$

If higher-order infinitesimals are neglected, the substantial increase in linear momentum is expressed in the form

$$d\mathbf{Q} = \mathbf{Q}' - \mathbf{Q} = m\,d\mathbf{V}_o - dm\,\mathbf{V}_{re} \qquad (29)$$

Consequently, the theorem of linear momentum leads to the fundamental relation

$$\mathbf{F} - \beta\mathbf{V}_{re} = m\mathbf{a}_o \qquad (30)$$

where

$$\beta = -\frac{dm}{dt}, \qquad \mathbf{a}_o = \frac{d\mathbf{V}_o}{dt} \qquad (31)$$

respectively denote the mass flow of propellant and the absolute acceleration of the solid part of the rocket. The following remarks are pertinent:

(a) The equation governing the translational motion of a rocket vehicle is formally identical with that of a constant mass vehicle, provided that the following fictitious system of external forces is considered: the actual external force **F** and the reactive force $-\beta\mathbf{V}_{re}$.

(b) By appropriate specialization of the system of external forces, Eq. (30) can be applied to cover the cases where the rocket is in flight, on a test stand, or on the ground (take-off and landing).

(c) The derivation of this section is subject to errors of two kinds: those due to neglecting the rotation of the rocket with respect to the Fixed Stars and those due to neglecting the relative momentum associated with the fluid particles within the rocket. Errors of the first type are generally negligible from an engineering point of view. Errors of the second type are zero when the motion of the fluid particles within the rocket is steady or quasi-steady with respect to the solid walls; this is because the relative momentum neglected in Eq. (27) and the relative momentum neglected in Eq. (28) are equal, so that Eq. (29) correctly expresses the substantial increase in linear momentum.

EXERCISES

1. Consider a rigid body, and denote the components of the velocity of the center of mass on the body axes by u, v, w, the components of the angular velocity by p, q, r, and the components of the external force by F_x, F_y, F_z. Show that the first of Eqs. (23) is equivalent to the scalar relationships (*Euler force equations*)

$$F_x = m(\dot{u} + qw - rv)$$

$$F_y = m(\dot{v} + ru - pw) \qquad (32)$$

$$F_z = m(\dot{w} + pv - qu)$$

2. Consider a rigid body, and assume that the body axes are central (the origin of the system is located at the center of mass) and principal (the axes are identical with the principal axes of inertia of the body). After the components of the external moment are denoted by M_x, M_y, M_z, show that the second of Eqs. (23) leads to the scalar relationships (*Euler moment equations*)

$$M_x = A\dot{p} + (C - B)qr$$

$$M_y = B\dot{q} + (A - C)rp \qquad (33)$$

$$M_z = C\dot{r} + (B - A)pq$$

where A, B, C are the principal and central moments of inertia and p, q, r the components of the angular velocity on the body axes.

3. With reference to Exercise 2, show that the angular momentum of a rigid body can be written in terms of its components on the principal and central axes as

$$\mathbf{K} = Ap\mathbf{i} + Bq\mathbf{j} + Cr\mathbf{k} \tag{34}$$

Starting from this expression, rederive the Euler moment equations (33).

4. For the system composed of a spinning rotor and a rigid body, derive the distribution of accelerations. Furthermore, derive the equations of forces (24) and moments (25).

REFERENCES

1. LEVI-CIVITA, T. and AMALDI, U., *Lezioni di Meccanica Razionale,* Nicola Zanichelli Editore, Bologna, 1930.
2. SYNGE, J. L. and GRIFFITH, B. A., *Principles of Mechanics,* McGraw-Hill Book Company, Inc., New York, 1949.
3. GOLDSTEIN, H., *Classical Mechanics,* Addison-Wesley Publishing Company, Inc., Reading, Mass., 1950.
4. ROSSER, J. B., NEWTON, R. R., and GROSS, G. L., *Mathematical Theory of Rocket Flight,* McGraw-Hill Book Company, Inc., New York, 1947.

CHAPTER 3

EQUATIONS OF MOTION FOR ROCKET
AND JET-POWERED VEHICLES

1. INTRODUCTION

In the previous chapter, an approximate derivation of the equations of motion of a rocket vehicle was presented. An extremely idealized model was employed in the sense that two facts were neglected: (a) that the rocket may rotate with respect to the Fixed Stars and (b) that the particles contained in the tanks, the piping system, the combustion chamber, and the nozzle have a relative velocity other than zero with respect to the solid walls of the vehicle.

In this chapter, the previous limitations are removed, and a rigorous derivation of the equations of motion is presented referring, for didactic purposes, to a rocket system in which no rotating machinery is present, that is, either a solid-propellant rocket or a liquid-propellant rocket whose feeding mechanism is operated by a pressurized inert gas (Fig. 1). The results are then extended to vehicles propelled by air-breathing jet engines which incorporate various types of inlets and outlets plus rotating machinery such as compressors and turbines. After the most general equations governing the translational-rotational motion of any vehicle are established, their application to stability and control analyses as well as to trajectory analyses is discussed. Furthermore, the hypotheses leading

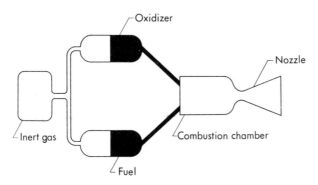

FIG. 1. Example of a liquid fuel rocket whose feeding mechanism is operated by pressurized inert gas.

27

to the uncoupling of the force equation from the moment equation are pointed out. Finally, in connection with trajectory analyses, the motion of the vehicle is discussed using either an absolute reference frame or a reference frame rigidly associated with the Earth.

2. ROCKET-POWERED VEHICLE

The derivation of the equations of motion for a rocket-powered vehicle requires particular care because of the important dynamic effects associated with the expulsion of high-speed particles from the nozzle.* The problem can be stated as follows: A rocket-powered vehicle expels particles at an arbitrary rate; therefore, the mass contained within the rocket is an arbitrary function of time. What are the equations describing the instantaneous motion of the rocket? In order to investigate this problem, two reference systems are needed (Fig. 2): a reference frame $\Omega\xi\eta\zeta$ rigidly associated with the Fixed Stars and a reference frame $Oxyz$ rigidly associated with the solid part of the rocket (body axes system). Furthermore, in accordance with Chapter 1, the following basic motions are considered: absolute motion or the motion of any point of the rocket with respect to $\Omega\xi\eta\zeta$, relative motion (subscript r) or the motion with respect to $Oxyz$, and transport motion (subscript t) or the ideal motion which a point would have with respect to $\Omega\xi\eta\zeta$ should it become fixed with respect to $Oxyz$.

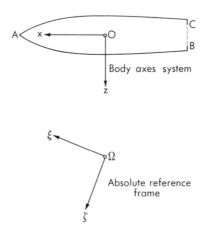

Fig. 2. Reference frames.

---

* The fundamental characteristic of the rocket motor is that the matter to be burned and ejected is entirely stored within the vehicle. The surrounding medium is not utilized for propulsion.

2.1 Equation of forces. If the rocket is regarded as a continuum, the relationship which describes its translational motion is given by

$$\mathbf{F} = \int_m \mathbf{a} \, dm \tag{1}$$

where $\mathbf{F}$ is the resultant external force and $\mathbf{a}$ the absolute acceleration of the infinitesimal mass dm. The subscript m to the integral sign indicates that the integration process is to be extended to the instantaneous mass located within the geometric boundary $ABCA$ of the rocket at time instant t (Fig. 2).

In order to integrate Eq. (1), it is necessary to have the distribution of accelerations inside the rocket, which, according to the theorem of composition of accelerations, is given by

$$\mathbf{a} = \mathbf{a}_o + \dot{\boldsymbol{\omega}} \times \mathbf{OP} + \boldsymbol{\omega} \times (\boldsymbol{\omega} \times \mathbf{OP}) + 2\boldsymbol{\omega} \times \mathbf{V}_r + \mathbf{a}_r \tag{2}$$

where $\boldsymbol{\omega}$ is the absolute angular velocity of the body axes systems and $\mathbf{a}_o$ the absolute acceleration of its origin. After combining Eqs. (1) and (2), one obtains the following result:

$$\mathbf{F} = m\mathbf{a}_o + \dot{\boldsymbol{\omega}} \times \int_m \mathbf{OP} \, dm + \boldsymbol{\omega} \times \left(\boldsymbol{\omega} \times \int_m \mathbf{OP} \, dm \right)$$
$$+ 2\boldsymbol{\omega} \times \int_m \mathbf{V}_r \, dm + \int_m \mathbf{a}_r \, dm \tag{3}$$

It should be noted that the relative velocity and the relative acceleration of the solid particles of the rocket are zero. Therefore, after the infinitesimal mass is written in the form $dm = \rho d\tau$, where ρ is the local density and $d\tau$ the infinitesimal volume, the integrals of the relative velocities and accelerations become

$$\int_m \mathbf{V}_r \, dm = \int_{m_f} \mathbf{V}_r \, dm$$
$$\int_m \mathbf{a}_r \, dm = \int_{m_f} \mathbf{a}_r \, dm = \int_{\tau_f} \rho \mathbf{a}_r \, d\tau \tag{4}$$

where m_f is the mass of the fluid particles and τ_f the associated volume.

The next step is to transform the integral of the relative accelerations into quantities associated with the fluid conditions at the exit of the rocket engine. If the unit vectors of the body axes system are denoted by $\mathbf{i}$, $\mathbf{j}$, $\mathbf{k}$ and the components of the relative velocity on these axes by u, v, w, the following formulas hold:

$$\mathbf{V}_r = u\mathbf{i} + v\mathbf{j} + w\mathbf{k} \tag{5}$$

$$\mathbf{a}_r = \frac{du}{dt} \mathbf{i} + \frac{dv}{dt} \mathbf{j} + \frac{dw}{dt} \mathbf{k}$$

where the derivatives of the velocity components are *substantial deriva-*

tives in the sense commonly accepted in Fluid Mechanics. After it is assumed that the fluid field within the rocket is described by relationships having the form

$$u = u(x, y, z, t), \qquad v = v(x, y, z, t), \qquad w = w(x, y, z, t) \qquad (6)$$

it can be shown that these substantial derivatives and the corresponding *local derivatives* are related by the well-known formulas

$$\frac{du}{dt} = \frac{\partial u}{\partial t} + \mathbf{V}_r \cdot \nabla u$$

$$\frac{dv}{dt} = \frac{\partial v}{\partial t} + \mathbf{V}_r \cdot \nabla v \qquad (7)$$

$$\frac{dw}{dt} = \frac{\partial w}{\partial t} + \mathbf{V}_r \cdot \nabla w$$

Consequently, after it is recalled that, because of the *continuity theorem*,

$$\frac{\partial \rho}{\partial t} + \nabla \cdot (\rho \mathbf{V}_r) = 0 \qquad (8)$$

Eqs. (7) can be rewritten in the form

$$\rho \frac{du}{dt} = \frac{\partial(\rho u)}{\partial t} + \nabla \cdot (\rho u \mathbf{V}_r)$$

$$\rho \frac{dv}{dt} = \frac{\partial(\rho v)}{\partial t} + \nabla \cdot (\rho v \mathbf{V}_r) \qquad (9)$$

$$\rho \frac{dw}{dt} = \frac{\partial(\rho w)}{\partial t} + \nabla \cdot (\rho w \mathbf{V}_r)$$

and imply that

$$\rho \mathbf{a}_r = \frac{\partial(\rho \mathbf{V}_r)}{\partial t} + \mathbf{H} \qquad (10)$$

where

$$\mathbf{H} = \nabla \cdot (\rho u \mathbf{V}_r)\mathbf{i} + \nabla \cdot (\rho v \mathbf{V}_r)\mathbf{j} + \nabla \cdot (\rho w \mathbf{V}_r)\mathbf{k} \qquad (11)$$

As a further step, *Gauss's divergence theorem** is applied, and leads to

$$\int_{\tau_f} \mathbf{H} \, d\tau = - \int_{\sigma_f} \rho(\mathbf{V}_r \cdot \mathbf{n})\mathbf{V}_r \, d\sigma \qquad (12)$$

---

* This theorem deals with the transformation of a volume integral into a surface integral and is stated as follows: If $\mathbf{F}$ is a vectorial function of the coordinates x, y, z which is defined in a volume τ bounded by the closed surface σ, then

$$\int_{\tau} \nabla \cdot \mathbf{F} \, d\tau = - \int_{\sigma} \mathbf{F} \cdot \mathbf{n} \, d\sigma$$

where $\mathbf{n}$ is a unit vector which is normal to the area element $d\sigma$ and positive when directed inward.

where σ_f is the surface bounding all of the fluid particles. Now, denote the mass flow crossing the unit area bounding the fluid particles by

$$\mu = -\rho \mathbf{V}_r \cdot \mathbf{n} \tag{13}$$

Since $\mu = 0$ everywhere except at points of the exit area of the engine S_e, the integral of the relative accelerations becomes

$$\int_m \mathbf{a}_r \, dm = \int_{m_f} \frac{1}{\rho} \frac{\partial(\rho \mathbf{V}_r)}{\partial t} \, dm + \int_{S_e} \mu \mathbf{V}_r \, d\sigma \tag{14}$$

Consequently, after Eqs. (3), (4), and (14) are combined, the following result is obtained:*

$$\mathbf{F} + \mathbf{C} + \mathbf{U} + \mathbf{R} = m\mathbf{a}_o + \dot{\omega} \times \int_m \mathbf{OP} \, dm + \omega \times \left(\omega \times \int_m \mathbf{OP} \, dm \right) \tag{15}$$

where the *Coriolis force*, the *force due to the unsteadiness of the relative motion*, and the *reactive force* are respectively defined by

$$\mathbf{C} = -2\omega \times \int_{m_f} \mathbf{V}_r \, dm$$

$$\mathbf{U} = -\int_{m_f} \frac{1}{\rho} \frac{\partial(\rho \mathbf{V}_r)}{\partial t} \, dm \tag{16}$$

$$\mathbf{R} = -\int_{S_e} \mu \mathbf{V}_r \, d\sigma$$

2.2 Equation of moments. If it is assumed that the reference point for the moments is the origin of the body axes system, the rotational motion of the rocket is described by the relationship

$$\mathbf{M} = \int_m \mathbf{OP} \times \mathbf{a} \, dm \tag{17}$$

where $\mathbf{M}$ is the resultant external moment. If the distribution of accelerations (2) is introduced and a procedure similar to that used in developing the equation of forces is employed, the following result can be shown to hold:

$$\mathbf{M} + \mathbf{M}_C + \mathbf{M}_U + \mathbf{M}_R = \left(\int_m \mathbf{OP} \, dm \right) \times \mathbf{a}_o$$
$$+ \int_m \mathbf{OP} \times [\dot{\omega} \times \mathbf{OP} + \omega \times (\omega \times \mathbf{OP})] \, dm \tag{18}$$

where the *Coriolis moment*, the *moment due to the unsteadiness of the*

---

* This equation differs from the simplified relationship (2–30) because of the presence of four additional terms, three of which are due to the rotation of the rocket with respect to the Fixed Stars and one, to the unsteadiness of the relative motion of the fluid within the engine.

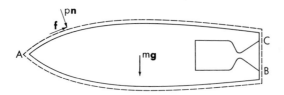

$$S_w \equiv \text{area CAB}$$
$$S_e \equiv \text{area BC}$$

FIG. 3. Control surface for the determination of the forces acting on a rocket-powered vehicle in flight.

relative motion, and the *reactive moment* are respectively defined by

$$\mathbf{M}_C = -2\int_{m_f} \mathbf{OP} \times (\boldsymbol{\omega} \times \mathbf{V}_r)\, dm$$

$$\mathbf{M}_U = -\int_{m_f} \mathbf{OP} \times \frac{1}{\rho} \frac{\partial(\rho \mathbf{V}_r)}{\partial t}\, dm \tag{19}$$

$$\mathbf{M}_R = -\int_{S_e} \mathbf{OP} \times \mu \mathbf{V}_r\, d\sigma$$

2.3 Solidification principle. It is of interest to note that the inertia terms appearing on the right side of Eqs. (15) and (18) are identical with those appearing in the equations of motion of a totally rigid body. This observation leads to the *principle of solidification* (Ref. 1): *The equations governing the instantaneous motion of a rocket-powered vehicle are formally identical with those of a totally rigid body, provided the following fictitious system of external forces is considered: the actual forces, the Coriolis force, the force due to the unsteadiness of the relative motion within the rocket, and the reactive force.*

3. ROCKET IN FLIGHT

For the particular case of a rocket-powered vehicle in flight, the external forces include gravitational forces and surface forces (Fig. 3). Consequently, if the variation of the acceleration of gravity within the rocket is neglected, the resultant force and the resultant moment are written as

$$\mathbf{F} = m\mathbf{g} + \int_{S_w + S_e} (p\mathbf{n} + \mathbf{f})\, d\sigma$$

$$\mathbf{M} = \left(\int_m \mathbf{OP}\, dm\right) \times \mathbf{g} + \int_{S_w + S_e} \mathbf{OP} \times (p\mathbf{n} + \mathbf{f})\, d\sigma \tag{20}$$

where **g** is the gravitational force per unit mass,* S_w the wetted area of the vehicle, S_e the exit area of the engine, p the local static pressure, and **f** the local tangential stress exerted by the surrounding medium on the control surface $ABCA$.

If p_o is the free-stream static pressure, the integrated effect of the vector $p_o\mathbf{n}$ over the closed surface $ABCA$ is zero, that is,

$$\int_{S_w+S_e} p_o\mathbf{n}\, d\sigma = 0$$

$$\int_{S_w+S_e} \mathbf{OP} \times p_o\mathbf{n}\, d\sigma = 0 \tag{21}$$

Consequently, the external force and the external moment can be rewritten in the form

$$\mathbf{F} = m\mathbf{g} + \int_{S_w+S_e} \boldsymbol{\pi}\, d\sigma$$

$$\mathbf{M} = \left[\int_m \mathbf{OP}\, dm\right] \times \mathbf{g} + \int_{S_w+S_e} \mathbf{OP} \times \boldsymbol{\pi}\, d\sigma \tag{22}$$

where the quantity

$$\boldsymbol{\pi} = (p - p_o)\mathbf{n} + \mathbf{f} \tag{23}$$

is called the *stress vector*.

After Eqs. (15) through (23) are combined, one obtains the results

$$\mathbf{T} + \mathbf{A} + \mathbf{U} + \mathbf{C} + m\mathbf{g} = m\mathbf{a}_o + \dot{\boldsymbol{\omega}} \times \int_m \mathbf{OP}\, dm + \boldsymbol{\omega} \times \left(\boldsymbol{\omega} \times \int_m \mathbf{OP}\, dm\right) \tag{24}$$

$$\mathbf{M}_T + \mathbf{M}_A + \mathbf{M}_U + \mathbf{M}_C + \left(\int_m \mathbf{OP}\, dm\right) \times \mathbf{g}$$

$$= \left(\int_m \mathbf{OP}\, dm\right) \times \mathbf{a}_o + \int_m \mathbf{OP} \times [\dot{\boldsymbol{\omega}} \times \mathbf{OP} + \boldsymbol{\omega} \times (\boldsymbol{\omega} \times \mathbf{OP})]\, dm$$

where the *thrust*, the *aerodynamic force*, the *moment due to the thrust*, and the *aerodynamic moment* are respectively defined as

$$\mathbf{T} = \int_{S_e} (\boldsymbol{\pi} - \mu\mathbf{V}_r)\, d\sigma$$

$$\mathbf{A} = \int_{S_w} \boldsymbol{\pi}\, d\sigma$$

$$\mathbf{M}_T = \int_{S_e} \mathbf{OP} \times (\boldsymbol{\pi} - \mu\mathbf{V}_r)\, d\sigma \tag{25}$$

$$\mathbf{M}_A = \int_{S_w} \mathbf{OP} \times \boldsymbol{\pi}\, d\sigma$$

---

* This vector is due to the attraction exerted by all the bodies of the Universe on the rocket-powered vehicle.

Hence, the aerodynamic force is the integrated effect of the stress vector over the wetted area of the aircraft; in turn, the thrust is equal to the reactive force plus the integrated effect of the stress vector over the exit area of the engine.

4. STABILITY AND CONTROL ANALYSES VERSUS TRAJECTORY ANALYSES

The dynamical equations (24), in combination with the appropriate kinematic relationships, are useful in stability and control analyses as well as in trajectory analyses. They are employed either simultaneously or in a simplified form, depending on the particular problem being considered. In this connection, the considerations which follow are of interest.

To control a vehicle in flight, it is necessary to vary the magnitude and the direction of the forces acting on the vehicle. This is usually achieved by means of devices of various kinds which permit varying the aerodynamic forces and/or the thrust. Owing to the great variety of such devices, an entirely general discussion is difficult. However, the main ideas can be clarified if, for the sake of discussion, one refers to a conventional configuration in which the pitching, yawing, and rolling motions are controlled by movable surfaces called the elevator, the rudder, and ailerons. If the three parameters which characterize the angular position of the elevator, the rudder, and the ailerons around their respective hinge lines are denoted by α_e, α_r, α_a, both the aerodynamic force and the aerodynamic moment obey functional relationships of the form

$$\mathbf{A} = \mathbf{A}(\alpha_e, \alpha_r, \alpha_a, \ldots)$$

$$\mathbf{M}_A = \mathbf{M}_A(\alpha_e, \alpha_r, \alpha_a, \ldots)$$

$$(26)$$

Consequently, it is plain to see that the dynamical equations (24) must, rigorously speaking, be solved simultaneously, since a change in the forces causes a change in the moments and vice versa. This is the point of view taken in stability and control analyses. On the other hand, there are many engineering problems where the hypotheses

$$\frac{\partial \mathbf{A}}{\partial \alpha_e} = \frac{\partial \mathbf{A}}{\partial \alpha_r} = \frac{\partial \mathbf{A}}{\partial \alpha_a} = 0 \qquad (27)$$

can be introduced, meaning that the deflections of the control surfaces have a negligible effect on the forces but a nonnegligible effect on the moments. Under these hypotheses, Eqs. (24) become uncoupled and form two noninteracting sets, in the sense that the equation of forces can be solved independently of that of moments. The latter equation is employed a posteriori to predict the deflections of the control surfaces necessary to maintain the aircraft along the path described by the first of Eqs. (24). This point of view is useful in all those cases where the attention of the observer is focused on the translational, rather than the rotational, behavior of the aircraft, that is, in trajectory studies. It amounts to regarding the aircraft as a *particle of variable mass* and, since it leads to substantial simplifications without great loss in accuracy, it is employed throughout the remainder of this book.

5. SIMPLIFIED EQUATION FOR TRAJECTORY ANALYSES

Although the first of Eqs. (24) describes the trajectory of a rocket for general conditions, it is customary to simplify it somewhat for application to engineering problems. More specifically, after it is assumed that (a) the motion of the fluid with respect to the aircraft is steady or quasi-steady, (b) the Coriolis force associated with the relative motion of the fluid with respect to the vehicle is negligible,* and (c) the inertia terms which depend on the rotation of the rocket with respect to the Fixed Stars are negligible, the following simplified equation describes the absolute motion of the rocket:

$$\mathbf{T} + \mathbf{A} + m\mathbf{g} = m\mathbf{a}_o \qquad (28)$$

5.1 Reference frame rigidly associated with the Earth. This section deals with trajectories which are traveled in the immediate neighborhood of the Earth and are characterized by relatively small time intervals, that is, small with respect to the period of revolution of the Earth around the Sun and the Moon around the Earth. For these applications, the Earth-vehicle system can be conceived as being isolated in space, which is the same as neglecting the differential effects of the Sun and the Moon on the motion of the Earth and the vehicle. Consequently, since the mass of the vehicle is negligible with respect to that of the Earth, the following idealization of the Earth's motion is possible: (a) the center Q of the Earth moves with constant absolute velocity; and (b) the absolute angular velocity of the Earth ω_e is constant and has the same direction as the polar axis.

Because of these hypotheses and in the light of the theorem of composition of accelerations, the following relationships can be readily established between the motion of the vehicle with respect to the Fixed Stars

---

* For all practical applications, the ratio of the Coriolis force to the reactive force is of the order of 10^{-3} or smaller.

and that relative to the Earth:

$$\mathbf{a}_o = \mathbf{a}_{oe} + 2\boldsymbol{\omega}_e \times \mathbf{V}_{oe} + \boldsymbol{\omega}_e \times (\boldsymbol{\omega}_e \times \mathbf{QO}) \qquad (29)$$

where $\mathbf{V}_{oe}$ and $\mathbf{a}_{oe}$ are the velocity and the acceleration of the vehicle with respect to the Earth and $\mathbf{QO}$ is the vector joining the center of the Earth with the instantaneous position of the vehicle. Consequently, Eq. (28) can be rewritten as

$$\mathbf{T} + \mathbf{A} + m\mathbf{g} = m[\mathbf{a}_{oe} + 2\boldsymbol{\omega}_e \times \mathbf{V}_{oe} + \boldsymbol{\omega}_e \times (\boldsymbol{\omega}_e \times \mathbf{QO})] \qquad (30)$$

where $2\boldsymbol{\omega}_e \times \mathbf{V}_{oe}$ is the *Coriolis acceleration* and $\boldsymbol{\omega}_e \times (\boldsymbol{\omega}_e \times \mathbf{QO})$ the *transport acceleration.*

Notice that the transport acceleration depends on the instantaneous latitude of the vehicle, being zero at the Poles and a maximum at the Equator where its order of magnitude is $10^{-3}g_o$ (the symbol g_o denotes the acceleration of gravity at sea level). Furthermore, the Coriolis acceleration depends on the modulus and the direction of the velocity of the vehicle with respect to the Earth, being zero when the flight path is parallel to the polar axis and a maximum when it is perpendicular to this axis; in the latter case, the order of magnitude of this acceleration is $10^{-3}g_o$ for present-day commercial aircraft but may increase to $10^{-1}g_o$ for vehicles travelling at either satellite speeds or velocities approaching the escape velocity.

In the light of these considerations, Eq. (30) can be approximated by either

$$\mathbf{T} + \mathbf{A} + m\mathbf{g} = m[\mathbf{a}_{oe} + 2\boldsymbol{\omega}_e \times \mathbf{V}_{oe}] \qquad (31)$$

or

$$\mathbf{T} + \mathbf{A} + m\mathbf{g} = m\mathbf{a}_{oe} \qquad (32)$$

depending on the degree of accuracy desired in engineering problems. In particular, Eq. (31) is calculated with a precision of $10^{-3}g_o$ and is of considerable interest in many problems characteristic of ballistic missiles, satellite vehicles, and spaceships departing for interplanetary expeditions. On the other hand, Eq. (32) neglects the Coriolis acceleration and is to be employed in those cases where the flight speeds are small compared to the escape velocity or in problems where the emphasis is placed on preliminary design estimates or comparative performance analyses.

6. MISCELLANEOUS TOPICS

Here, several miscellaneous topics are treated in order to complement the previous discussion as well as to extend its applicability to *jet-powered vehicles,* that is, vehicles powered by air-breathing jet engines.

6.1 Arbitrariness of the definitions of thrust and aerodynamic force. Both the exact and the approximate equations of motion indicate that the instantaneous translational motion of a rocket-powered vehicle does not depend on the individual values of the thrust and the aerodynamic force but rather on their sum

$$\mathbf{T} + \mathbf{A} = \int_{S_e} (\boldsymbol{\pi} - \mu \mathbf{V}_r) \, d\sigma + \int_{S_w} \boldsymbol{\pi} \, d\sigma \tag{33}$$

Consequently, it is possible to analyze the flight of a rocket-powered aircraft by discarding definitions (25) and adopting any other set of definitions consistent with Eq. (33). Nevertheless, there exists an important practical justification for the definitions employed in this chapter: the value of the thrust predicted with the first of Eqs. (25) is identical with that which can be measured on a test stand (see exercises).

6.2 Alternative expression for the thrust of a rocket. The expression indicated for the thrust can be transformed into a more familiar form if the following definitions are introduced:

$$\beta = \int_{S_e} \mu \, d\sigma$$

$$\mathbf{V}_{re} = \frac{1}{\beta} \int_{S_e} \mu \mathbf{V}_r \, d\sigma \tag{34}$$

$$p_e = \frac{1}{S_e} \int_{S_e} p \, d\sigma$$

where β is the over-all mass flow, $\mathbf{V}_{re}$ the average relative velocity, and p_e the average pressure over the exit area. If it is assumed that the tangential stress over the exit area is negligible, the thrust becomes

$$\mathbf{T} = -\beta \mathbf{V}_{re} + (p_e - p_o) S_e \mathbf{n}_e \tag{35}$$

and, clearly, is due to the superposition of a momentum component and a pressure component. Whereas the momentum thrust depends only on the flow conditions in the exit section of the rocket, the pressure thrust depends also on the conditions of the atmosphere; it increases with the altitude and reaches its maximum value at $h = \infty$, where $p_o = 0$.

6.3 Jet-powered vehicle. The derivation of the equations of motion for a jet-powered vehicle is accomplished by a procedure similar to that developed for a rocket-powered vehicle. However, three additional difficulties exist. First, air enters the vehicle through the inlet section of the engine; second, the fluid conditions at the inlet of the engine are, generally

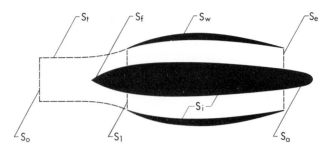

Fig. 4. Terminology employed for a jet-powered vehicle.

speaking, different from the free-stream conditions; and third, rotating machinery, such as compressors and turbines, may be present.

Although a great variety of configurations can be imagined, attention is focused on the one indicated in Fig. 4, where S_1 denotes the inlet area of the engine, S_e the exit area, S_f the forebody area (includes all the surfaces preceding the inlet section), S_a the afterbody area (includes all the surfaces following the exit section), S_i the area associated with the internal walls of the engine (includes rotating machinery, when present), S_o the cross-sectional area of the streamtube preceding the engine evaluated at a large distance from the aircraft, S_t the lateral area of the streamtube, and S_w the wetted area of the engine nacelle and the vehicle. Particular cases of this configuration are the rocket, the ramjet, the turbojet (with and without afterburner), and the turbofan; special subcases occur when the forebody area is absent (simple inlet) or when the afterbody area is absent (simple outlet). At any rate, regardless of the particular configuration, the various forms (28) through (32) of the equation of forces* are still valid, provided that the thrust and the aerodynamic force are defined as

$$\mathbf{T} = \int_{S_e + S_o} (\boldsymbol{\pi} - \mu \mathbf{V}_r)\, d\sigma$$

$$\mathbf{A} = \int_{S_t + S_w + S_a} \boldsymbol{\pi}\, d\sigma \tag{36}$$

6.4 Alternative expression for the thrust of a jet engine. The definition indicated for the thrust can be transformed into a more familiar form by a procedure similar to that used for the rocket. If the average pressure

---

* The equation of moments differs from that of a rocket because of the gyroscopic effects due to the rotating machinery. The calculation of the gyroscopic moment is to be carried out with the method outlined in Chapter 2.

$S_w \equiv$ area CAB

$S_i \equiv$ area CHKB

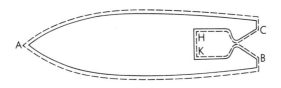

FIGURE 5

and relative velocity far away from the aircraft are denoted by p_o and $\mathbf{V}_{ro}$, the average pressure and relative velocity at the exit section by p_e and $\mathbf{V}_{re}$, and the moduli of the inlet and outlet mass flows by β_o and β_e, the following result can be derived:

$$\mathbf{T} = \beta_o \mathbf{V}_{ro} - \beta_e \mathbf{V}_{re} + (p_e - p_o)S_e \mathbf{n}_e \qquad (37)$$

Incidentally, the inlet and outlet mass flows satisfy the relationship

$$\beta_e = \beta_o + \beta \qquad (38)$$

where $\beta = -dm/dt$ is the mass of fuel injected into the combustion chamber per unit time.

EXERCISES

1. Consider a closed surface σ in the xyz-space. If p_o is a constant scalar quantity and $\mathbf{n}$ a unit vector normal to the area element $d\sigma$ (positive inward), show that

$$\int_\sigma p_o \mathbf{n}\, d\sigma = 0, \qquad \int_\sigma \mathbf{OP} \times p_o \mathbf{n}\, d\sigma = 0 \qquad (39)$$

2. With reference to the rotational motion of a rocket vehicle, derive the equation of moments (18) making use of the vectorial identity

$$\begin{aligned}
\mathbf{OP} \times \mathbf{H} = \quad & \nabla \cdot \{\rho \mathbf{V}_r[(\mathbf{OP} \times \mathbf{V}_r) \cdot \mathbf{i}]\}\mathbf{i} \\
& + \nabla \cdot \{\rho \mathbf{V}_r[(\mathbf{OP} \times \mathbf{V}_r) \cdot \mathbf{j}]\}\mathbf{j} \\
& + \nabla \cdot \{\rho \mathbf{V}_r[(\mathbf{OP} \times \mathbf{V}_r) \cdot \mathbf{k}]\}\mathbf{k}
\end{aligned} \qquad (40)$$

3. For a rocket-powered vehicle, consider the system of particles bounded by the wetted area S_w and the inner walls of the engine S_i (Fig. 5). Assuming that the mass of the propellant burning in the combustion chamber and flowing in the nozzle at a given time instant is small

$S_o \equiv$ area CEFB
$S_e \equiv$ area BC

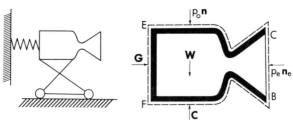

FIGURE 6

with respect to the mass of the vehicle, prove that

$$T = \int_{S_i} \boldsymbol{\pi} \, d\sigma \tag{41}$$

which means that the thrust is actually the integrated effect of the stress vector over the inner walls of the engine.

4. Consider an axially-symmetric rocket engine mounted on a carriage in a test stand (Fig. 6), and assume that the axis of the engine is horizontal. Assume that the rocket, which is placed against a thrust gauge, is fired and that steady conditions are reached for the flow in the nozzle. Neglecting the transport acceleration due to the daily rotation of the Earth around its polar axis and assuming a constant pressure p_o over the surface S_o, show that the force **G** transmitted by the thrust gauge to the walls of the rocket is given by

$$\mathbf{G} = \beta \mathbf{V}_{re} - (p_e - p_o)S_e\mathbf{n}_e \tag{42}$$

that is, prove that

$$\mathbf{G} = -\mathbf{T} \tag{43}$$

5. For the configuration indicated in Fig. 4, show that the definitions of thrust and aerodynamic force can be rewritten in the equivalent form

$$\mathbf{T} = \int_{S_i} \boldsymbol{\pi} \, d\sigma - \int_{S_1} \boldsymbol{\pi} \, d\sigma - \beta_0(\mathbf{V}_{r1} - \mathbf{V}_{ro})$$

$$\mathbf{A} = \int_{S_f+S_1+S_w+S_a} \boldsymbol{\pi} \, d\sigma + \beta_0(\mathbf{V}_{r1} - \mathbf{V}_{ro}) \tag{44}$$

Generally speaking, therefore, the thrust is not identical with the integrated effect of the stress vector over the internal area of the engine. However, the identity in question occurs for an engine operating in such a way that the inlet conditions and the free-stream conditions are identical.

REFERENCES

1. GANTMACHER, F. R. and LEVIN, L. M., *Equations of Motion of a Rocket*, NACA TM No. 1255, 1950.
2. ROSSER, J. B., NEWTON, R. R., and GROSS, G. L., *Mathematical Theory of Rocket Flight*, McGraw-Hill Book Company, Inc., New York, 1947.
3. MATTIOLI, E., *Spinta e Resistenza nella Propulsione a Razzo*, L'Aerotecnica, Vol. 34, No. 4, 1954.
4. SUTTON, G. P., *Rocket Propulsion Elements*, John Wiley and Sons, Inc., New York, 1956.
5. KUETHE, A. M. and SCHETZER, J. D., *Foundations of Aerodynamics*, John Wiley and Sons, Inc., New York, 1950.
6. PRANDTL, L. and TIETJENS, O. G., *Fundamentals of Hydro-and-Aeromechanics*, McGraw-Hill Book Company, Inc., New York, 1934.
7. KLEIN, H., *The Calculation of the Scoop Drag for a General Configuration in a Supersonic Stream*, Douglas Aircraft Company, Inc., Santa Monica Division, Report No. SM–13744, 1950.
8. WYATT, D. M. D., *Aerodynamic Forces Associated with Inlets of Turbojet Installations*, Aerospace Engineering, Vol. 10, No. 10, 1951.
9. WEATHERSTON, R. C., *Thrust and Drag*, ARS Journal, Vol. 22, No. 6, 1952.
10. MIELE, A., *Equations of Motion of a Rocket-Powered Aircraft*, Boeing Scientific Research Laboratories, Flight Sciences Laboratory, TR No. 20, 1960.

CHAPTER 4

SCALAR EQUATIONS FOR FLIGHT
OVER A FLAT EARTH

1. INTRODUCTION

This chapter is concerned with trajectories characterized by short ranges and/or velocities which are small with respect to the escape velocity. For the analysis of these trajectories, the Earth can be regarded as ideally flat and nonrotating, so that the general dynamical equation reduces to the simplified form represented by Eq. (3–32). The latter is rewritten as

$$\mathbf{T} + \mathbf{A} + m\mathbf{g} = m\mathbf{a} = m\frac{d\mathbf{V}}{dt} \qquad (1)$$

where $\mathbf{T}$ is the thrust, $\mathbf{A}$ the aerodynamic force, m the mass, $\mathbf{g}$ the acceleration of gravity, $\mathbf{a}$ the acceleration of the aircraft with respect to the Earth (note that the subscripts o and e used in Chapter 3 are dropped here, since no ambiguity is possible), and t the time. Furthermore, the symbol

$$\mathbf{V} = \frac{d\mathbf{EO}}{dt} \qquad (2)$$

denotes the velocity of the aircraft with respect to the Earth, $\mathbf{EO}$ being the vector which joins point E on the surface of the Earth with the aircraft.

In the following sections, the scalar equations associated with the vectorial equations (1) and (2) are derived for the general case of paths in a three-dimensional space. These equations are then reduced to those relevant to flight in either a vertical plane or a horizontal plane. To do so, it is necessary to define several reference systems and derive rules relevant to the transformation of coordinates from one system to another.

2. BASIC COORDINATE SYSTEMS

The coordinate systems of interest for flight over a flat Earth are the following (Fig. 1): the ground axes system $EXYZ$, the local horizon system $Ox_hy_hz_h$, the wind axes system $Ox_wy_wz_w$, and the body axes system $Ox_by_bz_b$. These systems are now described with the assumption that the aircraft has a plane of symmetry (Refs. 1 and 6).

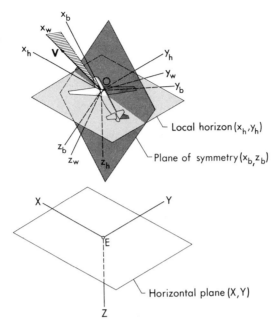

FIG. 1. Coordinate systems for flight over a flat Earth.

The *ground axes system* is fixed with respect to the Earth and is defined as follows: its origin E is a point on the Earth's surface; the Z-axis is vertical and positive downward; the X-axis and the Y-axis are contained in a horizontal plane and are directed in such a way that the trihedral $EXYZ$ is right-handed.

The *local horizon system* is defined as follows: its origin O is a point in the plane of symmetry of the vehicle; its axes and the corresponding axes of the ground system are always parallel.

If the atmosphere is assumed to be at rest with respect to the Earth, the *wind axes system* is defined as follows: the x_w-axis is tangent to the flight path and is positive forward; the z_w-axis is perpendicular to the x_w-axis, contained in the plane of symmetry, and positive downward for the normal flight attitude of the aircraft; the y_w-axis is perpendicular to the $x_w z_w$-plane and is directed in such a way that the trihedral $Ox_w y_w z_w$ is right-handed.

Finally, the *body axes system* is defined as follows: the x_b-axis is contained in the plane of symmetry and is positive forward; the z_b-axis is perpendicular to the x_b-axis, contained in the plane of symmetry, and positive downward for the normal flight attitude of the aircraft; the y_b-axis is perpendicular to the plane of symmetry and is directed in such a way that the trihedral $Ox_b y_b z_b$ is right-handed.

TABLE 1

DIRECTION COSINES OF THE WIND AXES WITH RESPECT TO
THE LOCAL HORIZON

	$\mathbf{i}_w$	$\mathbf{j}_w$	$\mathbf{k}_w$
$\mathbf{i}_h$	$\cos \gamma \cos \chi$	$\sin \mu \sin \gamma \cos \chi$ $-\cos \mu \sin \chi$	$\cos \mu \sin \gamma \cos \chi$ $+\sin \mu \sin \chi$
$\mathbf{j}_h$	$\cos \gamma \sin \chi$	$\sin \mu \sin \gamma \sin \chi$ $+\cos \mu \cos \chi$	$\cos \mu \sin \gamma \sin \chi$ $-\sin \mu \cos \chi$
$\mathbf{k}_h$	$-\sin \gamma$	$\sin \mu \cos \gamma$	$\cos \mu \cos \gamma$

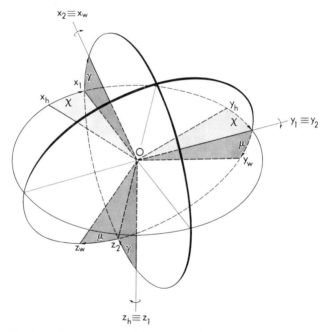

FIG. 2. System of rotations leading from the local horizon to the wind axes.

3. ANGULAR RELATIONSHIPS

In this section, the angular relationships between the different co-ordinate systems are derived; more specifically, attention is focused on the following pairs: local horizon-ground axes, wind axes-local horizon, and body axes-wind axes.

3.1 Local horizon-ground axes. Since the local horizon axes and the ground axes are always parallel, the following matrix relationship exists between the corresponding unit vectors:

$$\begin{bmatrix} \mathbf{i}_h \\ \mathbf{j}_h \\ \mathbf{k}_h \end{bmatrix} = \begin{bmatrix} \mathbf{i}_e \\ \mathbf{j}_e \\ \mathbf{k}_e \end{bmatrix} \tag{3}$$

where the subscript e refers to the ground system.

3.2 Wind axes-local horizon. The orientation of the wind axes with respect to the local horizon can be described in terms of three angular parameters. Although an infinite number of combinations of parameters can be imagined, the particular system which has become standard in aerodynamics is based on the three successive rotations* of *velocity yaw* χ, *velocity pitch* γ, and *velocity roll* μ. To define these rotations, it is convenient to introduce two intermediate coordinate systems whose properties are as follows (Fig. 2): the system $Ox_1y_1z_1$ is obtained from the local horizon system by means of a rotation χ around the z_h-axis; the system $Ox_2y_2z_2$ is obtained from $Ox_1y_1z_1$ by means of a rotation γ around the y_1-axis; the wind axes system is obtained from $Ox_2y_2z_2$ by means of a rotation μ around the x_2-axis.

These partial transformations are described by the matrix equations

$$\begin{bmatrix} \mathbf{i}_1 \\ \mathbf{j}_1 \\ \mathbf{k}_1 \end{bmatrix} = \begin{bmatrix} \cos\chi & \sin\chi & 0 \\ -\sin\chi & \cos\chi & 0 \\ 0 & 0 & 1 \end{bmatrix} \begin{bmatrix} \mathbf{i}_h \\ \mathbf{j}_h \\ \mathbf{k}_h \end{bmatrix} \tag{4}$$

$$\begin{bmatrix} \mathbf{i}_2 \\ \mathbf{j}_2 \\ \mathbf{k}_2 \end{bmatrix} = \begin{bmatrix} \cos\gamma & 0 & -\sin\gamma \\ 0 & 1 & 0 \\ \sin\gamma & 0 & \cos\gamma \end{bmatrix} \begin{bmatrix} \mathbf{i}_1 \\ \mathbf{j}_1 \\ \mathbf{k}_1 \end{bmatrix} \tag{5}$$

$$\begin{bmatrix} \mathbf{i}_w \\ \mathbf{j}_w \\ \mathbf{k}_w \end{bmatrix} = \begin{bmatrix} 1 & 0 & 0 \\ 0 & \cos\mu & \sin\mu \\ 0 & -\sin\mu & \cos\mu \end{bmatrix} \begin{bmatrix} \mathbf{i}_2 \\ \mathbf{j}_2 \\ \mathbf{k}_2 \end{bmatrix} \tag{6}$$

in which each scalar matrix is orthogonal. Consequently, after a matrix

---

* All rotations considered in this chapter are positive in the counterclockwise sense. It is emphasized that these rotations should not be confused with those of *yaw*, *pitch*, and *roll*, which are generally employed to designate the orientation of the *body axes* with respect to the local horizon.

multiplication is performed, the relationship between the wind axes and the local horizon is given by

$$
\begin{bmatrix} \mathbf{i}_w \\ \mathbf{j}_w \\ \mathbf{k}_w \end{bmatrix} = \begin{bmatrix} \cos\gamma\cos\chi & \cos\gamma\sin\chi & -\sin\gamma \\ \begin{matrix}\sin\mu\sin\gamma\cos\chi \\ -\cos\mu\sin\chi\end{matrix} & \begin{matrix}\sin\mu\sin\gamma\sin\chi \\ +\cos\mu\cos\chi\end{matrix} & \sin\mu\cos\gamma \\ \begin{matrix}\cos\mu\sin\gamma\cos\chi \\ +\sin\mu\sin\chi\end{matrix} & \begin{matrix}\cos\mu\sin\gamma\sin\chi \\ -\sin\mu\cos\chi\end{matrix} & \cos\mu\cos\gamma \end{bmatrix} \begin{bmatrix} \mathbf{i}_h \\ \mathbf{j}_h \\ \mathbf{k}_h \end{bmatrix} \quad (7)
$$

where the scalar matrix is also orthogonal (Table 1).

3.3 Body axes-wind axes. Since the x_b, z_b, z_w-axes are contained in the plane of symmetry of the aircraft, only two angular coordinates, the *sideslip angle* σ and the *angle of attack* α, are necessary to determine the orientation of the body axes with respect to the wind axes. The system of rotations necessary to perform the transformation from the wind axes to the body axes is easily understood, if an intermediate coordinate system is introduced. Its properties are the following (Fig. 3): the system $Ox_3y_3z_3$ is obtained from the wind axes system by means of a rotation σ around the z_w-axis; in turn, the body axes system is obtained from $Ox_3y_3z_3$ by means of a rotation α around the y_3-axis. In matrix notation, these partial rotations are expressed by

$$
\begin{bmatrix} \mathbf{i}_3 \\ \mathbf{j}_3 \\ \mathbf{k}_3 \end{bmatrix} = \begin{bmatrix} \cos\sigma & \sin\sigma & 0 \\ -\sin\sigma & \cos\sigma & 0 \\ 0 & 0 & 1 \end{bmatrix} \begin{bmatrix} \mathbf{i}_w \\ \mathbf{j}_w \\ \mathbf{k}_w \end{bmatrix} \quad (8)
$$

$$
\begin{bmatrix} \mathbf{i}_b \\ \mathbf{j}_b \\ \mathbf{k}_b \end{bmatrix} = \begin{bmatrix} \cos\alpha & 0 & -\sin\alpha \\ 0 & 1 & 0 \\ \sin\alpha & 0 & \cos\alpha \end{bmatrix} \begin{bmatrix} \mathbf{i}_3 \\ \mathbf{j}_3 \\ \mathbf{k}_3 \end{bmatrix} \quad (9)
$$

so that the relationship between the body axes and the wind axes becomes (Table 2)

$$
\begin{bmatrix} \mathbf{i}_b \\ \mathbf{j}_b \\ \mathbf{k}_b \end{bmatrix} = \begin{bmatrix} \cos\alpha\cos\sigma & \cos\alpha\sin\sigma & -\sin\alpha \\ -\sin\sigma & \cos\sigma & 0 \\ \sin\alpha\cos\sigma & \sin\alpha\sin\sigma & \cos\alpha \end{bmatrix} \begin{bmatrix} \mathbf{i}_w \\ \mathbf{j}_w \\ \mathbf{k}_w \end{bmatrix} \quad (10)
$$

4. EVOLUTORY VELOCITY

In this section, the evolutory velocity, that is, the angular velocity of the wind axes with respect to the Earth axes, is calculated. To do so, con-

TABLE 2

DIRECTION COSINES OF THE BODY AXES WITH RESPECT TO
THE WIND AXES

	$\mathbf{i}_b$	$\mathbf{j}_b$	$\mathbf{k}_b$
$\mathbf{i}_w$	$\cos\alpha\cos\sigma$	$-\sin\sigma$	$\sin\alpha\cos\sigma$
$\mathbf{j}_w$	$\cos\alpha\sin\sigma$	$\cos\sigma$	$\sin\alpha\sin\sigma$
$\mathbf{k}_w$	$-\sin\alpha$	0	$\cos\alpha$

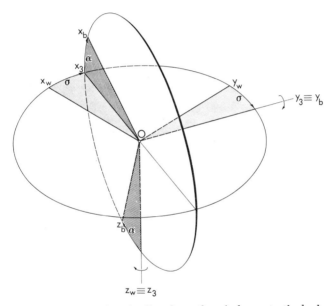

FIG. 3. System of rotations leading from the wind axes to the body axes.

sider the behavior of the aircraft between time instants t and $t + dt$, and denote the infinitesimal variations of the velocity yaw angle, the velocity pitch angle, and the velocity roll angle by $d\chi$, $d\gamma$, $d\mu$. Since these infinitesimal scalar rotations occur around the z_h-axis, the y_1-axis, and the x_2-axis, respectively, the infinitesimal vectorial rotation is represented by

$$d\mathbf{\Omega}_w = d\mu\mathbf{i}_2 + d\gamma\mathbf{j}_1 + d\chi\mathbf{k}_h \qquad (11)$$

Hence, in accordance with Chapter 1, the evolutory velocity becomes

$$\mathbf{\omega}_w = \frac{d\mathbf{\Omega}_w}{dt} = \dot{\mu}\mathbf{i}_2 + \dot{\gamma}\mathbf{j}_1 + \dot{\chi}\mathbf{k}_h \qquad (12)$$

Owing to the fact that the previous unit vectors and those of the wind axes system are related by the matrix equation

$$
\begin{bmatrix} \mathbf{i}_2 \\ \mathbf{j}_1 \\ \mathbf{k}_h \end{bmatrix} = \begin{bmatrix} 1 & 0 & 0 \\ 0 & \cos\mu & -\sin\mu \\ -\sin\gamma & \sin\mu\cos\gamma & \cos\mu\cos\gamma \end{bmatrix} \begin{bmatrix} \mathbf{i}_w \\ \mathbf{j}_w \\ \mathbf{k}_w \end{bmatrix}
\tag{13}
$$

the evolutory velocity can be rewritten in terms of its components on the wind axes as

$$
\boldsymbol{\omega}_w = p_w \mathbf{i}_w + q_w \mathbf{j}_w + r_w \mathbf{k}_w
\tag{14}
$$

where

$$
\begin{bmatrix} p_w \\ q_w \\ r_w \end{bmatrix} = \begin{bmatrix} 1 & 0 & -\sin\gamma \\ 0 & \cos\mu & \sin\mu\cos\gamma \\ 0 & -\sin\mu & \cos\mu\cos\gamma \end{bmatrix} \begin{bmatrix} \dot{\mu} \\ \dot{\gamma} \\ \dot{\chi} \end{bmatrix}
\tag{15}
$$

5. KINEMATIC RELATIONSHIPS

In this section, the scalar relationships corresponding to the vectorial equation (2) are derived. It is observed that, since the velocity is collinear with the x_w-axis, the left-hand side of Eq. (2) can be represented by

$$
\mathbf{V} = V\mathbf{i}_w = V[\cos\gamma\cos\chi\,\mathbf{i}_h + \cos\gamma\sin\chi\,\mathbf{j}_h - \sin\gamma\,\mathbf{k}_h]
\tag{16}
$$

It is also observed that the vector joining the origin of the ground system with the aircraft can be written in the form

$$
\mathbf{EO} = X\mathbf{i}_h + Y\mathbf{j}_h + Z\mathbf{k}_h
\tag{17}
$$

Since the altitude above sea level satisfies the relation

$$
h = -Z + \text{Const}
\tag{18}
$$

the time derivative of this vector becomes

$$
\frac{d\mathbf{EO}}{dt} = \dot{X}\mathbf{i}_h + \dot{Y}\mathbf{j}_h - \dot{h}\mathbf{k}_h
\tag{19}
$$

Consequently, if Eqs. (2), (16), and (19) are combined, the following relationships are derived:

$$
\begin{aligned}
\dot{X} &= V\cos\gamma\cos\chi \\
\dot{Y} &= V\cos\gamma\sin\chi \\
\dot{h} &= V\sin\gamma
\end{aligned}
\tag{20}
$$

6. DYNAMIC RELATIONSHIPS

In this section, the vectorial equation (1) is reduced to its equivalent scalar form. The method employed is analogous to that of the previous section and consists of determining the components of each vector on the wind axes.

First, in analogy with the sideslip angle and the angle of attack, the *thrust sideslip angle* ν and the *thrust angle of attack* ϵ are introduced. These angles are the successive rotations to which the wind axes system must be subjected in order to turn the x_w-axis in a direction parallel to the thrust. Consequently, the thrust becomes

$$\mathbf{T} = T[\cos \epsilon \cos \nu \, \mathbf{i}_w + \cos \epsilon \sin \nu \mathbf{j}_w - \sin \epsilon \mathbf{k}_w] \tag{21}$$

Second, the aerodynamic force is written in terms of its components on the wind axes as*

$$\mathbf{A} = -(D\mathbf{i}_w + Q\mathbf{j}_w + L\mathbf{k}_w) \tag{22}$$

where D is the *drag*, Q the *side force*, and L the *lift*. Third, if it is noted that the acceleration of gravity has the same direction as the Z-axis, the following relation is obtained:

$$\mathbf{g} = g[-\sin \gamma \mathbf{i}_w + \sin \mu \cos \gamma \mathbf{j}_w + \cos \mu \cos \gamma \mathbf{k}_w] \tag{23}$$

Fourth, after calculating the time derivative of Eq. (16), one obtains the following expression for the acceleration of the aircraft relative to the Earth:

$$\frac{d\mathbf{V}}{dt} = \dot{V}\mathbf{i}_w + V \frac{d\mathbf{i}_w}{dt} \tag{24}$$

where the dot sign denotes a derivative with respect to time. In consideration of Poisson's formulas, the time rate of change of the unit vector tangent to the flight path and the evolutory velocity are related by

$$\frac{d\mathbf{i}_w}{dt} = \boldsymbol{\omega}_w \times \mathbf{i}_w = r_w\mathbf{j}_w - q_w\mathbf{k}_w \tag{25}$$

Consequently, if the equation of forces is combined with Eqs. (21) through (25), the following scalar equations are derived:

$$T \cos \epsilon \cos \nu - D - mg \sin \gamma - m\dot{V} = 0$$

$$T \cos \epsilon \sin \nu - Q + mg \sin \mu \cos \gamma - mVr_w = 0 \tag{26}$$

$$T \sin \epsilon + L - mg \cos \mu \cos \gamma - mVq_w = 0$$

---

* No special significance is implied in the signs appearing on the right-hand side of Eq. (22). These signs merely reflect the convention adopted in this book with regard to the positive values for the drag, the side force, and the lift.

and, in consideration of Eq. (15), can be rewritten in the form

$$T \cos \epsilon \cos \nu - D - mg \sin \gamma - m\dot{V} = 0$$

$$T \cos \epsilon \sin \nu - Q + mg \sin \mu \cos \gamma$$
$$+ mV \left(-\dot{\chi} \cos \mu \cos \gamma + \dot{\gamma} \sin \mu \right) = 0 \qquad (27)$$

$$T \sin \epsilon + L - mg \cos \mu \cos \gamma$$
$$- mV(\dot{\chi} \sin \mu \cos \gamma + \dot{\gamma} \cos \mu) = 0$$

where the mass is variable and is related to the engine mass flow β in the following manner:

$$\dot{m} + \beta = 0 \qquad (28)$$

7. AIRCRAFT AND ENGINE CHARACTERISTICS

The translational motion of an aircraft having variable mass and operating in a three-dimensional space over a flat Earth is described by the seven equations (20), (27), and (28). Contained in these relations are the five functions

$$f_1 = D, \quad f_2 = Q, \quad f_3 = L, \quad f_4 = T, \quad f_5 = \beta \qquad (29)$$

which depend on the characteristics of the aircraft and the engine. Hence, in order to understand the nature of the differential system, a discussion of these functions is necessary.

If the characteristics of the aircraft and the engine are evaluated from a quasi-steady point of view, the functions (29) can be assumed to have the form

$$f_k = f_k(h, V, \sigma, \alpha, \pi, \nu, \epsilon), \quad k = 1, \ldots, 5 \qquad (30)$$

where π is a variable controlling the engine performance and is called the *engine control parameter, thrust control parameter,* or *power setting.* As an example, π can be identified with the rotor speed or the corrected rotor speed of a turbojet or turbofan engine, with the fuel-to-air ratio or the corrected fuel-to-air ratio of a ramjet engine, and with the combustion chamber pressure or the propellant mass flow of a rocket engine (see Chapter 7).

An important particular case occurs when the aircraft sideslip angle and the thrust sideslip angle are simultaneously zero, that is,

$$\sigma = \nu = 0 \qquad (31)$$

Under this condition, the side force of a symmetric configuration is

$Q = 0$; furthermore, the remaining functions (30) reduce to

$$f_k = f_k(h, V, \alpha, \pi, \epsilon), \qquad k = 1, 3, 4, 5 \tag{32}$$

A further simplification is possible, if it can be assumed that (a) the parameters controlling the aircraft do not interact with those controlling the engine and (b) the engine performance is independent of the inclination of the thrust. Under these hypotheses, the functions (32) are written in the form

$$D = D(h, V, \alpha), \qquad L = L(h, V, \alpha) \tag{33}$$

$$T = T(h, V, \pi), \qquad \beta = \beta(h, V, \pi) \tag{34}$$

whose justification is presented in Chapters 6 and 7. It is emphasized that these relationships are only approximations of the actual behavior of aircraft and engines. In fact, a change in the thrust control parameter generally affects both the drag and the lift; conversely, a change in the angle of attack usually affects the thrust of the engine.

8. GENERAL DISCUSSION AND PARTICULAR CASES

In the light of the functional relationships (30), the differential system composed of Eqs. (20), (27), and (28) has one independent variable, the time, and thirteen dependent variables, which include the seven derivated variables (*state variables*)

$$X, Y, h, V, \chi, \gamma, m \tag{35}$$

and the six nonderivated variables (*control variables*)

$$\mu, \sigma, \alpha, \pi, \nu, \epsilon \tag{36}$$

This means that the number of degrees of freedom* is

$$n = 13 - 7 = 6 \tag{37}$$

which is logical, since it is possible to control the flight path by controlling the time history of the rudder deflection, the elevator deflection, the aileron deflection, the thrust control parameter, the thrust sideslip angle, and the thrust angle of attack.†

---

* By definition, the *number of mathematical degrees of freedom* of a differential system is equal to the difference between the number of dependent variables and the number of equations.

† In the present discussion, it is assumed that the engine is gimballed with respect to the aircraft, so that the thrust angle of attack and the thrust sideslip angle are independent of both the angle of attack and the sideslip angle of the aircraft.

8.1 Specified maneuver of the controls. Suppose that the controls of the aircraft and the engine are manipulated in such a way that the six nonderivated variables (36) are prescribed functions of the time. In this case, the integration of the equations of motion consists of determining the time history of the remaining seven derivated variables (35) subject to appropriate initial and/or final conditions. Since all the equations are of the first order, the general solution depends on seven integration constants. These constants can be identified, for instance, with the initial values of the seven derivated variables of the problem.

8.2 Engine fixed with respect to the aircraft. If the engine is fixed with respect to the aircraft, the angles defining the orientation of the engine and the aircraft with respect to the flight path are no longer independent but are related by the matrix equation

$$\begin{bmatrix} \cos \alpha \cos \sigma & \cos \alpha \sin \sigma & -\sin \alpha \\ -\sin \sigma & \cos \sigma & 0 \\ \sin \alpha \cos \sigma & \sin \alpha \sin \sigma & \cos \alpha \end{bmatrix} \begin{bmatrix} \cos \epsilon \cos \nu \\ \cos \epsilon \sin \nu \\ -\sin \epsilon \end{bmatrix} = \begin{bmatrix} K_1 \\ K_2 \\ K_3 \end{bmatrix} \quad (38)$$

where the constants appearing on the right-hand side are the direction cosines of the thrust with respect to the body axes. By matrix multiplication, the above expression leads to the relationships

$$\cos \epsilon \cos \alpha \cos (\nu - \sigma) + \sin \epsilon \sin \alpha = K_1$$

$$\cos \epsilon \sin (\nu - \sigma) = K_2 \quad (39)$$

$$\cos \epsilon \sin \alpha \cos (\nu - \sigma) - \sin \epsilon \cos \alpha = K_3$$

of which only two are independent because

$$K_1^2 + K_2^2 + K_3^2 = 1 \quad (40)$$

Consequently, the equations of motion must be completed by any two of Eqs. (39). Since the new differential system involves nine equations and thirteen dependent variables, the number of degrees of freedom becomes $n = 4$. This result is logical in view of the possibility of controlling the flight path by means of the rudder, the elevator, the aileron, and the thrust control parameter.

8.3 Flight in a vertical plane. In this section, attention is focused on the class of paths which are flown in a vertical plane with the thrust and velocity vectors contained in the plane of symmetry. This category of trajectories is represented by the mathematical conditions

$$Y = \text{Const}, \quad \nu = \sigma = 0 \quad (41)$$

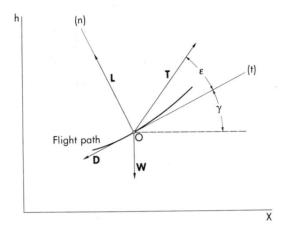

FIG. 4. Forces acting on the aircraft for flight in a vertical plane.

the first of which, in combination with the kinematic relationship in the Y-direction, leads to $\chi = 0$. Since the zero-sideslip condition and the symmetry of the aircraft imply that $Q = 0$, the dynamical relationship in the y_w-direction admits the solution $\mu = 0$, meaning that the plane of symmetry is vertical at all time instants. Consequently, the motion of the aircraft in a vertical plane (Fig. 4) is represented by the five differential equations*

$$\dot{X} - V \cos \gamma = 0$$

$$\dot{h} - V \sin \gamma = 0$$

$$T \cos \epsilon - D - m(g \sin \gamma + \dot{V}) = 0 \qquad (42)$$

$$T \sin \epsilon + L - m(g \cos \gamma + V\dot{\gamma}) = 0$$

$$\dot{m} + \beta = 0$$

which involve the eight dependent variables

$$X, h, V, \gamma, m, \alpha, \pi, \epsilon \qquad (43)$$

and admit $n = 3$ degrees of freedom. This is logical, since the flight path can be varied by controlling the time history of the elevator deflection, the thrust control parameter, and the thrust angle of attack. On the

---

* Generally speaking, the scalar equations on the wind axes and those on the principal axes (tangent, principal normal, binormal) are not identical. However, this identity exists for the particular case of flight in a vertical plane.

other hand, if the engine is fixed with respect to the aircraft, these equations must be completed by the relationship

$$\epsilon - \alpha = \text{Const} \tag{44}$$

so that the number of degrees of freedom becomes $n = 2$.

8.4 Flight in a horizontal plane. This section considers the class of paths which are flown in a horizontal plane with the thrust and velocity vectors contained in the plane of symmetry. This category of trajectories is represented by the mathematical conditions

$$h = \text{Const}, \qquad \nu = \sigma = 0 \tag{45}$$

the first of which, in combination with the kinematic relationship in the vertical direction, leads to $\gamma = 0$ at all time instants. After considering that $Q = 0$, one concludes that the motion of the aircraft in a horizontal plane (Fig. 5) is represented by the six differential equations

$$\dot{X} - V \cos \chi = 0$$
$$\dot{Y} - V \sin \chi = 0$$
$$T \cos \epsilon - D - m\dot{V} = 0$$
$$g \sin \mu - V\dot{\chi} \cos \mu = 0 \tag{46}$$
$$T \sin \epsilon + L - m(g \cos \mu + V\dot{\chi} \sin \mu) = 0$$
$$\dot{m} + \beta = 0$$

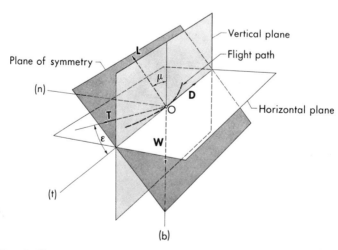

FIG. 5. Forces acting on the aircraft for flight in a horizontal plane.

which include the nine dependent variables

$$X, Y, V, \chi, m, \mu, \alpha, \pi, \epsilon \tag{47}$$

and admit $n = 3$ degrees of freedom. If the engine is fixed with respect to the aircraft, these equations must be completed by Eq. (44), so that the number of degrees of freedom reduces to $n = 2$.

In practice, it is customary to replace the third, fourth, and fifth of Eqs. (46) by the equivalent set

$$T \cos \epsilon - D - m\dot{V} = 0$$

$$(T \sin \epsilon + L) \sin \mu - mV\dot{\chi} = 0 \tag{48}$$

$$(T \sin \epsilon + L) \cos \mu - mg = 0$$

which can be obtained by projecting the equation of forces on the axes of the principal trihedral (tangent, principal normal, binormal).

EXERCISES

1. Consider an aircraft flying in a vertical plane in such a way that $\sigma = \nu = \epsilon = 0$. Show that the dynamical equation leads to the following scalar relationships on the local horizon axes:

$$(T - D) \cos \gamma - L \sin \gamma = m\ddot{X}$$

$$(T - D) \sin \gamma + L \cos \gamma - mg = m\ddot{h} \tag{49}$$

2. For an aircraft flying in a horizontal plane in such a way that $\sigma = \nu = \epsilon = 0$, show that the dynamical equation yields the following scalar relationships on the local horizon axes:

$$(T - D) \cos \chi - L \sin \mu \sin \chi = m\ddot{X}$$

$$(T - D) \sin \chi + L \sin \mu \cos \chi = m\ddot{Y} \tag{50}$$

$$L \cos \mu - mg = 0$$

3. Show that the unit vectors associated with the principal trihedral of the trajectory are given by

$$\begin{bmatrix} \mathbf{t} \\ \mathbf{n} \\ \mathbf{b} \end{bmatrix} = \begin{bmatrix} 1 & 0 & 0 \\ 0 & A & -B \\ 0 & B & A \end{bmatrix} \begin{bmatrix} \mathbf{i}_w \\ \mathbf{j}_w \\ \mathbf{k}_w \end{bmatrix} \tag{51}$$

where

$$A = \frac{r}{V} r_w, \qquad B = \frac{r}{V} q_w \tag{52}$$

(the symbol r denotes the radius of curvature of the trajectory).

4. Show that the radius of curvature of the trajectory described by the aircraft is given by

$$r = \frac{V}{\sqrt{(\dot{\gamma})^2 + (\dot{\chi}\cos\gamma)^2}}\tag{53}$$

and, for a right turn in a horizontal plane, simplifies to

$$r = \frac{V^2}{g}\cot\mu\tag{54}$$

5. Denoting the angular velocity of the body axes system with respect to the Earth by $\boldsymbol{\omega}_b$, prove that this vector and the evolutory velocity satisfy the relationship

$$\boldsymbol{\omega}_b - \boldsymbol{\omega}_w = \dot{\sigma}\mathbf{k}_w + \dot{\alpha}\mathbf{j}_b\tag{55}$$

Under what conditions are the angular velocity of the aircraft and the evolutory velocity identical?

6. Denote the components of the angular velocity of the aircraft on the body axes by p_b, q_b, r_b. Show that these components and the components of the evolutory velocity on the wind axes satisfy the matrix relationship

$$\begin{bmatrix} p_b \\ q_b - \dot{\alpha} \\ r_b \end{bmatrix} = \begin{bmatrix} \cos\alpha\cos\sigma & \cos\alpha\sin\sigma & -\sin\alpha \\ -\sin\sigma & \cos\sigma & 0 \\ \sin\alpha\cos\sigma & \sin\alpha\sin\sigma & \cos\alpha \end{bmatrix}\begin{bmatrix} p_w \\ q_w \\ r_w + \dot{\sigma} \end{bmatrix}\tag{56}$$

which can be rewritten as

$$\begin{bmatrix} p_b + \dot{\sigma}\sin\alpha \\ q_b - \dot{\alpha} \\ r_b - \dot{\sigma}\cos\alpha \end{bmatrix} = \begin{bmatrix} \cos\alpha\cos\sigma & \cos\alpha\sin\sigma & -\sin\alpha \\ -\sin\sigma & \cos\sigma & 0 \\ \sin\alpha\cos\sigma & \sin\alpha\sin\sigma & \cos\alpha \end{bmatrix}$$

$$\times \begin{bmatrix} 1 & 0 & -\sin\gamma \\ 0 & \cos\mu & \sin\mu\cos\gamma \\ 0 & -\sin\mu & \cos\mu\cos\gamma \end{bmatrix}\begin{bmatrix} \dot{\mu} \\ \dot{\gamma} \\ \dot{\chi} \end{bmatrix}\tag{57}$$

7. Consider a rocket-powered aircraft, and assume that (a) the equation of moments (3–24) is approximately valid for the case where the body axes system is replaced by a central reference frame (reference frame whose origin is always superimposed on the instantaneous center of mass), (b) the central reference frame is directionally invariant with respect to the aircraft, and (c) the Coriolis moment as well as the moment

due to the unsteadiness of the relative motion are negligible. Show that the moment equation leads to the matrix relationship

$$
\begin{bmatrix} l_A + l_T \\ m_A + m_T \\ n_A + n_T \end{bmatrix} = \begin{bmatrix} \cos \alpha \cos \sigma & -\sin \sigma & \sin \alpha \cos \sigma \\ \cos \alpha \sin \sigma & \cos \sigma & \sin \alpha \sin \sigma \\ -\sin \alpha & 0 & \cos \alpha \end{bmatrix} \begin{bmatrix} A\dot{p}_b + (C - B)q_b r_b \\ B\dot{q}_b + (A - C)r_b p_b \\ C\dot{r}_b + (B - A)p_b q_b \end{bmatrix}
$$

(58)

where l_A, m_A, n_A are the components of the aerodynamic moment on the wind axes, l_T, m_T, n_T the components of the moment due to the thrust on the wind axes, p_b, q_b, r_b the components of the angular velocity of the vehicle on the body axes, and A, B, C the principal and central moments of inertia of the vehicle.

REFERENCES

1. SCHULZ, W. and LUDWIG, R., *Die Koordinatensysteme der Flugmechanik*, ZFW, Vol. 2, Nos. 3–4, 1954.
2. ABZUG, M. J., *Applications of Matrix Operators to the Kinematics of Airplane Motion*, Journal of the Aerospace Sciences, Vol. 23, No. 7, 1956.
3. FRAZER, R. A., DUNCAN, W. J., and COLLAR, A. R., *Elementary Matrices*, Cambridge University Press, Cambridge, 1947.
4. BRAND, L., *Vector Analysis*, John Wiley and Sons, Inc., New York, 1957.
5. PERLIS, S., *Theory of Matrices*, Addison-Wesley Publishing Company, Inc., Reading, Mass., 1952.
6. MIELE, A., *Coordinate Systems and Equations of Motion for Flight Over a Spherical Earth*, Boeing Scientific Research Laboratories, Flight Sciences Laboratory, TR No. 17, 1959.

CHAPTER 5

SCALAR EQUATIONS FOR FLIGHT OVER A SPHERICAL EARTH

1. INTRODUCTION

In the previous chapter, the scalar equations governing the flight of an aircraft over an ideally flat, nonrotating Earth were derived. In this chapter, the more general case of flight over a spherical, rotating Earth is considered with the assumptions that the trajectory is flown in the immediate neighborhood of the Earth and that the inertia term associated with the transport acceleration is negligible with respect to the weight. Consequently, the general dynamical equation is employed in the simplified form represented by Eq. (3–31), which is rewritten here as

$$\mathbf{T} + \mathbf{A} + m\mathbf{g} = m\left(\frac{d\mathbf{V}}{dt} + 2\boldsymbol{\omega}_e \times \mathbf{V}\right) \tag{1}$$

where $\mathbf{T}$ is the thrust, $\mathbf{A}$ the aerodynamic force, m the mass, $\mathbf{g}$ the acceleration of gravity, t the time, and $\boldsymbol{\omega}_e$ the angular velocity of the Earth with respect to the Fixed Stars. Furthermore, the symbol

$$\mathbf{V} = \frac{d\mathbf{EO}}{dt} \tag{2}$$

denotes the velocity of the aircraft with respect to the Earth, where $\mathbf{EO}$ is the vector joining point E on the surface of the Earth with the aircraft.

In the following sections, the scalar equations associated with the vectorial relations (1) and (2) are derived for the general case of paths in a three-dimensional space and then reduced to those relevant to flight in a great-circle plane. To do so, it is necessary to define several coordinate systems and establish relationships which describe the position and the motion of one system with respect to another (Ref. 4).

2. BASIC COORDINATE SYSTEMS

The coordinate systems of interest for flight over a spherical Earth are the Earth axes system $Ex_ey_ez_e$, the curvilinear ground system $EXYZ$, the local horizon system $Ox_hy_hz_h$, the wind axes system $Ox_wy_wz_w$, and the body axes system $Ox_by_bz_b$. While the terminology for the wind axes and

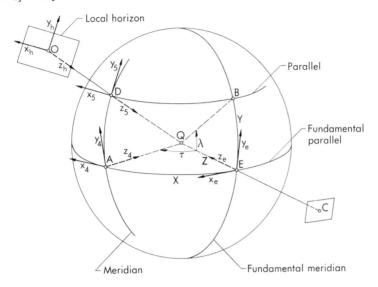

FIG. 1. Coordinate systems for flight over a spherical Earth.

the body axes is identical with that of Chapter 4, new definitions are needed for the Earth axes system, the curvilinear ground system, and the local horizon system.

2.1 Earth axes system. The Earth axes system is a Cartesian reference frame which is rigidly attached to the Earth. Its origin E is a point on the Earth's surface; the z_e-axis is vertical and positive downward; the x_e-axis and the y_e-axis are tangent to the Earth's surface and are directed in such a way that the trihedral $Ex_ey_ez_e$ is right-handed. Incidentally, the great circle tangent to the x_e-axis (not necessarily the geographic Equator) is called the *fundamental parallel*, while the great circle tangent to the y_e-axis is called the *fundamental meridian* (Fig. 1). Furthermore, a *meridian* is the intersection of the surface of the Earth and a plane perpendicular to the fundamental parallel, and a *parallel* is the intersection of the Earth's surface with a plane parallel to the fundamental parallel.

2.2 Curvilinear ground system. The curvilinear ground system is an orthogonal reference frame which is fixed to the Earth. Its origin E is a point on the Earth's surface; the X-coordinate is measured from E on the fundamental parallel; the Y-coordinate is measured from E on the fundamental meridian; and the Z-coordinate is measured radially from E. Furthermore, the positive senses for X, Y, Z are consistent with the positive senses for the Earth axes.

Denote, now, by O the instantaneous position of the aircraft and by D the intersection of the radial line passing through O with the Earth's surface. Indicate by A the intersection of the meridian passing through D with the fundamental parallel, by B the intersection of the parallel through D with the fundamental meridian, and by C the point where the spherical surface passing through the aircraft intersects the radial line passing through E. Clearly, if the aircraft moves with respect to the Earth, its projections A, B, C simultaneously move; consequently, the three coordinates X, Y, Z suffice to determine the position of point O with respect to the Earth.

2.3 Local horizon system. The local horizon system is a Cartesian reference frame having the following properties: its origin O is identical with the instantaneous position of the aircraft; the z_h-axis is vertical and positive downward; the x_h-axis and the y_h-axis are contained in the plane tangent to the spherical surface passing through the aircraft (*local horizon*) and are such that the trihedral $Ox_hy_hz_h$ is right-handed; in particular, the x_h-axis is parallel to the tangent to the parallel passing through D, while the y_h-axis is parallel to the tangent to the meridian passing through D.

3. ANGULAR RELATIONSHIPS

In this section, the angular relationships between the different coordinate systems are derived. In particular, attention is focused on the following pairs: local horizon-Earth axes, wind axes-local horizon, and body axes-wind axes.

3.1 Local horizon-Earth axes. The orientation of the local horizon with respect to the Earth axes can be described in terms of two angular parameters, the *longitude* τ and the *latitude* λ. The rotations necessary to perform the transformation from one system to another are easily understood, if two intermediate coordinate systems are introduced. Their properties are illustrated in Fig. 1: the system $Ax_4y_4z_4$ is obtained from the Earth axes by means of a rotation τ around the y_e-axis plus a translation;* the system $Dx_5y_5z_5$ is obtained from $Ax_4y_4z_4$ by means of a rotation λ around the x_4-axis plus a translation; finally, the local horizon system is such that its axes and the corresponding axes of the system $Dx_5y_5z_5$ are parallel and have the same positive sense. In matrix-vector

---

* When dealing with coordinate system transformations, the only angle that is positive in the clockwise sense is τ; all other angles are positive in the counterclockwise sense.

notation, these partial rotations are expressed as

$$
\begin{bmatrix} \mathbf{i}_4 \\ \mathbf{j}_4 \\ \mathbf{k}_4 \end{bmatrix} = \begin{bmatrix} \cos \tau & 0 & \sin \tau \\ 0 & 1 & 0 \\ -\sin \tau & 0 & \cos \tau \end{bmatrix} \begin{bmatrix} \mathbf{i}_e \\ \mathbf{j}_e \\ \mathbf{k}_e \end{bmatrix} \tag{3}
$$

$$
\begin{bmatrix} \mathbf{i}_5 \\ \mathbf{j}_5 \\ \mathbf{k}_5 \end{bmatrix} = \begin{bmatrix} 1 & 0 & 0 \\ 0 & \cos \lambda & \sin \lambda \\ 0 & -\sin \lambda & \cos \lambda \end{bmatrix} \begin{bmatrix} \mathbf{i}_4 \\ \mathbf{j}_4 \\ \mathbf{k}_4 \end{bmatrix} \tag{4}
$$

$$
\begin{bmatrix} \mathbf{i}_h \\ \mathbf{j}_h \\ \mathbf{k}_h \end{bmatrix} = \begin{bmatrix} \mathbf{i}_5 \\ \mathbf{j}_5 \\ \mathbf{k}_5 \end{bmatrix} \tag{5}
$$

Since the curvilinear coordinates and the angles of rotation are related by

$$
X = r_o \tau, \qquad Y = r_o \lambda \tag{6}
$$

where r_o is the radius of the Earth, the total rotation is written in the form

$$
\begin{bmatrix} \mathbf{i}_h \\ \mathbf{j}_h \\ \mathbf{k}_h \end{bmatrix} = \begin{bmatrix} \cos\left(\dfrac{X}{r_o}\right) & 0 & \sin\left(\dfrac{X}{r_o}\right) \\ -\sin\left(\dfrac{X}{r_o}\right)\sin\left(\dfrac{Y}{r_o}\right) & \cos\left(\dfrac{Y}{r_o}\right) & \cos\left(\dfrac{X}{r_o}\right)\sin\left(\dfrac{Y}{r_o}\right) \\ -\sin\left(\dfrac{X}{r_o}\right)\cos\left(\dfrac{Y}{r_o}\right) & -\sin\left(\dfrac{Y}{r_o}\right) & \cos\left(\dfrac{X}{r_o}\right)\cos\left(\dfrac{Y}{r_o}\right) \end{bmatrix} \begin{bmatrix} \mathbf{i}_e \\ \mathbf{j}_e \\ \mathbf{k}_e \end{bmatrix} \tag{7}
$$

Incidentally, if the limiting process $r_o \to \infty$ is carried out, the square matrix appearing in the previous relationship reduces to a unit matrix; consequently, Eq. (7) reduces to Eq. (4–3), which was already calculated for the flat Earth case.

3.2 Wind axes-local horizon. The orientation of the wind axes with respect to the local horizon can be described in terms of the velocity yaw angle χ, the velocity pitch angle γ, and the velocity roll angle μ, exactly as in Chapter 4. Therefore, the relationship between the wind axes and the local horizon is given by

$$
\begin{bmatrix} \mathbf{i}_w \\ \mathbf{j}_w \\ \mathbf{k}_w \end{bmatrix} = \begin{bmatrix} \cos \gamma \cos \chi & \cos \gamma \sin \chi & -\sin \gamma \\ \sin \mu \sin \gamma \cos \chi - \cos \mu \sin \chi & \sin \mu \sin \gamma \sin \chi + \cos \mu \cos \chi & \sin \mu \cos \gamma \\ \cos \mu \sin \gamma \cos \chi + \sin \mu \sin \chi & \cos \mu \sin \gamma \sin \chi - \sin \mu \cos \chi & \cos \mu \cos \gamma \end{bmatrix} \begin{bmatrix} \mathbf{i}_h \\ \mathbf{j}_h \\ \mathbf{k}_h \end{bmatrix} \tag{8}
$$

3.3 Body axes-wind axes. The orientation of the body axes with respect to the wind axes can be described in terms of the sideslip angle σ and the angle of attack α, which are defined exactly as in Chapter 4. Consequently, the following relationship holds:

$$
\begin{bmatrix} \mathbf{i}_b \\ \mathbf{j}_b \\ \mathbf{k}_b \end{bmatrix} = \begin{bmatrix} \cos\alpha\cos\sigma & \cos\alpha\sin\sigma & -\sin\alpha \\ -\sin\sigma & \cos\sigma & 0 \\ \sin\alpha\cos\sigma & \sin\alpha\sin\sigma & \cos\alpha \end{bmatrix} \begin{bmatrix} \mathbf{i}_w \\ \mathbf{j}_w \\ \mathbf{k}_w \end{bmatrix} \tag{9}
$$

4. ANGULAR VELOCITIES

In this section, the angular velocity of one reference system with respect to another is calculated. Attention is focused on the following pairs: local horizon-Earth axes and wind axes-Earth axes.

4.1 Local horizon-Earth axes. Because the partial rotations necessary to pass from the Earth axes to the local horizon occur around the y_e-axis and the x_4-axis, the infinitesimal angular displacement of the local horizon with respect to the Earth is given by*

$$
d\mathbf{\Omega}_h = d\lambda \mathbf{i}_4 - d\tau \mathbf{j}_e \tag{10}
$$

Consequently, the angular velocity of the local horizon with respect to the Earth becomes

$$
\boldsymbol{\omega}_h = \frac{d\mathbf{\Omega}_h}{dt} = \dot{\lambda}\mathbf{i}_4 - \dot{\tau}\mathbf{j}_e \tag{11}
$$

which, in consideration of Eqs. (3) through (6), can be rewritten in the form

$$
\boldsymbol{\omega}_h = \frac{\dot{Y}}{r_o}\mathbf{i}_h - \frac{\dot{X}}{r_o}\cos\left(\frac{Y}{r_o}\right)\mathbf{j}_h + \frac{\dot{X}}{r_o}\sin\left(\frac{Y}{r_o}\right)\mathbf{k}_h \tag{12}
$$

4.2 Wind axes-Earth axes. The over-all rotation necessary to pass from the Earth axes to the wind axes stems from the superimposition of the partial rotation necessary to pass from the Earth axes to the local horizon and the partial rotation necessary to pass from the local horizon to the wind axes. Hence, the infinitesimal angular displacement of the wind

---

* A negative sign precedes $d\tau$, since this rotation is positive in the clockwise sense.

axes with respect to the Earth is given by

$$d\mathbf{\Omega}_w = d\mathbf{\Omega}_h + (d\mu\mathbf{i}_2 + d\gamma\mathbf{j}_1 + d\chi\mathbf{k}_h) \tag{13}$$

where the unit vectors $\mathbf{i}_2$, $\mathbf{j}_1$, $\mathbf{k}_h$ are defined exactly as in Chapter 4. Furthermore, the evolutory velocity, that is, the angular velocity of the wind axes with respect to the Earth, becomes

$$\boldsymbol{\omega}_w = \frac{d\mathbf{\Omega}_w}{dt} = \boldsymbol{\omega}_h + (\dot{\mu}\mathbf{i}_2 + \dot{\gamma}\mathbf{j}_1 + \dot{\chi}\mathbf{k}_h) \tag{14}$$

In accordance with Chapter 4, the unit vectors characterizing the rotation of the wind axes with respect to the local horizon are related to the unit vectors of the wind axes system by the matrix equation

$$\begin{bmatrix} \mathbf{i}_2 \\ \mathbf{j}_1 \\ \mathbf{k}_h \end{bmatrix} = \begin{bmatrix} 1 & 0 & 0 \\ 0 & \cos\mu & -\sin\mu \\ -\sin\gamma & \sin\mu\cos\gamma & \cos\mu\cos\gamma \end{bmatrix} \begin{bmatrix} \mathbf{i}_w \\ \mathbf{j}_w \\ \mathbf{k}_w \end{bmatrix} \tag{15}$$

Consequently, after Eqs. (8), (12), (14), and (15) are combined, the evolutory velocity can be written in the form

$$\boldsymbol{\omega}_w = p_w\mathbf{i}_w + q_w\mathbf{j}_w + r_w\mathbf{k}_w \tag{16}$$

where

$$\begin{bmatrix} p_w \\ q_w \\ r_w \end{bmatrix} = \begin{bmatrix} 1 & 0 & -\sin\gamma \\ 0 & \cos\mu & \sin\mu\cos\gamma \\ 0 & -\sin\mu & \cos\mu\cos\gamma \end{bmatrix} \begin{bmatrix} \dot{\mu} \\ \dot{\gamma} \\ \dot{\chi} \end{bmatrix}$$

$$+ \begin{bmatrix} \cos\gamma\cos\chi & \cos\gamma\sin\chi & -\sin\gamma \\ \begin{matrix} \sin\mu\sin\gamma\cos\chi \\ -\cos\mu\sin\chi \end{matrix} & \begin{matrix} \sin\mu\sin\gamma\sin\chi \\ +\cos\mu\cos\chi \end{matrix} & \sin\mu\cos\gamma \\ \begin{matrix} \cos\mu\sin\gamma\cos\chi \\ +\sin\mu\sin\chi \end{matrix} & \begin{matrix} \cos\mu\sin\gamma\sin\chi \\ -\sin\mu\cos\chi \end{matrix} & \cos\mu\cos\gamma \end{bmatrix} \begin{bmatrix} \dfrac{\dot{Y}}{r_o} \\ -\dfrac{\dot{X}}{r_o}\cos\left(\dfrac{Y}{r_o}\right) \\ \dfrac{\dot{X}}{r_o}\sin\left(\dfrac{Y}{r_o}\right) \end{bmatrix} \tag{17}$$

Incidentally, if the limiting process $r_o \to \infty$ is carried out, the second of the product matrices on the right-hand side of Eq. (17) reduces to a null matrix; hence, the components of the evolutory velocity on the wind axes become identical with those already derived for the case of a flat Earth.

5. KINEMATIC RELATIONSHIPS

In this section, the scalar relationships corresponding to the vectorial equation (2) are derived. Since the velocity is collinear with the x_w-axis, the left-hand side of Eq. (2) can be represented as

$$\mathbf{V} = V\mathbf{i}_w = V\left(\cos\gamma\cos\chi\mathbf{i}_h + \cos\gamma\sin\chi\mathbf{j}_h - \sin\gamma\mathbf{k}_h\right) \qquad (18)$$

Furthermore, the vector joining the origin of the Earth axes system with the aircraft is given by

$$\mathbf{EO} = \mathbf{EQ} - (r_o + h)\mathbf{k}_h \qquad (19)$$

where $\mathbf{EQ}$ is a vector rigidly attached to the Earth and h the altitude above sea level. Consequently, if the time derivative of the previous equation is calculated, the following result is derived:

$$\frac{d\mathbf{EO}}{dt} = -\dot{h}\mathbf{k}_h - (r_o + h)\frac{d\mathbf{k}_h}{dt} \qquad (20)$$

where, because of Poisson's formulas, the time derivative of the unit vector perpendicular to the local horizon is given by

$$\frac{d\mathbf{k}_h}{dt} = \boldsymbol{\omega}_h \times \mathbf{k}_h = -\frac{\dot{X}}{r_o}\cos\left(\frac{Y}{r_o}\right)\mathbf{i}_h - \frac{\dot{Y}}{r_o}\mathbf{j}_h \qquad (21)$$

As a final step, Eqs. (2), (18), (20), and (21) are combined, leading to the following kinematic relationships:

$$\dot{X} = V\frac{r_o}{r_o + h}\frac{\cos\gamma\cos\chi}{\cos(Y/r_o)}$$

$$\dot{Y} = V\frac{r_o}{r_o + h}\cos\gamma\sin\chi \qquad (22)$$

$$\dot{h} = V\sin\gamma$$

These relationships are a generalization of Eqs. (4–20), which were calculated for a flat Earth. In fact, they contain Eqs. (4–20) as a particular case, as can be seen by carrying out the limiting process $r_o \to \infty$.

6. DYNAMIC RELATIONSHIPS

In this section, the scalar relationships corresponding to the vectorial equation (1) are derived. This equation differs from Eq. (4–1) because of the presence of the inertia term associated with the Coriolis acceleration

$$\mathbf{a}_c = 2\boldsymbol{\omega}_e \times \mathbf{V} \qquad (23)$$

If p_{ew}, q_{ew}, r_{ew} denote the components of the angular velocity of the Earth on the wind axes, the Coriolis acceleration can be written as

$$\mathbf{a}_c = 2V(r_{ew}\mathbf{j}_w - q_{ew}\mathbf{k}_w) \tag{24}$$

Consequently, after the law of variation of the acceleration of gravity with the altitude

$$g = g_o \left(\frac{r_o}{r_o + h}\right)^2 \tag{25}$$

is considered, the dynamical equation can be resolved into the following scalar relationships on the wind axes:

$$T \cos \epsilon \cos \nu - D - mg_o \left(\frac{r_o}{r_o + h}\right)^2 \sin \gamma - m\dot{V} = 0$$

$$T \cos \epsilon \sin \nu - Q + mg_o \left(\frac{r_o}{r_o + h}\right)^2 \sin \mu \cos \gamma - mV(r_w + 2r_{ew}) = 0$$
$$\tag{26}$$

$$T \sin \epsilon + L - mg_o \left(\frac{r_o}{r_o + h}\right)^2 \cos \mu \cos \gamma - mV(q_w + 2q_{ew}) = 0$$

where the mass is variable and is related to the engine mass flow by

$$\dot{m} + \beta = 0 \tag{27}$$

Incidentally, the components of the angular velocity of the Earth on the wind axes depend on the instantaneous flight condition of the aircraft. Furthermore, they are related to the corresponding components on the Earth axes p_e, q_e, r_e by the matrix relationship

$$
\begin{bmatrix} p_{ew} \\ q_{ew} \\ r_{ew} \end{bmatrix} =
\begin{bmatrix}
\cos \gamma \cos \chi & \cos \gamma \sin \chi & -\sin \gamma \\
\begin{array}{c} \sin \mu \sin \gamma \cos \chi \\ -\cos \mu \sin \chi \end{array} & \begin{array}{c} \sin \mu \sin \gamma \sin \chi \\ +\cos \mu \cos \chi \end{array} & \sin \mu \cos \gamma \\
\begin{array}{c} \cos \mu \sin \gamma \cos \chi \\ +\sin \mu \sin \chi \end{array} & \begin{array}{c} \cos \mu \sin \gamma \sin \chi \\ -\sin \mu \cos \chi \end{array} & \cos \mu \cos \gamma
\end{bmatrix}
$$

$$
\times
\begin{bmatrix}
\cos\left(\dfrac{X}{r_o}\right) & 0 & \sin\left(\dfrac{X}{r_o}\right) \\
-\sin\left(\dfrac{X}{r_o}\right)\sin\left(\dfrac{Y}{r_o}\right) & \cos\left(\dfrac{Y}{r_o}\right) & \cos\left(\dfrac{X}{r_o}\right)\sin\left(\dfrac{Y}{r_o}\right) \\
-\sin\left(\dfrac{X}{r_o}\right)\cos\left(\dfrac{Y}{r_o}\right) & -\sin\left(\dfrac{Y}{r_o}\right) & \cos\left(\dfrac{X}{r_o}\right)\cos\left(\dfrac{Y}{r_o}\right)
\end{bmatrix}
\begin{bmatrix} p_e \\ q_e \\ r_e \end{bmatrix} \tag{28}
$$

where the scalar quantities p_e, q_e, r_e are known for each given Earth axes system and must be consistent with

$$\omega_e = \sqrt{p_e^2 + q_e^2 + r_e^2} \tag{29}$$

7. DISCUSSION

The translational motion of an aircraft having variable mass and operating in a three-dimensional space over a spherical earth is described by the thirteen equations (17), (22), (26), (27), and (28). Contained in these relations are the five functions

$$f_1 = D, \quad f_2 = L, \quad f_3 = Q, \quad f_4 = T, \quad f_5 = \beta \tag{30}$$

which depend on the characteristics of the aircraft and the engine. If, in accordance with Chapter 4, these functions are assumed to have the form

$$f_k = f_k(h, V, \sigma, \alpha, \pi, \nu, \epsilon), \quad k = 1, \ldots, 5 \tag{31}$$

where π is the control parameter of the engine, the previous differential system has the following features: there is one independent variable, the time, and there are nineteen dependent variables, which include the eight derivated variables

$$X, Y, h, V, \chi, \gamma, \mu, m \tag{32}$$

and the eleven nonderivated variables

$$\sigma, \alpha, \pi, \nu, \epsilon, p_w, q_w, r_w, p_{ew}, q_{ew}, r_{ew} \tag{33}$$

Consequently, the number of degrees of freedom is

$$n = 19 - 13 = 6 \tag{34}$$

which is logical in view of the possibility of controlling the time history of the rudder deflection, the elevator deflection, the aileron deflection, the thrust control parameter, the thrust sideslip angle, and the thrust angle of attack. Incidentally, these degrees of freedom reduce to $n = 4$, if the engine is fixed with respect to the aircraft.

7.1 **Flight in a great-circle plane.** The class of paths which are flown in a great-circle plane in such a way that the velocity roll angle and the thrust sideslip angle are always zero is now considered (Fig. 2). This particular motion is expressed mathematically by the conditions

$$Y = 0, \quad \mu = \nu = 0 \tag{35}$$

the first of which means that the great circle under consideration is identical with the fundamental parallel. Because of the hypotheses, the velocity yaw angle is $\chi = 0$ at all time instants. Furthermore, the components of the evolutory velocity on the wind axes simplify to

$$p_w = 0, \quad q_w = \dot{\gamma} - \frac{\dot{X}}{r_o}, \quad r_w = 0 \tag{36}$$

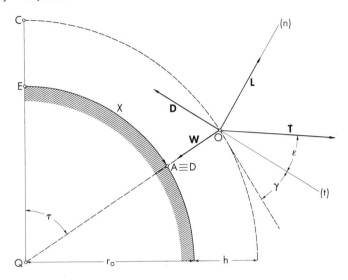

FIG. 2. Forces acting on the aircraft in a great-circle plane.

while the components of the angular velocity of the Earth become

$$p_{ew} = p_e \cos\left(\gamma - \frac{X}{r_o}\right) - r_e \sin\left(\gamma - \frac{X}{r_o}\right)$$

$$q_{ew} = q_e = \omega_e \cos\varphi_e \qquad (37)$$

$$r_{ew} = p_e \sin\left(\gamma - \frac{X}{r_o}\right) + r_e \cos\left(\gamma - \frac{X}{r_o}\right)$$

where φ_e is the angle of inclination of the polar axis with respect to the perpendicular to the plane of the motion.

As a final result, the kinematic and dynamic relationships describing the motion of an aircraft in a great-circle plane are given by

$$\dot{X} = V \frac{r_o}{r_o + h} \cos\gamma$$

$$\dot{h} = V \sin\gamma$$

$$T \cos\epsilon - D - mg_o\left(\frac{r_o}{r_o + h}\right)^2 \sin\gamma = m\dot{V} \qquad (38)$$

$$T \sin\epsilon + L - mg_o\left(\frac{r_o}{r_o + h}\right)^2 \cos\gamma = mV\left[\dot{\gamma} - \frac{V\cos\gamma}{r_o + h} + 2\omega_e \cos\varphi_e\right]$$

$$\dot{m} + \beta = 0$$

while the dynamic relationship in the y_w-direction leads to

$$Q = -2mV\left[p_e \sin\left(\gamma - \frac{X}{r_o}\right) + r_e \cos\left(\gamma - \frac{X}{r_o}\right)\right] \tag{39}$$

and, clearly, indicates that the Coriolis force associated with the rotation of the Earth with respect to the Fixed Stars is to be balanced by the side force. The latter can be generated, for example, by means of a sideslip angle other than zero.

In theory, Eqs. (38) and (39) must be solved simultaneously. In practice, if the sideslip angle is small, its effect on the drag, the lift, the thrust, and the engine mass flow can be neglected. Under such conditions, the above differential system becomes uncoupled, and the trajectory of the aircraft in the great-circle plane can be computed by means of Eqs. (38) only; in turn, Eq. (39) is employed a posteriori in order to predict the time history of the sideslip angle necessary to maintain the aircraft in the great-circle plane.

Under the previous approximation, Eqs. (38) include the eight dependent variables

$$X, h, V, \gamma, m, \alpha, \pi, \epsilon \tag{40}$$

and admit $n = 3$ degrees of freedom, which is logical in view of the possibility of controlling the time history of the angle of attack, the thrust control parameter, and the thrust angle of attack. These degrees of freedom reduce to $n = 2$, if the engine is fixed with respect to the aircraft.

REFERENCES

1. SCHULZ, W. and LUDWIG, R., *Die Koordinatensysteme der Flugmechanik*, ZFW, Vol. 2, Nos. 3–4, 1954.
2. ABZUG, M. J., *Applications of Matrix Operators to the Kinematics of Airplane Motion*, Journal of the Aerospace Sciences, Vol. 23, No. 7, 1956.
3. GOLDSTEIN, H., *Classical Mechanics*, Addison-Wesley Publishing Company, Inc., Reading, Mass., 1950.
4. MIELE, A., *Coordinate Systems and Equations of Motion for Flight Over a Spherical Earth*, Boeing Scientific Research Laboratories, Flight Sciences Laboratory, TR No. 17, 1959.

CHAPTER 6

AERODYNAMIC FORCES

by

KERMIT E. VAN EVERY * and ANGELO MIELE

1. INTRODUCTION

The study of the aerodynamic forces acting on vehicles of all types is of fundamental interest to the engineer involved in planning flight operations and in designing a vehicle for a given mission. Owing to the many possible combinations of speed regimes and aircraft components, the literature on the subject is immense. However, since a complete discussion of aerodynamics is beyond the scope of this textbook, the objectives of this chapter are necessarily limited. Thus, only those elements which are necessary for the analytical development of the theory of flight paths and for the understanding of the qualitative relationships between Flight Mechanics and Aerodynamic Design are presented.

1.1 Components of the aerodynamic force. According to Chapter 3, the aerodynamic force acting on a vehicle is defined as

$$\mathbf{A} = \int_{\Sigma} [\Delta p \mathbf{n} + \mathbf{f}] \, d\sigma \tag{1}$$

where Δp is the difference between the local static pressure and the free-stream static pressure, $\mathbf{n}$ the unit vector normal to the area element $d\sigma$ (positively directed inward), $\mathbf{f}$ the local tangential stress exerted by the air on the vehicle, and Σ an appropriate reference area (the wetted area for rocket vehicles or the sum of the wetted area, the streamtube area, and the afterbody area for jet-powered vehicles). In accordance with Chapters 4 and 5, this aerodynamic force can be resolved into components on the wind axes as follows:

$$\mathbf{A} = -(D\mathbf{i}_w + Q\mathbf{j}_w + L\mathbf{k}_w) \tag{2}$$

where D is the drag, Q the side force, L the lift and where $\mathbf{i}_w$, $\mathbf{j}_w$, $\mathbf{k}_w$ are the unit vectors associated with the wind axes system. Consequently,

---

* Chief of Technical Sections, Douglas Aircraft Company, Aircraft Division.

after Eqs. (1) and (2) are combined, the following results are obtained:

$$D = - \int_{\Sigma} (\Delta p \mathbf{n} \cdot \mathbf{i}_w + \mathbf{f} \cdot \mathbf{i}_w)\, d\sigma$$

$$Q = - \int_{\Sigma} (\Delta p \mathbf{n} \cdot \mathbf{j}_w + \mathbf{f} \cdot \mathbf{j}_w)\, d\sigma \qquad (3)$$

$$L = - \int_{\Sigma} (\Delta p \mathbf{n} \cdot \mathbf{k}_w + \mathbf{f} \cdot \mathbf{k}_w)\, d\sigma$$

1.2 Aerodynamic coefficients. The components of the aerodynamic force are customarily represented in terms of three dimensionless coefficients, which are called the *coefficients of drag, side force, and lift* and are defined as

$$C_D = \frac{D}{qS}, \qquad C_Q = \frac{Q}{qS}, \qquad C_L = \frac{L}{qS} \qquad (4)$$

where

$$q = \tfrac{1}{2}\rho V^2 \qquad (5)$$

is the free-stream dynamic pressure and S is an appropriate reference area (the planform area for a wing or the maximum cross-sectional area for a fuselage). Consequently, if

$$C_p = \frac{\Delta p}{q}, \qquad C_f = \frac{f}{q} \qquad (6)$$

denote the *pressure coefficient* and the *skin friction coefficient* and $\mathbf{t}$ is a unit vector parallel to the tangential stress, the following results are obtained:

$$C_D = - \frac{1}{S} \int_{\Sigma} (C_p \mathbf{n} \cdot \mathbf{i}_w + C_f \mathbf{t} \cdot \mathbf{i}_w)\, d\sigma$$

$$C_Q = - \frac{1}{S} \int_{\Sigma} (C_p \mathbf{n} \cdot \mathbf{j}_w + C_f \mathbf{t} \cdot \mathbf{j}_w)\, d\sigma \qquad (7)$$

$$C_L = - \frac{1}{S} \int_{\Sigma} (C_p \mathbf{n} \cdot \mathbf{k}_w + C_f \mathbf{t} \cdot \mathbf{k}_w)\, d\sigma$$

These equations indicate that, in order to evaluate the aerodynamic characteristics of a configuration, the pressure coefficient and the skin friction coefficient must be known at all points of the surface Σ. While this study is a fundamental objective of Aerodynamics, it must be omitted here for obvious considerations of space. Consequently, only a few general elements are presented in the following sections. In particular, although the figures indicate the qualitative behavior of typical vehicles, they are not intended to provide data for computing the aerodynamic characteristics of arbitrary configurations.

1.3 Realms of Fluid Mechanics. In the absence of effects of a thermal nature, the fundamental dimensionless variables in the aerodynamics of a perfect gas are the *Mach number*, the *Reynolds number*, and the *Knudsen number*. These variables, which characterize the compressibility, viscosity, and rarefaction of a flow field, are respectively defined as

$$M = \frac{V}{a}, \qquad R_e = \frac{\rho V l}{\mu}, \qquad K_n = \frac{\lambda}{l} \qquad (8)$$

where V is the velocity of the aircraft, l is a characteristic length of the flow field and where ρ, μ, a, λ respectively denote the density, the dynamic viscosity, the speed of sound, and the mean free path corresponding to the free-stream conditions. Notice that the speed of sound is given by

$$a = \sqrt{kR\theta} \qquad (9)$$

where k denotes the ratio of the specific heats, R the air constant, and θ the free-stream absolute temperature; furthermore, within the assumptions of the kinetic theory, the mean free path is expressed by Chapman's law

$$\lambda = \frac{\mu}{\rho} \sqrt{\frac{\pi}{2R\theta}} \qquad (10)$$

Consequently, definitions (8) lead to the relationship

$$K_n = \sqrt{\frac{\pi k}{2}} \frac{M}{R_e} \qquad (11)$$

from which it is clear that the ratio of Mach number to Reynolds number has the same order of magnitude as the Knudsen number and, therefore, is a measure of the flow rarefaction. In this connection, three basic degrees of rarefaction can be defined, that is, negligible, moderate, and high; the corresponding flows are called *continuum flow, transition flow,* and *free molecular flow*. In particular, continuum flow is defined by the inequality $M/R_e \gg 1$, while free molecular flow is identified by the inequality $M/R_e \gg 1$.

In the succeeding sections, a discussion of the continuum and free molecular flows is presented, with emphasis on the former. The reason for this is that, in the majority of problems encountered in Flight Mechanics, the continuum flow theory is either entirely valid or can be extrapolated to predict the aerodynamic forces with sufficient accuracy far into the realm of transition flow. On the other hand, the free molecular flow approach is indispensable in problems where the aerodynamic forces, even though negligible with respect to the gravitational forces, are applied over long periods of time and, consequently, produce important effects on the nature of the resulting trajectories.*

---

* The decay and lifetime of satellite orbits are examples of such problems.

2. CONTINUUM FLOW

In this section, a flow satisfying the condition $M/R_e \ll 1$ is considered, that is, a flow which can be mathematically treated as a continuum. For this case, the space surrounding the aircraft can usually be separated into two regions: a very thin inner region, which is immediately adjacent to the surface of the aircraft and is characterized by the fact that viscosity effects are important (*boundary layer*); and an outer region, where viscosity effects can be neglected, so that the flow can be treated as inviscid.

Depending on the degree of compressibility, the inner and outer flows can be separated into *incompressible subsonic, compressible subsonic, transonic, supersonic,* and *hypersonic.* Although the interval of free-stream Mach numbers corresponding to each of these regimes is determined by the geometry of the body, the angle of attack, and the sideslip angle, the following values are typical:

Incompressible subsonic flow	$0 < M < 0.5$
Compressible subsonic flow	$0.5 < M < 0.8$
Transonic flow	$0.8 < M < 1.2$
Supersonic flow	$1.2 < M < 5$
Hypersonic flow	$5 < M$

2.1 Arbitrary drag polar. In the following sections, a symmetric aircraft operating at zero sideslip angle is considered; since the side force is zero, attention is focused on the drag and lift only. If effects of a thermal nature are neglected and if it is assumed that the geometry of the body is specified, both theory and experimental data indicate that the pressure coefficient and the skin friction coefficient obey the laws*

$$C_p = C_p(\alpha, M, R_e, P), \qquad C_f = C_f(\alpha, M, R_e, P) \tag{12}$$

where α is the angle of attack and P a point on the surface Σ. Consequently, the evaluation of the surface integrals (7) yields the functional relationships

$$C_D = C_D(\alpha, M, R_e), \qquad C_L = C_L(\alpha, M, R_e) \tag{13}$$

which are illustrated in Fig. 1 for a typical subsonic aircraft. At relatively low angles of attack, the effect of flow separation from the rear portion of the wing is negligible, and the lift coefficient varies linearly with the

---

* As long as flow separation does not occur, the variation of the pressure coefficient with the Reynolds number and the variation of the skin friction coefficient with the angle of attack are negligible.

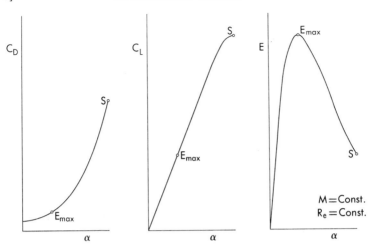

FIG. 1. Drag coefficient, lift coefficient, and aerodynamic efficiency versus the angle of attack.

angle of attack and is almost independent of the Reynolds number. On the other hand, at relatively high angles of attack, the effect of flow separation is important, and the lift coefficient varies nonlinearly with the angle of attack and depends strongly on the Reynolds number; furthermore, it reaches a maximum value at a point S called the *stalling point*. Generally speaking, conventional aircraft do not fly at angles of attack beyond the stalling point, owing to stability and control considerations. Elimination of the angle of attack from the parametric equations (13) leads to the relationship

$$C_D = C_D(C_L, M, R_e) \tag{14}$$

which is called the *drag polar* and is plotted in Fig. 2.

2.2 Lift-to-drag ratio. An important parameter of an aircraft is the *lift-to-drag ratio* or *aerodynamic efficiency* (Figs. 1 and 2)

$$E = \frac{L}{D} = \frac{C_L}{C_D} \tag{15}$$

which depends on the Mach number, the Reynolds number, and the angle of attack (or the lift coefficient). If the Mach number and the Reynolds number are given, the aerodynamic efficiency has a maximum with respect to the lift coefficient, which occurs at the point where the straight line from the origin is tangent to the polar diagram. Representative values of E_{max} are 10–25 for subsonic aircraft, 5–10 for supersonic aircraft, and 1–5 for hypervelocity vehicles.

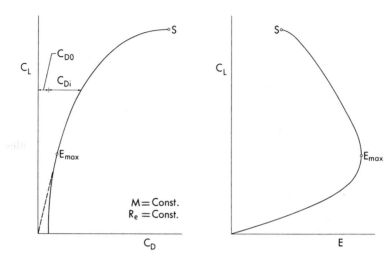

FIG. 2. Drag polar of an aircraft and aerodynamic efficiency versus the lift coefficient.

2.3 Drag terminology. The over-all drag is customarily separated into components whose significance is associated with either the physical nature of the flow field or the geometry of the body. Although many decompositions are possible, only two have become widely accepted in both Fluid Mechanics and Flight Mechanics.

The first decomposition is a direct consequence of the first of Eqs. (7) and consists of dividing the over-all drag into the *friction drag* and the *pressure drag*.* The former is due to the integrated effect of the tangential stresses acting over the area Σ, and the latter, to the integrated effect of the normal stresses. In coefficient form, this is written as

$$C_D = C_{Df} + C_{Dp} \qquad (16)$$

where C_{Df} is the *friction drag coefficient* and C_{Dp} the *pressure drag coefficient.*

The second decomposition consists of dividing the over-all drag into the *zero-lift drag* and the *induced drag*,† the latter term indicating every kind of drag which depends on the lift, regardless of its physical origin.

---

* The pressure drag can be present in several ways, for instance, through vortex shedding (subsonic and supersonic vortex drag), flow separation (subsonic form drag), and formation of shock waves (supersonic wave drag).

† Historically speaking, the term *induced drag* was used initially to designate the drag associated with the vortex system shedding from the wing. To prevent confusion, this kind of drag is referred to here as the *vortex drag.*

In coefficient form, this is written as

$$C_D = C_{DO} + C_{Di} \tag{17}$$

where C_{DO} is the *zero-lift drag coefficient* and C_{Di} the *induced drag coefficient* (Fig. 2). It is obvious that the zero-lift drag is composed of both friction drag and pressure drag; an analogous remark holds for the induced drag, although its main constituent is pressure drag.

2.4 Parabolic drag polar. There are many aircraft configurations for which the induced drag coefficient is a quadratic function of the lift coefficient for subsonic speeds and for some interval of values of the lift coefficient. Hence, if K denotes a constant characteristic of the aircraft such that

$$C_{Di} = KC_L^2 \tag{18}$$

the total drag coefficient becomes

$$C_D = C_{DO} + KC_L^2 \tag{19}$$

and implies that

$$E = \frac{C_L}{C_{DO} + KC_L^2} \tag{20}$$

The drag polar represented by Eq. (19) is called the *parabolic drag polar* and is characterized by the following maximum value of the aerodynamic efficiency:

$$E_{\max} = \frac{1}{2\sqrt{KC_{DO}}} \tag{21}$$

The corresponding lift coefficient is given by

$$C_L = \sqrt{\frac{C_{DO}}{K}} \tag{22}$$

and implies that

$$\frac{C_{Di}}{C_{DO}} = 1 \tag{23}$$

Hence, *for an aircraft flying in the subsonic regime, the lift-to-drag ratio is a maximum when the induced drag equals the zero-lift drag.*

It must be emphasized that the parabolic polar, while extremely helpful for engineering purposes, is only an approximation of the experimental polar. Its accuracy depends on the lift coefficient as well as the geometry of the configuration and is now discussed for positive lift coefficients and for both symmetric and asymmetric configurations.

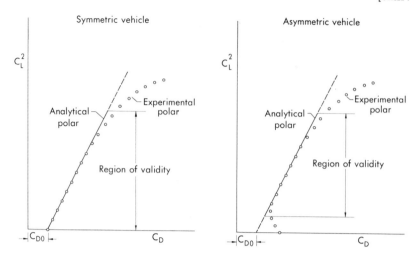

Fig. 3. Limits of validity of the parabolic polar for both symmetric and asymmetric configurations.

If the configuration is *symmetric* (that is, if its main components are an unwarped, uncambered wing and a body of revolution with its axis in the plane of the wing chords), the drag coefficient of the experimental polar has a minimum at $C_L = 0$. For this configuration, the available experimental data show that the approximation (19) holds for every lift coefficient below that for which some appreciable flow separation from the wing occurs (Fig. 3). In many cases, this limiting lift coefficient is identical with or proportional to the *buffeting lift coefficient* C_{LB}, that is, the lift coefficient at which the aircraft begins to shake due to the turbulence associated with flow separation.

If the configuration is *asymmetric*, the drag coefficient of the experimental polar no longer has a minimum at $C_L = 0$ but at some lift coefficient C_{LM} other than zero. Thus, a more general form of the drag polar is the following:

$$C_D = C_{DM} + K(C_L - C_{LM})^2 \qquad (24)$$

where C_{DM} is the minimum drag coefficient. However, for lift coefficients which are higher than that corresponding to the minimum drag coefficient but lower than that for appreciable flow separation (this is the region where the airplane normally flies), the parabolic polar can still be utilized, providing that the following convention is adopted: the term C_{DO} no longer indicates the actual value of zero-lift drag coefficient but a fictitious value obtained by fitting the experimental data with the quadratic law (19) and extrapolating this law to $C_L = 0$ (see Fig. 3).

2.5 Generalized drag polar. An interesting generalization of the previous discussion arises when the induced drag coefficient is represented in the form

$$C_{Di} = KC_L^x \tag{25}$$

The resulting new polar is given by

$$C_D = C_{DO} + KC_L^x \tag{26}$$

and is called the *generalized drag polar;* it can be employed to represent the behavior of the aircraft in any flow regime, if the zero-lift drag coefficient C_{DO}, the induced drag factor K, and the exponent x are regarded to be functions of both the Mach number and the Reynolds number.[*]

When the generalized polar is employed, the aerodynamic efficiency is given by

$$E = \frac{C_L}{C_{DO} + KC_L^x} \tag{27}$$

and, for a given Mach number and Reynolds number, attains the following maximum value:

$$E_{\max} = \frac{1}{x}\left(\frac{x-1}{C_{DO}}\right)^{(x-1)/x}\left(\frac{1}{K}\right)^{1/x} \tag{28}$$

for the lift coefficient given by

$$C_L = \left[\frac{C_{DO}}{K(x-1)}\right]^{1/x} \tag{29}$$

which implies that

$$\frac{C_{Di}}{C_{DO}} = \frac{1}{x-1} \tag{30}$$

For thin-winged configurations operating at moderately supersonic speeds, the approximation $x = 2$ can be employed, as in the subsonic case;[†] hence, the aerodynamic efficiency is a maximum when the induced drag equals the zero-lift drag. On the other hand, for thin-winged configurations operating in the hypervelocity domain, the approximation $x = 3/2$ is pertinent; hence, the aerodynamic efficiency is a maximum when the induced drag is twice the zero-lift drag.

---

[*] For a given lift coefficient, the dependence of the induced drag coefficient on the Reynolds number is negligible over the entire spectrum of flight speeds. On the other hand, the dependence of the zero-lift drag coefficient and the induced drag coefficient on the Mach number is negligible only for low subsonic speeds and hypervelocity speeds.

[†] The engineering practice is to use the parabolic approximation at transonic speeds also, even though this is not fully justified from a theoretical standpoint.

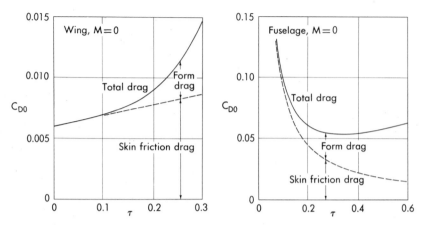

Fig. 4. Zero-lift drag coefficient of a typical two-dimensional wing and a typical body of revolution versus the thickness ratio.

3. LOW SUBSONIC AIRCRAFT

In this section, configurations designed for low subsonic flight are discussed. First, the zero-lift drag and the induced drag are analyzed; then, the aerodynamic characteristics of some typical jet aircraft are illustrated.

3.1 Subsonic incompressible flow. The zero-lift drag of a subsonic aircraft is composed of friction drag and pressure drag; the latter is due to the flow separation and is usually called the *form drag* (see Fig. 4). For a given Reynolds number and for a family of geometrically related bodies, the relative importance of the form drag with respect to the friction drag is largely dependent on the *thickness ratio* τ, that is, the ratio of the maximum thickness to the chord for a wing or of the maximum diameter to the length for a fuselage.* However, since the thickness ratios used for a wing rarely exceed 20% and those used for a fuselage rarely exceed 15%, it is concluded that the form drag can be neglected with respect to the friction drag, at least as far as preliminary design is concerned. This conclusion, in combination with the fact that interference effects are generally small in the subsonic realm, justifies the *wetted area method*. According to this method, a uniform skin friction coefficient can be assumed for the different surfaces of the aircraft; thus, if the contributions of the streamtube area and the afterbody area are neglected, the

---

* The reciprocal of the thickness ratio of a body is referred to as the *fineness ratio*.

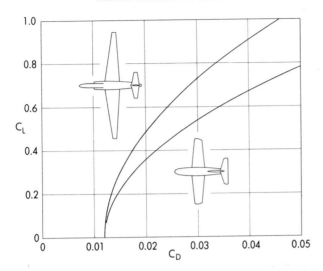

F$_{IG}$. 5. Subsonic drag polars of a typical high-altitude reconnaissance aircraft and a typical jet trainer.

zero-lift drag coefficient of the configuration becomes

$$C_{DO} \cong C_f \frac{S_w}{S} \tag{31}$$

where S_w is the wetted area and S the wing surface. Incidentally, the average skin friction coefficient depends on the Reynolds number, the roughness of the surfaces, and the nature of the boundary layer (laminar or turbulent); the typical value $C_f = 0.003$ can be of use for preliminary design analyses.

The induced drag of a subsonic aircraft is mainly pressure drag, more specifically, vortex drag associated with the system of trailing vortices issuing from the wing. Owing to the fact that the vortex drag coefficient of a wing with an elliptic spanwise lift distribution is given by*

$$\frac{C_L^2}{\pi \mathcal{R}} \tag{32}$$

it has become customary to represent the induced drag coefficient of an entire configuration in the form

$$C_{Di} = \frac{C_L^2}{\pi \mathcal{R} e} \tag{33}$$

---

*The symbol $\mathcal{R} = b^2/S$ denotes the *aspect ratio* of a wing with span b and planform area S.

where *e, Oswald's efficiency* factor, accounts for the nonellipticity of the lift distribution over the wing, the increase in the skin friction drag of the wing with the angle of attack, and the increase in the fuselage drag with the angle of attack. Practical values of Oswald's factor range in the neighborhood of 0.6–0.9.

3.2 Examples. In connection with the previous discussion, two examples of drag polars are shown in Fig. 5. One refers to a high-altitude reconnaissance jet having an aspect ratio of 11, and the other, to a jet trainer with an aspect ratio of 6. For the same lift coefficient, the induced drag coefficient of the jet trainer is about 80% larger than that of the reconnaissance jet.

4. HIGH SUBSONIC—LOW TRANSONIC AIRCRAFT

In this section, configurations designed for high subsonic–low transonic flight are discussed; as an example, the aerodynamic characteristics of a typical jet transport are presented.

4.1 Subsonic compressible flow. When the free-stream Mach number exceeds the typical value 0.5, compressibility effects begin to be noticeable. However, even though the zero-lift drag coefficient and the induced drag factor change with respect to the incompressible flow values, this change can be neglected as long as the local Mach numbers are subsonic.

As the free-stream Mach number increases, the local Mach numbers increase at all points of the surface of the aircraft. Finally, a special condition is reached such that the highest local Mach number is one; this condition is called the critical condition, and the corresponding free-stream Mach number, the *critical Mach number* M_C.

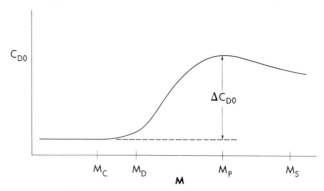

FIG. 6. Transonic drag terminology.

4.2 Low transonic flow. When the free-stream Mach number exceeds the critical Mach number, the flow becomes transonic, that is, locally supersonic over some region of the aircraft. The subsequent transition from supersonic back to subsonic flow occurs through a system of shock waves, and the associated pressure drag is called the *wave drag*. Incidentally, the drag increase due to the shock waves becomes noticeable only after the critical Mach number has been exceeded by a considerable margin (Fig. 6); for this reason, extensive use has been made of the *Mach number for drag divergence* M_D, which is rather arbitrarily defined as the Mach number at which the drag coefficient starts to increase rapidly.

Since the velocity perturbations caused by the wing are greater than those caused by the fuselage, the local Mach numbers over the wing are greater than those over the fuselage. Consequently, in order to design an aircraft for high subsonic–low transonic flight, the drag divergence Mach number of the wing and, hence, the critical Mach number of the wing must be made as high as possible (Ref. 8).

One method for delaying the drag rise of a configuration is to use sweptback wings (Fig. 7), since the critical Mach number is essentially determined by the component of the free-stream velocity normal to the leading edge. Consequently, if a two-dimensional wing is swept by an angle Λ, the critical Mach number increases according to the factor $1/\cos \Lambda$; in practice, owing to three-dimensional tip effects and fuselage interference effects, the benefit of the sweep is reduced considerably. The

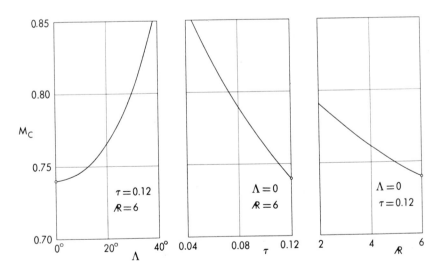

FIG. 7. Influence of the angle of sweep, the thickness ratio, and the aspect ratio on the critical Mach number of a typical wing.

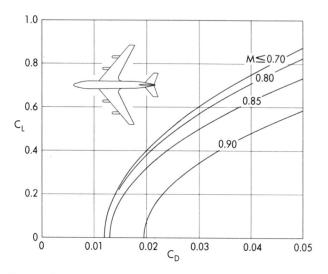

FIG. 8. Drag polar of a typical jet transport at high subsonic-low transonic speeds.

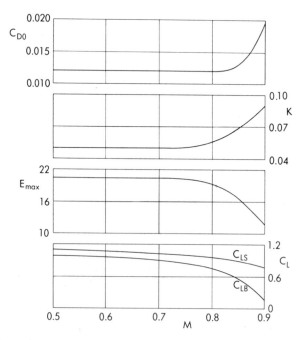

FIG. 9. Aerodynamic characteristics of a typical jet transport at high subsonic-low transonic speeds.

other methods commonly employed in order to increase the critical Mach number consist of decreasing the thickness ratio and the aspect ratio (Fig. 7). The underlying principle of these methods is evident, since they both result in a decrease of the velocity disturbance caused by the wing.

4.3 Example. In connection with the previous discussion, the drag polar of a typical high subsonic–low transonic multijet transport is indicated in Fig. 8. Furthermore, Fig. 9 shows the zero-lift drag coefficient, the induced drag factor, the maximum aerodynamic efficiency, the stalling lift coefficient, and the buffeting lift coefficient versus the Mach number.

5. SUPERSONIC AIRCRAFT

In this section, the main characteristics of configurations designed for supersonic flight are discussed. First, the behavior of an aircraft at high transonic and supersonic Mach numbers is analyzed; then, the characteristics of a typical supersonic aircraft are illustrated.

5.1 High transonic flow. When the free-stream Mach number exceeds the drag divergence Mach number, the zero-lift drag coefficient increases rapidly because of the formation of shock waves. However, this increase is not indefinite, and a maximum value is reached at the *Mach number for peak drag* M_P (see Fig. 6). Incidentally, the existence of a maximum for the drag coefficient in the transonic region is qualitatively evident if one thinks in terms of the linearized theory of two-dimensional wings, which predicts a pressure coefficient inversely proportional to $\sqrt{1 - M^2}$ in subsonic flow and to $\sqrt{M^2 - 1}$ in supersonic flow (Ref. 6).

If an aircraft is designed to be supersonic, it is usually desirable that its *peak drag coefficient* be as low as possible. The methods for decreasing the peak drag coefficient are identical with those for increasing the critical Mach number, that is, sweeping the wing, decreasing the thickness ratio, and decreasing the aspect ratio (Fig. 10). This is obvious, since the effect of any of these methods is to decrease the strength of the shock-wave system.

Interference effects in the transonic range are generally greater than those in the subsonic range due to the higher velocity perturbations over both the wing and the fuselage. When combined, these perturbations often result in large supersonic regions which contribute substantially to the wave drag. In order to decrease this interference drag, it is particularly useful to employ *Whitcomb's area rule*. Whitcomb's idea is that the disturbances caused by a wing-fuselage combination at a great distance from the body are independent of the particular arrangement and are a

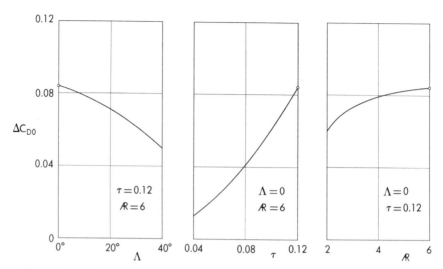

Fig. 10. Influence of the angle of sweep, the thickness ratio, and the aspect ratio on the peak drag coefficient of a typical wing.

function of only the cross-sectional area distribution. It follows that, for each wing-fuselage combination, there exists an equivalent body of revolution having equal wave drag and that the drag of this equivalent body must be decreased in order to decrease the drag of the combination. Thus, by indenting the fuselage, it is possible to add the wing to the configuration with only a small variation in the cross-sectional area distribution of the equivalent body, that is, with only a small variation in the over-all wave drag with respect to that of the basic fuselage. Incidentally, the area rule is most effective in cases where $\mathcal{R} \sqrt[3]{\tau} < 1$, where $\mathcal{R}$ is the aspect ratio and τ the thickness ratio.

5.2 Supersonic flow. The supersonic flow regime starts when the free-stream Mach number satisfies the inequality $M > M_S$, where M_S, the *upper critical Mach number,* is the free-stream Mach number at which the lowest local Mach number is one (Fig. 6).

As in the case of subsonic flow, the zero-lift drag can be decomposed into the friction drag and the pressure drag; the latter is due to the formation of shock waves and, therefore, is called the wave drag. For a family of geometrically related wings, the friction drag coefficient is practically independent of τ, while the wave drag coefficient increases as τ^2 (Fig. 11); hence, it is extremely important to use small thickness ratios. However, even though the thickness ratios used in engineering practice rarely exceed 6%, the pressure drag at supersonic speeds is usually a considerable fraction of the over-all zero-lift drag.

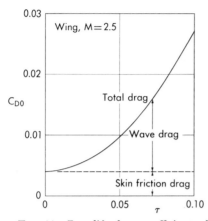

FIG. 11. Zero-lift drag coefficient of a typical two-dimensional wing versus the thickness ratio.

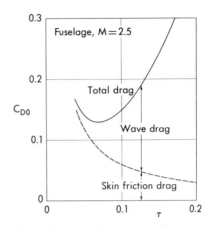

FIG. 12. Zero-lift drag coefficient of a typical body of revolution versus the thickness ratio.

With regard to the fuselage, the example of Fig. 12 shows that the friction drag coefficient is inversely proportional to τ, while the wave drag coefficient increases as τ^2; hence, for a given cross-sectional area, a thickness ratio minimizing the over-all zero-lift drag exists, which is about 7% in this particular example. Should the volume be prescribed and the cross-sectional area free, then the friction drag would become inversely proportional to $\tau^{1/3}$ and the wave drag directly proportional to $\tau^{8/3}$; hence, the thickness ratio minimizing the over-all zero-lift drag would be much smaller, that is, about 4%.

The induced drag of a supersonic aircraft is mainly pressure drag and, in accordance with the physical nature of the flow field, is usually separated into the wave drag due to lift and the vortex drag associated with the system of vortices issuing from the wing. While the wave drag is never zero, the vortex drag is zero for a wing of infinite span, as in subsonic flow. At any rate, since the theory of linearized flows predicts that both the wave drag due to lift and the vortex drag are, in coefficient form, proportional to C_L^2, the parabolic approximation can be assumed for the drag polar.

There exist several wing planforms which have been subjected to a thorough analytical investigation in recent years: the straight wing, the swept wing, the arrow wing, the delta wing, and the diamond wing. Among these, the delta wing deserves particular mention. Even though this wing is not necessarily the best for every design, the following positive features are of interest: (a) at transonic and moderate supersonic Mach numbers, its zero-lift drag is considerably less than that

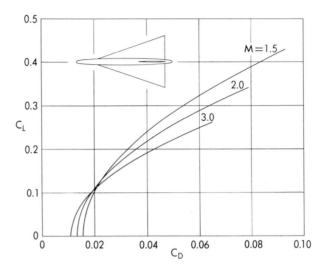

FIG. 13. Drag polar of a typical jet aircraft at supersonic speeds.

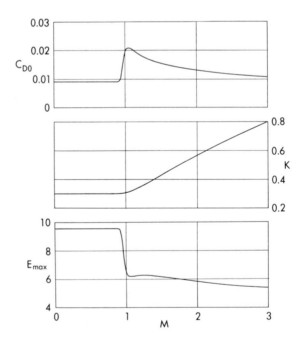

FIG. 14. Aerodynamic characteristics of a typical jet aircraft at supersonic speeds.

of a straight wing having equal thickness ratio and aspect ratio; (b) its peak drag coefficient is below that of the straight wing and considerably delayed; (c) its maximum aerodynamic efficiency is greater than that of the straight wing at moderate supersonic speeds; and (d) owing to the different spanwise distribution of the aerodynamic load, lower thickness ratios can be utilized, a circumstance which has a beneficial effect on both the zero-lift drag coefficient and the maximum aerodynamic efficiency.

5.3 Example. In connection with the previous discussion, the drag polar of a multijet, delta-wing aircraft designed for operation at moderate supersonic speeds is indicated in Fig. 13 for several values of the Mach number. Furthermore, Fig. 14 shows the zero-lift drag coefficient, the induced drag factor, and the maximum aerodynamic efficiency versus the Mach number.

6. HYPERSONIC VEHICLES

In this section, configurations designed for hypersonic flight are discussed. In particular, the characteristics of a typical ballistic missile and a typical hypervelocity glider are illustrated.

6.1 Hypersonic flow. Hypersonic flow is a highly supersonic flow, more specifically, according to some authors, a flow in which the Mach number exceeds five. The main characteristics of this flow are that (a) the shock waves originating at the leading edge of the body lie close to the body so that a strong interaction with the boundary layer may occur and (b) because of the extreme temperatures in the region between the shock waves and the body, the consideration of real gas effects (molecular vibration, dissociation, and ionization) may be necessary when analyzing the flow field (Ref. 2).

As the Mach number increases, the shock waves move closer to the body. At very high Mach numbers, a rough picture of hypersonic flow is provided, if it is assumed that the shock waves are identical with the surface of the body at least in its front part (*Newtonian flow*); consequently, the pressure coefficients can be determined with the simple assumption that the molecules crossing the shock layer conserve the tangential component of the velocity but lose the normal component.

6.2 Ballistic missile. A most striking application of the hypersonic flow theory is the analysis of a ballistic missile. Aerodynamically, a ballistic missile is designed to fly the greatest portion of its trajectory at zero lift, since steering is usually achieved by gimballing the engine; geometrically,

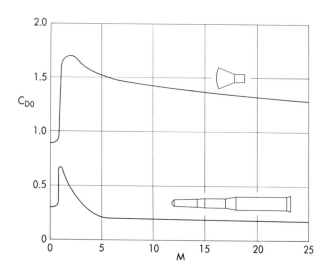

F<small>IG</small>. 15. Aerodynamic characteristics of a typical long-range missile and a typical high-drag reentry capsule.

a ballistic missile is a body of revolution with a nose and a blunt base. With respect to the nose, drag considerations would favor a rather pointed form. However, because of the severity of the heat transfer problem encountered during reentry, a blunt form may be desirable. In the first place, the convective heating rate at the nose can be reduced by increasing the radius of curvature. In the second place, for a relatively light missile, a further reduction in the peak heating rate as well as in the overall heat transferred during reentry is possible, if a high pressure drag design is used for the body (see Chapter 14).

Customarily, the zero-lift drag of a missile is separated into the friction drag, the pressure drag of the forebody or wave drag, and the pressure drag of the base. The latter, called the *base drag*, is particularly important for hypersonic vehicles and exists because the streamlines are unable to follow the contour of the base; hence, the pressure behind the base is much smaller than that on the body surface forward of the base.

The aerodynamic characteristics of a typical long-range missile are given by the lower curve of Fig. 15. This curve can be applied to both the take-off and reentry configurations, the reason being that the change in the cross-sectional area is approximately proportional to the change in the drag for the particular example under consideration. Also shown in Fig. 15 are the aerodynamic characteristics of a typical high-drag capsule used for manned reentry.

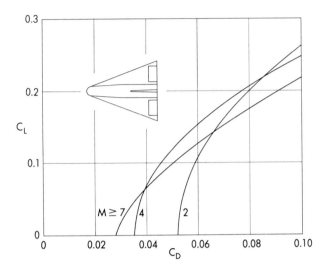

FIG. 16. Drag polar of a typical hypervelocity glider.

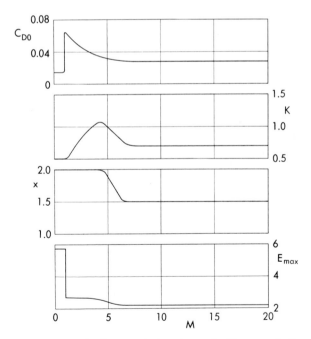

FIG. 17. Aerodynamic characteristics of a typical hypervelocity glider.

6.3 Hypervelocity glider. Another important application of the hypersonic flow theory is the analysis of a hypervelocity glider, that is, a vehicle which has lifting surfaces and is designed for operation at extremely high speeds. The design of this vehicle is a compromise between aerodynamic and heat transfer requirements. In fact, while a wing with sharp leading edges and a pointed fuselage are desirable from the standpoint of aerodynamic efficiency, the heat transfer problem is such that the leading edges of all the planar surfaces as well as the nose of the fuselage must be blunt. Since this circumstance introduces a high drag penalty and reduces the aerodynamic efficiency, the leading edge of the wing must be sharply swept, thus decreasing both the drag and the heat transfer. In conclusion, the probable configuration of a hypervelocity glider seems to be a delta planform with a blunt leading edge and a blunt fuselage; the drag polar of such a vehicle is illustrated in Fig. 16, while Fig. 17 shows the relationship between the coefficients of the polar and the Mach number. Incidentally, for small angles of attack and very high Mach numbers, the induced drag coefficient tends to the limiting value

$$C_{Di} = \frac{C_L^{3/2}}{\sqrt{2}}$$ (34)

which can be determined by applying the Newtonian flow theory to a flat plate and utilizing the circumstance that, for small angles of attack, the lift coefficient is proportional to α^2, while the drag coefficient is proportional to α^3.

7. FREE MOLECULAR FLOW

In this section, a flow satisfying the condition $M/R_e \gg 1$ is considered, that is, a flow which must be treated with the kinetic theory of gases. For this flow, the incident molecules are undisturbed by the presence of the vehicle, while the re-emitted molecules collide with the free-stream molecules only at a great distance from the body; hence, the aerodynamic forces are essentially governed by the interaction of the impinging molecules and the surface (Ref. 3).

Although the details of this interaction are not well known, the simplest treatments available so far have been concerned with two idealized models, that of the *specular reflection* and that of the *diffuse reflection,* the latter being closer to reality. In the specular model, the molecules hitting the surface are reflected optically; this means that the tangential component of the velocity is unchanged, while the normal component is reversed. In the diffuse model, the molecules hitting the surface are re-emitted with a Maxwellian distribution corresponding to the surface temperature.

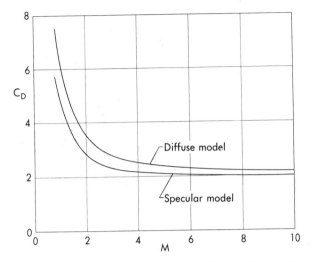

F I G. 18. Drag coefficient of a sphere in free-molecular flow.

If it is assumed that (a) the sideslip angle is zero, (b) the geometry of the body is given, (c) the model of reflection is specified, and (d) the body temperature and the free-stream temperature are identical in the diffuse model, the pressure coefficient and the skin friction coefficient can be shown to obey the laws*

$$C_p = C_p(\alpha, M, P), \qquad C_f = C_f(\alpha, M, P) \tag{35}$$

where P is a point on the surface Σ. Consequently, the evaluation of the surface integrals (7) yields the functional relationships

$$C_D = C_D(\alpha, M), \qquad C_L = C_L(\alpha, M) \tag{36}$$

which, after the parameter α is eliminated, lead to the expression

$$C_D = C_D(C_L, M) \tag{37}$$

which is called the drag polar in free molecular flow.

If the body under consideration is a sphere, the lift coefficient is always zero, and Eq. (37) reduces to the form

$$C_D = C_D(M) \tag{38}$$

---

* In a free molecular flow, the parameter $a = \sqrt{kR\theta}$ cannot be interpreted as the speed of propagation of weak pressure waves (speed of sound) but only as a mathematical reference velocity. Any physical significance attributed to it can be derived only from its proportionality to the velocity of thermal agitation of the molecules $\sqrt{2R\theta}$.

which is plotted in Fig. 18 for both the specular and diffuse cases. The
approximate conclusion to be derived from this graph is that, in the
absence of chemical reactions, particle showers, sputtering of surface material, and effects due to electric charges, the asymptotic value $C_D = 2$
can be employed in the range of velocities characteristic of satellite orbits.

8. AERODYNAMIC COMPONENTS IN A SPECIFIED ATMOSPHERE

In Section 2, continuum flow was considered, and the aerodynamic
coefficients of a given aircraft were represented as a function of the angle
of attack, the Mach number, and the Reynolds number; in Section 7, free
molecular flow was analyzed and the coefficients were represented as
functions of the angle of attack and the Mach number. While this representation is independent of the atmospheric properties, there are many
problems in Flight Mechanics which necessitate the representation of the
aerodynamic components in an arbitrarily specified atmosphere.

For example, consider the continuum flow regime and rewrite Eqs. (13)
in the form

$$\frac{2D}{\rho S V^2} = f_1\left(\alpha, \frac{V}{a}, \frac{\rho V l}{\mu}\right)$$

$$\frac{2L}{\rho S V^2} = f_2\left(\alpha, \frac{V}{a}, \frac{\rho V l}{\mu}\right)$$

(39)

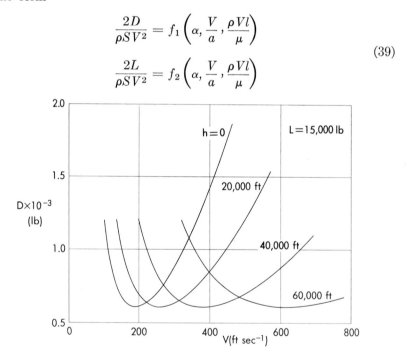

FIG. 19. Drag of a high altitude reconnaissance jet as a function of the velocity
and the altitude for a given lift.

Observe that, for a given atmospheric model (for instance, the 1959 ARDC Model Atmosphere), the density, the viscosity, and the speed of sound are known functions of the altitude, that is,

$$\rho = \rho(h), \quad \mu = \mu(h), \quad a = a(h) \tag{40}$$

Consequently, after Eqs. (39) and (40) are combined, the following functional relationships are obtained:[*]

$$D = D(h, V, \alpha), \quad L = L(h, V, \alpha) \tag{41}$$

which, after α is eliminated, imply that

$$D = D(h, V, L) \tag{42}$$

8.1 Example. In connection with the previous discussion, a numerical example has been prepared relative to the high altitude reconnaissance jet described in Fig. 5. In Fig. 19, the drag function (42) is plotted versus the velocity and the altitude under the assumptions that the wing surface is $S = 600 \text{ ft}^2$ and that the lift is $L = 15,000 \text{ lb}$. For each given altitude, there exists a velocity such that the over-all drag is a minimum; con-

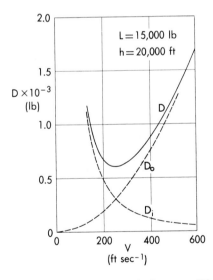

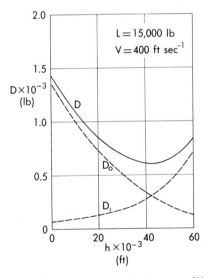

FIG. 20. Variation of the zero-lift drag, the induced drag, and the over-all drag with the velocity for a given lift and a given altitude.

FIG. 21. Variation of the zero-lift drag, the induced drag, and the over-all drag with the altitude for a given lift and a given velocity.

---

[*] Analogous functional relationships can be shown to hold for the free molecular flow regime.

versely, for each given velocity, there exists an altitude where the over-all drag is a minimum. Incidentally, the existence of these stationary points can be explained as follows: (a) the over-all drag is the sum of the zero-lift drag and the induced drag; (b) for a given altitude, the zero-lift drag increases monotonically with the velocity, while the induced drag decreases (Fig. 20); and (c) for a given velocity, the zero-lift drag decreases monotonically with the altitude, while the induced drag increases (Fig. 21).

ACKNOWLEDGMENT

The authors are indebted to Mrs. Doris McCann and Mrs. Irene Goldsmith (Douglas Aircraft Company), Miss Martha E. Graham (Boeing Scientific Research Laboratories), Dr. Alfred J. Eggers (NASA), Professors Martin H. Bloom (Polytechnic Institute of Brooklyn) and Joseph H. Clarke (Brown University), as well as Professors Harold M. DeGroff and Robert J. Goulard (Purdue University) for constructive criticism.

REFERENCES

1. HOERNER, S. F., *Fluid-Dynamic Drag*, S. F. Hoerner, Midland Park, N.J., 1958.
2. HAYES, W. D. and PROBSTEIN, R. F., *Hypersonic Flow Theory*, Academic Press, New York, 1959.
3. SCHAAF, S. A. and CHAMBRÉ, P. L., *Flow of Rarefied Gases*, High Speed Aerodynamics and Jet Propulsion, Vol. III, Princeton University Press, Princeton, N.J., 1958.
4. DONOVAN, A. F. and LAWRENCE, H. R., Editors, *Aerodynamic Components of Aircraft at High Speeds*, High Speed Aerodynamics and Jet Propulsion, Vol. VII, Princeton University Press, Princeton, N.J., 1957.
5. NIELSEN, J. N., *Missile Aerodynamics*, McGraw-Hill Book Company, Inc., New York, 1960.
6. VON KÁRMÁN, T., *Supersonic Aerodynamics. Principles and Applications*, Journal of the Aerospace Sciences, Vol. 14, No. 7, 1947.
7. EGGERS, A. J., ALLEN, H. J., and NEICE, S. E., *A Comparative Analysis of the Performance of Long-Range Hypervelocity Vehicles*, NACA TN No. 4046, 1957.
8. VAN EVERY, K. E., *Aerodynamics of High-Speed Airplanes*, SAE Quarterly Transactions, Vol. 3, No. 2, 1949.

CHAPTER 7

PROPULSION SYSTEMS

by

JOHN W. CONNORS* and JERRY GREY†

1. INTRODUCTION

This chapter contains a discussion of the basic principles, thermo-dynamic cycles, and performance characteristics of those propulsion systems which are of interest for aeronautical applications. Since a detailed discussion of the engine components is beyond the scope of this textbook, each powerplant is treated from an over-all point of view; furthermore, the main performance characteristics, the *thrust* and the *specific fuel consumption*, are presented only in the functional form which is useful for Flight Mechanics applications.

Propulsion systems can be divided into three broad groups: (a) single-flow systems, (b) multiflow systems, and (c) hybrid systems. A *single-flow system* is one in which thrust is produced by the acceleration of one propulsive stream; the rocket, the ramjet, and the turbojet (with and without afterburner) belong to this category. A *multiflow system* is one in which thrust is produced by the acceleration of more than one pro-pulsive stream; the turbofan, the turboprop, and the reciprocating engine are examples of such a system, although only the first of these engines is analyzed here. Finally, a *hybrid system* is formed by combining two single-flow systems; for example, the turbojet and the ramjet can be com-bined to form the turboramjet; other such systems are the ramrocket, the turborocket, and the ducted rocket.

2. ROCKET

The rocket is a comparative newcomer to the field of propulsion and has one outstanding characteristic: it is capable of operating beyond the Earth's atmosphere. Even though several types of rockets have been perfected, they are all functionally the same in that they include a cham-

---

* Project Engineer, Advanced Propulsion Group, Pratt and Whitney Aircraft Division of United Aircraft Corporation; also, Adjunct Associate Professor of Mechanical Engineering, Rensselaer Polytechnic Institute.

† Associate Professor of Aeronautical Engineering, Princeton University.

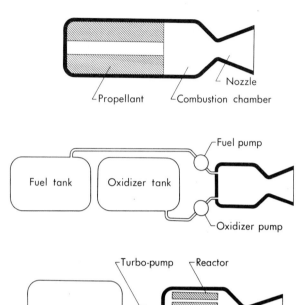

FIG. 1. Schematic diagrams of a solid propellant rocket (top), a liquid propellant rocket (center), and a nuclear rocket (bottom).

ber in which thermal energy is delivered to the working fluid and a nozzle in which this energy is transformed into the kinetic energy necessary for propulsion purposes. Among the particular arrangements which are possible, the following must be mentioned (Fig. 1): (a) the *solid propellant rocket,* in which the propellant is contained in the combustion chamber; (b) the *liquid propellant rocket,* in which the propellants are stored in appropriate tanks and fed to the combustion chamber by means of turbo-pumps or pressurized inert gases; and (c) the *nuclear rocket,* in which the energy resulting from the fission process in the reactor is transferred to a working fluid (Ref. 4).

Regardless of the particular arrangement, however, the thrust of a rocket engine is expressed by Eq. (3–35), which is rewritten here in the form

$$T = \beta V_e + S_e(p_e - p) \tag{1}$$

where β is the propellant mass flow, V_e the average relative velocity at the exit (note that the subscript r used in Chapter 3 is dropped here, since no ambiguity is possible), S_e the exit area, p_e the average static pressure over the exit section, and p the static ambient pressure (the subscript o used in Chapter 3 is dropped here, since no ambiguity is possible). In turn, after the acceleration of gravity at sea level is indicated by g_o, the specific propellant consumption is defined as

$$c = \frac{\beta g_o}{T} \qquad (2)$$

and is clearly a measure of the efficiency of the engine.* Typical values of the specific propellant consumption of present-day rockets range in the neighborhood of 10–15 hr^{-1}.

In a dimensionless form, the thrust and the specific propellant consumption are customarily represented by means of the coefficients

$$K_T = \frac{T}{p_c S_t}, \qquad K_c = \frac{c a_c}{g_o} \qquad (3)$$

where p_c and a_c are the pressure and the speed of sound corresponding to stagnation conditions in the combustion chamber and S_t is the area of the nozzle throat. While the performance analysis of a nozzle is necessary in order to evaluate these coefficients (Refs. 1 through 3), only the final results are presented here in functional form.

If it is assumed that (a) the flow is one-dimensional, steady, adiabatic, and frictionless, (b) the gas is perfect, and (c) no chemical reactions occur in the nozzle, the following relationships can be shown to hold:

$$K_T = K_T\left(\frac{S_e}{S_t}, \frac{p_c}{p}\right)$$

$$K_c = K_c\left(\frac{S_e}{S_t}, \frac{p_c}{p}\right) \qquad (4)$$

and are plotted in Fig. 2 with the assumption that the ratio of the specific heats is $k = 1.2$. As the graph indicates, for a given pressure ratio p_c/p, there is an area ratio which maximizes the thrust coefficient. When this condition occurs, the exit pressure equals the ambient pressure and the associated flow is termed correctly expanded. In this connection, the dashed line in Fig. 2 is the geometrical locus of the points where $p_e = p$; while the domain on the left of this line is representative of under-expanded nozzles ($p_e > p$), the domain on the right corresponds to over-expanded nozzles ($p_e < p$).

---

* The efficiency can also be expressed by means of the specific impulse, that is, the reciprocal of the specific propellant consumption.

TABLE 1

PERFORMANCE OF SEVERAL ROCKET PROPELLANTS

	Types of propellants	p_c (lb in^{-2})	θ_c (°R)	m	c (hr^{-1})	V_e (ft sec^{-1})
Solid propellants	GALCIT composite (asphalt + potassium perchlorate)	1,000	4,300	30	18.5	6,300
	JPN ballistite (nitrocellulose + nitroglycerin)	1,000	5,700	28	15.7	7,400
Liquid propellants	Liquid oxygen—JP4	500	6,300	22	13.6	8,500
	Liquid fluorine—hydrazine	500	8,200	19	11.4	10,200
	Liquid oxygen—hydrogen	500	5,000	9	9.9	11,700
	Liquid fluorine—hydrogen	500	5,500	9	9.6	12,100
Nuclear propellants	Hydrogen	500	5,000	2	4.7	24,700

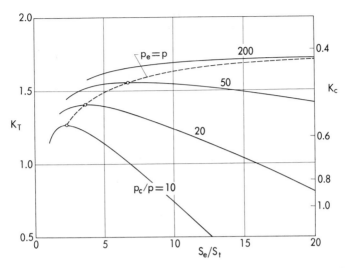

Fig. 2. Coefficients of thrust and specific propellant consumption of a rocket versus the area ratio and the pressure ratio.

Consider, now, a constant-geometry rocket equipped with a conventional Laval nozzle and designed in such a way that correct expansion is achieved at some altitude above sea level. At altitudes below the design altitude, overexpansion occurs and may cause a significant loss in thrust due to subambient pressures acting along a portion of the divergent section of the nozzle. Conversely, underexpansion occurs at altitudes above the design altitude and is accompanied by an increase in the thrust, which reaches its highest value at $h = \infty$, where $p = 0$.

It is obvious from Eqs. (3) and (4) that, for a given area ratio and pressure ratio, the specific propellant consumption is inversely proportional to the speed of sound in the combustion chamber and, consequently, is directly proportional to $\sqrt{m/\theta_c}$, where m is the molecular weight of the combustion products and θ_c the chamber temperature. This explains why nuclear rockets exhibit superior performance despite the limitations imposed on the chamber temperature;* the absence of a combustion process permits the selection of propellants having a low molecular weight (Table 1). Conversely, the same circumstance explains the shortcomings of solid propellant rockets, since their combustion products are characterized by a mean molecular weight which is higher than that of comparable liquid propellant rockets.

---

* The temperature of the propellants employed in current nuclear rockets is limited by the melting point of the core material and, hence, is generally lower than that of chemical rockets.

3. SINGLE-FLOW, AIR-BREATHING PROPULSION SYSTEMS

According to Eq. (3–37), the thrust of any single-flow, air-breathing propulsion system is given by*

$$T = \beta_e V_e - \beta_a V + S_e(p_e - p) \qquad (5)$$

where β_e is the exit mass flow, β_a the mass flow of air, and V the free-stream velocity. Furthermore, the specific fuel consumption is defined as

$$c = \frac{\beta g_o}{T} = \frac{\mu \beta_a g_o}{T} \qquad (6)$$

where

$$\beta = \beta_e - \beta_a, \qquad \mu = \beta/\beta_a \qquad (7)$$

are the mass flow of fuel and the fuel-to-air ratio. Typical values of the specific fuel consumption range in the neighborhood of 2.5–3.5 hr^{-1} for a ramjet, 2–3 hr^{-1} for a turbojet with afterburner, and 1–2 hr^{-1} for a simple turbojet.

In a dimensionless form, the thrust and the specific fuel consumption are represented by the following coefficients:

$$K_T = \frac{T}{p S_R}, \qquad K_c = \frac{c a_*}{g_o} \sqrt{\frac{\theta_*}{\theta}} = \frac{c a_*^2}{g_o a} \qquad (8)$$

where S_R is a fixed reference area of the engine (usually the inlet lip area for a ramjet and the maximum frontal area for a turbojet), θ the free-stream temperature, a the free-stream speed of sound, θ_* the static temperature at the tropopause, and a_* the speed of sound at the tropopause.

In order to determine how the coefficients of thrust and specific fuel consumption depend upon certain similarity parameters which are characteristic of the engine and the free-stream conditions, the analysis of the engine cycle is necessary (Refs. 1 through 3); however, since this analysis is beyond the scope of the textbook, only the final results are presented here in a functional form for a number of specific powerplants.

3.1 Ramjet. The ramjet engine, an important and useful propulsion system at moderate and high supersonic Mach numbers, is the least complex of the single-flow, air-breathing propulsion systems, since the compression process is accomplished by ram effect rather than by turbomachinery. However, because of this, the ramjet cannot produce thrust below a certain minimum Mach number.

---

* The symbols V_e, V, β_a employed here replace the symbols V_{re}, V_{ro}, β_o used in Chapter 3.

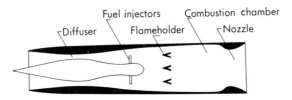

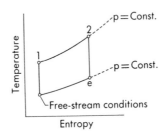

FIG. 3. Ramjet.

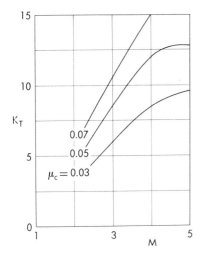

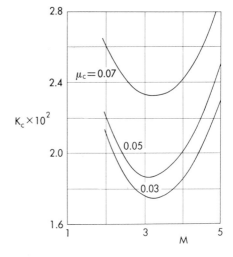

FIG. 4. Coefficient of thrust of a typical ramjet.

FIG. 5. Coefficient of specific fuel consumption of a typical ramjet.

The schematic drawing and the *ideal thermodynamic cycle* of this engine are indicated in Fig. 3. The air is decelerated and compressed isentropically from free-stream conditions to the subsonic state 1 in a diffuser. Fuel is then sprayed into the gas stream by means of injectors. A constant pressure combustion process occurs between states 1 and 2, beginning immediately behind the flameholders and spreading downstream into the unburned mixture to produce a relatively uniform temperature profile at the nozzle inlet. Finally, an isentropic expansion from state 2 to state e (ambient pressure) takes place in the nozzle.

In this cycle, called the Brayton cycle, heat is added over a range of temperatures from states 1 to 2 and rejected over a range of temperatures from state e to the free-stream state. Hence, for the same maximum temperature, the thermodynamic efficiency is somewhat less than that of the Carnot cycle, in which heat addition occurs at maximum temperature and heat rejection, at minimum temperature. In practice, irreversibility effects in the components cause the actual cycle to depart significantly from the ideal one.

The analytical representation of the ramjet performance is simple and straightforward, if it is assumed that (a) the flow is one-dimensional and steady, (b) the gas is perfect, (c) no chemical reaction occurs in the nozzle, (d) the combustion efficiency is constant and the fuel-to-air ratio is much less than unity, (e) Reynolds number effects are negligible, and (f) the ramjet geometry is either fixed or an arbitrarily specified function of the Mach number. Under these hypotheses, the coefficients of thrust and specific fuel consumption can be shown to obey the functional relationships

$$K_T = K_T(M, \mu_c), \qquad K_c = K_c(M, \mu_c) \tag{9}$$

where $M = V/a$ is the free-stream Mach number and

$$\mu_c = \mu \frac{\theta_*}{\theta} = \mu \left(\frac{a_*}{a}\right)^2 \tag{10}$$

is the *corrected fuel-to-air ratio*, a parameter which is proportional to the ratio of the stagnation enthalpy increase associated with the combustion process to the free-stream static enthalpy. These relationships are plotted in Figs. 4 and 5 for a variable-geometry ramjet which is designed for sustained operation at $M = 5$ and utilizes fuel with a lower heating value of 18,500 BTU lb^{-1}. It should be noted that, at high supersonic Mach numbers there is a limitation to the thrust which is imposed by the maximum allowable temperature of the combustion chamber walls. In addition to this temperature boundary, several other limitations exist to the performance of a particular ramjet. Thus, stable combustion can be maintained only if the combustion chamber pressure (which, in turn, is determined by the free-stream conditions and the corrected fuel-to-air ratio) is greater than the flame-out pressure. Also, excessive stresses in the engine structure can be prevented only if the combustion chamber pressure is smaller than the maximum allowable value.

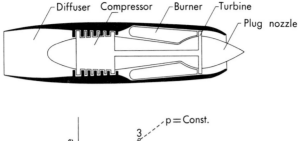

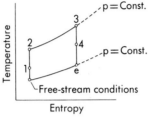

FIG. 6. Turbojet.

3.2 Turbojet. The turbojet engine, whose range of application varies between Mach numbers zero and three, can be regarded as a modification of the ramjet in the sense that a mechanical compressor and a turbine are present, thus enabling the engine to produce static thrust.

There is no difference between the *ideal thermodynamic cycle* of a ramjet and that of a turbojet. The latter is indicated in Fig. 6 along with a schematic drawing of an axial flow engine. The air undergoes an isentropic compression from the free-stream condition to state 1 in the diffuser and a further isentropic compression to state 2 in the compressor. Then, by means of a constant-pressure combustion process, heat is added from states 2 to 3; more specifically, a stoichiometric mixture of fuel and air is burned locally in the combustion zone. Immediately downstream, additional air is mixed with the combustion products to bring the temperature down to a value commensurate with reasonable turbine life. Subsequently, the air expands isentropically through the turbine from state 3 to state 4 doing an amount of work equal to the work of compression from states 1 to 2. Finally, a further isentropic expansion from states 4 to e (ambient pressure) occurs in the nozzle.

Under hypotheses similar to those of Section 3.1, the dimensionless representation of the turbojet performance is analogous to that of a ramjet and is given by

$$K_T = K_T(M, \mu_c)$$

$$K_c = K_c(M, \mu_c) \tag{11}$$

$$N_c = N_c(M, \mu_c)$$

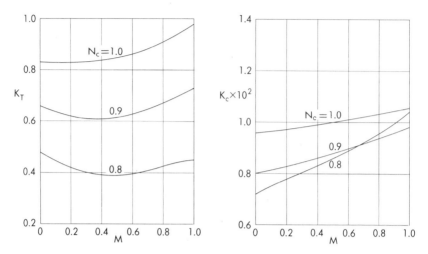

FIG. 7. Performance of a typical subsonic turbojet.

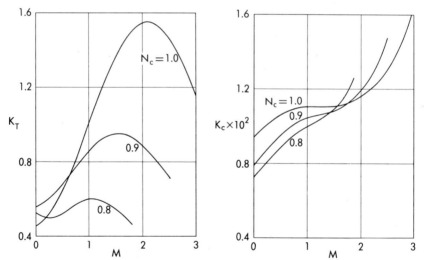

FIG. 8. Performance of a typical supersonic turbojet.

where

$$N_c = \frac{N}{N_{\max}} \sqrt{\frac{\theta_*}{\theta}} = \frac{N}{N_{\max}} \frac{a_*}{a} \quad (12)$$

is the *corrected rotor speed*, N the actual rotor speed (number of revolutions per unit time of the turbine-compressor unit), and $N_{\max}$ the maximum permissible rotor speed. The corrected rotor speed is proportional to the square root of the ratio of the stagnation enthalpy increase across the compressor to the free-stream static enthalpy and can be employed in place of the corrected fuel-to-air ratio as an independent variable. In fact, elimination of μ_c from the parametric equations (11) yields the new functional equations

$$K_T = K_T(M, N_c), \qquad K_c = K_c(M, N_c) \tag{13}$$

which are plotted in Fig. 7 for a typical constant-geometry subsonic turbojet and in Fig. 8 for a typical variable-geometry supersonic turbojet. Both of these turbojets have single-spool compressors with a moderate compression ratio.

It must be emphasized that, while the above performance curves are mathematically correct, they are restricted in practice by several physical limitations. Thus, the combustion chamber pressure is bounded by a lower limit (the flame-out pressure) and an upper limit (the maximum allowable pressure for which the engine is designed). Also, the temperatures at the outlet of the compressor and at the inlet of the turbine must be lower than certain limiting values which depend on the design of these engine components. Finally, the rotational speed is to be less than a maximum value which depends on the structural design of the engine.

3.3 Turbojet with afterburner. The turbojet with afterburner combines the characteristics of a turbojet and those of a ramjet. Because of the low fuel-to-air ratios used in turbojets, the gaseous mixture leaving the turbine contains enough unburned air to support further combustion. Consequently, if additional fuel is injected and burned in the tailpipe, a considerable increase in thrust can be obtained, the only limitation being imposed by the maximum temperature which the walls of the tailpipe can withstand. Since this limiting temperature is more than 1000° R higher than the corresponding limiting temperature at the turbine inlet, it is obvious that the thrust of an afterburning engine is considerably greater than that of a nonafterburning engine with the same airflow handling capacity. The specific fuel consumption, however, is generally higher.

The schematic diagram and *the ideal cycle* of a turbojet engine with an afterburner are indicated in Fig. 9. The thermodynamic states between free-stream conditions and state 4 are identical with those of the nonafterburning turbojet. However, instead of expanding through the nozzle from state 4 (turbine discharge) to ambient pressure, a further combustion occurs in the tailpipe, bringing the gas to state 5, from which it then expands through the nozzle to ambient pressure.

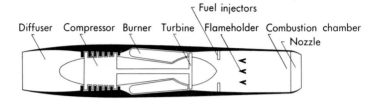

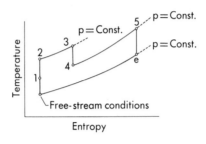

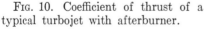

FIG. 9. Turbojet with afterburner.

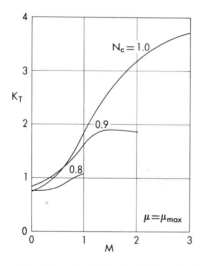

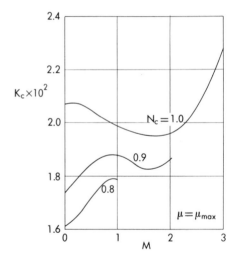

FIG. 10. Coefficient of thrust of a typical turbojet with afterburner.

FIG. 11. Coefficient of specific fuel consumption of a typical turbojet with afterburner.

If the fuel is injected in the afterburner in such a way that the resulting temperature is equal to the maximum permissible, the dimensionless representation of the performance becomes identical with that of the simple turbojet. This means that the functional equations (13) are still valid and are plotted in Figs. 10 and 11 for a typical engine.

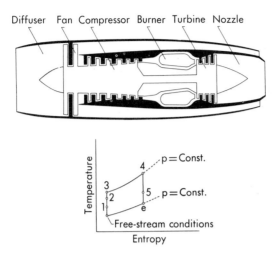

FIG. 12. Turbofan.

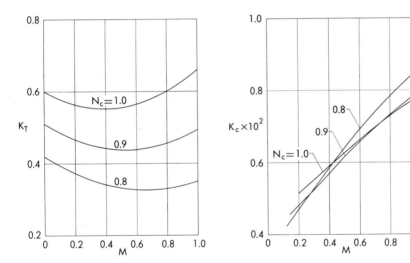

FIG. 13. Coefficient of thrust of a typical turbofan.

FIG. 14. Coefficient of specific fuel consumption of a typical turbofan.

4. MULTIFLOW PROPULSION SYSTEMS

In this section, attention is focused on one particular type of multiflow system, the *turbofan*. This engine, which currently finds its application at medium and high subsonic speeds, is a modification of the turbojet in that the turbine drives not only the compressor but also a fan; the latter compresses both the main stream of air which is channeled through the engine (primary flow) and the supplementary stream (secondary flow) which is ducted around the engine and discharged into the atmosphere. The main characteristic of the turbofan is that the thrust is greater than that of a turbojet with the same primary airflow capacity and, hence, its specific fuel consumption is lower; however, the thrust per unit frontal area is also lower.

The schematic drawing and the *ideal thermodynamic cycle* of this engine are indicated in Fig. 12. Both the primary and secondary flows are compressed isentropically from the free-stream condition to state 1 (fan inlet), whereupon an isentropic compression occurs across the fan, bringing both streams to state 2 (fan outlet). At this point, the two streams are separated, with the secondary stream expanding isentropically to ambient pressure in the nozzle. The primary stream undergoes a further compression and reaches state 3 (outlet of the compressor). Heat is then added from states 3 to 4 in a constant pressure burner; afterwards, the gas expands to state 5 through the turbine and then to state e in the nozzle. The dimensionless representation of the performance is identical with that of the simple turbojet and is indicated in Figs. 13 and 14 for a typical design.

5. HYBRID PROPULSION SYSTEMS

In the following paragraphs, two types of hybrid systems are discussed: the turboramjet and the ramrocket.

The *turboramjet* (Fig. 15-top), a combination of the turbojet and the ramjet, is designed to combine the high Mach number capability of the ramjet with the low Mach number capability of the turbojet. This power-plant is essentially a turbojet mounted inside a duct with an additional

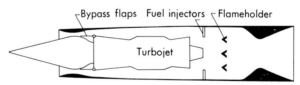

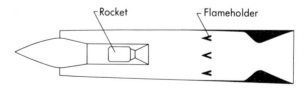

FIG. 15. Schematic diagram of a turboramjet (top) and a ramrocket (bottom).

combustion chamber downstream. At low flight speeds, the controllable flaps located at the compressor inlet close the bypass duct, and the power-plant operates either as a simple turbojet or as one with an afterburner; at high flight speeds, the flaps shut off the turbojet, and the powerplant operates as a ramjet.

The *ramrocket* consists of a rocket mounted inside a ramjet (Fig. 15-bottom). In the rocket combustion chamber, a richer-than-stoichiometric mixture is burned, and the fuel-rich combustion products are then mixed with air which flows in the annular passage around the rocket. Subsequently, a further combustion takes place in the downstream chamber, as in a ramjet. The ramrocket is quite a flexible powerplant; its operational range is somewhere between the rocket and the ramjet, depending on the relative sizes of the two component engines. However, because of the characteristics of the fuel employed, it is a compromised powerplant and, therefore, does not operate as efficiently as either of the component powerplants at the two ends of its propulsion spectrum.

6. PERFORMANCE IN A SPECIFIED ATMOSPHERE

In the previous sections, the coefficients of thrust and specific fuel consumption were represented as functions of, at most, two dimensionless parameters. This representation holds regardless of the distribution of the atmospheric properties versus the altitude; furthermore, it is instrumental in determining the engine performance in an arbitrarily specified atmosphere. To illustrate this point, which is important for Flight Mechanics analyses, consider a turbojet engine, and rewrite the functional equations (13) in the form

$$\frac{T}{pS_R} = f_1\left(\frac{V}{a}, \frac{N}{N_{\max}}\frac{a_*}{a}\right)$$

$$\frac{ca_*^2}{g_o a} = f_2\left(\frac{V}{a}, \frac{N}{N_{\max}}\frac{a_*}{a}\right) \tag{14}$$

Observe that, for a given atmospheric model (for instance, the 1959 ARDC Model Atmosphere), the pressure and the speed of sound are known functions of the altitude, that is,

$$p = p(h), \qquad a = a(h) \tag{15}$$

Consequently, after Eqs. (14) and (15) are combined, the following relationships are obtained:

$$T = T(h, V, N), \qquad c = c(h, V, N) \tag{16}$$

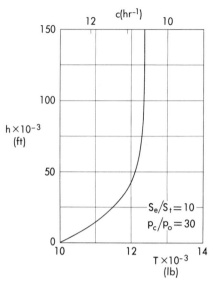

FIG. 16. Variation of the thrust and the specific propellant consumption of a rocket with the altitude.

If the above procedure is repeated for any of the engines analyzed in this chapter, it can be seen that the following generalized representation of the performance is possible:

$$T = T(h, V, \pi), \qquad c = c(h, V, \pi) \tag{17}$$

where h is the altitude, V the velocity, and π a variable called the *engine control parameter, thrust control parameter, or power setting.* The choice of this variable depends on the particular engine; thus, π can be identified with the combustion chamber pressure or the propellant mass flow of a rocket, with the fuel-to-air ratio or the corrected fuel-to-air ratio of a ramjet, and with the rotor speed or the corrected rotor speed of a turbojet and a turbofan.

As an example, Fig. 16 shows the variation of the thrust and the specific fuel consumption with the altitude for a rocket engine capable of developing a thrust of 10,000 lb at sea level with a combustion chamber pressure $p_c = 30$ atm. The propellant employed has a molecular weight of 19 and a chamber temperature of 6,400°R, so that the speed of sound in the combustion chamber is 4,500 ft sec^{-1}; the associated exit velocity is 10,200 ft sec^{-1}. As another example, Figs. 17 and 18 show the thrust and the specific fuel consumption of a turbojet capable of developing a sea-level static thrust of 10,000 lb at $N = N_{\max}$.

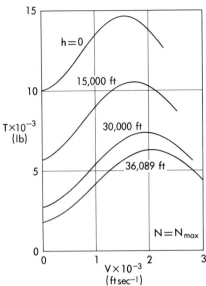

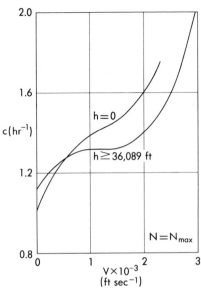

FIG. 17. Thrust developed by a typical supersonic turbojet.

FIG. 18. Specific fuel consumption
of a typical supersonic turbojet.

6.1 Approximate methods. In Flight Mechanics, it is often useful to represent the thrust and the specific fuel consumption in the approximate form

$$T = T_*(V, \pi)\left(\frac{\rho}{\rho_*}\right)^x, \qquad c = c_*(V, \pi)\left(\frac{\rho}{\rho_*}\right)^y \qquad (18)$$

where x and y are constants and the asterisk denotes quantities evaluated

TABLE 2

VALUES OF THE EXPONENTS x AND y IN THE TROPOSPHERE

Type of engine	x		y	
	Approximate lower limit	Approximate upper limit	Approximate lower limit	Approximate upper limit
Ramjet	1.1	1.4	0.0	0.1
Turbojet	0.3	1.0	−0.1	0.2
Turbojet with afterburner	0.6	1.1	−0.1	0.2
Turbofan	0.8	1.0	0	0.2

at the tropopause. For the air-breathing engines discussed in the present chapter, the values of the constants are

$$x = 1, \qquad y = 0 \tag{19}$$

in the isothermal stratosphere. Concerning the troposphere, numerical analyses yield the approximate results summarized in Table 2.

ACKNOWLEDGMENT

The authors are indebted to Messrs. Walter Doll and William H. Sens (Pratt and Whitney Aircraft Division of United Aircraft Corporation) for their helpful discussions.

REFERENCES

1. SUTTON, G. P., *Rocket Propulsion Elements*, John Wiley and Sons, Inc., New York, 1956.
2. HODGE, J., *Cycles and Performance Estimation*, Academic Press, New York, 1955.
3. ZUCROW, M. J., *Aircraft and Missile Propulsion, Vol. 2*, John Wiley and Sons, Inc., New York, 1958.
4. BUSSARD, R. W. and DE LAUER, R. D., *Nuclear Rocket Propulsion*, McGraw-Hill Book Company, Inc., New York, 1958.

Part II

QUASI-STEADY FLIGHT OVER A FLAT EARTH

INTRODUCTION TO PART II

The prediction of flight performance serves a twofold purpose: to determine the operational utility of an aircraft or missile which has already been designed and to determine the basic configuration of an aircraft or missile for a given mission. Because of the extent and complexity of the topics involved, the task of organizing the subject matter in an entirely rational manner is practically impossible. However, separation of the material according to the character of the motion (quasi-steady and non-steady) is desirable, since it results in two basically different mathematical problems.

The *quasi-steady approach* is useful in the analysis of those flight conditions which are characterized by negligible accelerations. Initially developed for piston-engined aircraft, this approach is also of interest for aircraft propelled by air-breathing jet engines. Its main characteristic is that, in almost every case having engineering interest, each point of the flight path can be investigated independently of those preceding and those following. Thus, the so-called point performance can be studied within the framework of elementary algebra. Furthermore, the optimum flight conditions can be obtained by using the Ordinary Theory of Maxima and Minima.

The *nonsteady approach* is of interest in the analysis of the flight paths of rocket-powered aircraft, missiles, satellite carriers, skip vehicles, and hypersonic gliders and in the study of the transient behavior of aircraft propelled by air-breathing jet engines. When this approach is used, the flight path can no longer be treated from a local point of view but must be considered in its entirety. In particular, the nucleus of the problems of performance optimization shifts from the domain of the Ordinary Theory of Maxima and Minima into the realm of the Calculus of Variations, so that the analytical difficulties are increased by an order of magnitude.

This part of the book is concerned with the performance of a jet-powered aircraft in quasi-steady motion over a flat Earth. Despite the simplifications associated with neglecting the acceleration terms, the extent of the subject matter is enormous owing to the great variety of flow regimes (subsonic, transonic, supersonic), drag polars (parabolic, nonparabolic), idealized powerplants (constant thrust, constant power), actual powerplants (turbojet, turbofan, ramjet), and flight conditions (gliding flight, level flight, quasi-level flight, climbing flight, turning flight). Consequently, the attainment of explicit solutions which are simultaneously valid for every case and subcase is out of reach. Nevertheless, if the drag, the thrust, and the specific fuel consumption are expressed in functional form, it is possible to formulate the performance problem in general and to predict functionally the nature of the solutions (Chapter 8).

If particular hypotheses are employed in the representation of the characteristics of the aircraft and the engine, considerable simplifications are possible; more specifically, analytical solutions become possible, and appropriate similarity parameters can be introduced. In this connection, three groups of problems are treated in the following chapters. First, attention is focused on an aircraft whose drag polar is parabolic with constant coefficients and whose powerplant characteristics are independent of the velocity. This combination, which yields a first approximation to subsonic vehicles powered by turbojet or turbofan engines, is investigated in Chapter 9; analytical solutions are emphasized. Then, the parabolic approximation is removed, and Chapter 10 analyzes the case of an aircraft whose drag polar is general; numerical solutions to several performance problems are presented. Finally, compressibility effects are considered in Chapter 11 in connection with high subsonic, transonic, and supersonic aircraft whose aerodynamic and engine characteristics are arbitrarily dependent on the Mach number; both the parabolic and the nonparabolic cases are investigated.

CHAPTER 8

INTRODUCTION TO THE PROBLEM
OF AIRCRAFT PERFORMANCE

1. INTRODUCTION

An important characteristic of aircraft propelled by air-breathing jet engines is that the inertia terms appearing in the dynamical equations are generally negligible along a major portion of the trajectory.* Consequently, the quasi-steady approach to aircraft performance is logical and permits substantial analytical simplifications of the problem. In spite of these simplifications, the great variety of speed regimes, aircraft configurations, and powerplants prohibits the attainment of explicit solutions which are simultaneously valid for every case and subcase. Nevertheless, if the drag, the thrust, and the specific fuel consumption are expressed in functional form, it is possible to formulate the performance problem in general and to predict functionally the nature of the solutions. This is the topic treated in the following pages in which a panoramic survey of the quasi-steady performance problem is offered. Because of the introductory nature of this chapter, the engineering statements are generally presented without proof and, therefore, will be justified later. To clarify the statements, figures are included; however, they do not apply to every vehicle but represent the typical behavior of a turbojet aircraft at speeds where compressibility effects are negligible.

There are two fundamental problems in quasi-steady flight: point performance problems and integral performance problems (Ref. 3). *Point performance problems* are concerned with the investigation of the local properties of the flight path, while *integral performance problems* are concerned with the study of the flight path as a whole, that is, with the over-all behavior of the aircraft between specified initial and final points. Since the acceleration terms are neglected in the dynamical equations, a point performance problem consists of solving a set of nonlinear algebraic relationships;† consequently, the optimum flight conditions can be ob-

---

*This is not the same as stating that the trajectory is rectilinear and flown with constant velocity.

†The major difference between quasi-steady flight and nonsteady flight is that the dynamical equations are algebraic in the quasi-steady case and differential in the nonsteady case.

tained by using the Ordinary Theory of Maxima and Minima. On the other hand, an integral performance problem consists of integrating the equations of motion subject to the appropriate command programs for the controls of the aircraft as well as to the appropriate initial and/or final conditions; while the rigorous study of the optimum flight conditions must be carried out with the Calculus of Variations, quasi-steady flight has the following characteristic: in the majority of problems having engineering interest, the optimum conditions calculated with the point performance approach are identical with those calculated with the integral perform-ance approach (see Ref. 4 and Volume 2).

2. FLIGHT IN A VERTICAL PLANE

In this section, a trajectory flown in a vertical plane is considered, and the following assumptions are employed: (a) the Earth is flat, and the acceleration of gravity is constant; (b) the inertia terms are negligible in the dynamical equations; (c) the thrust is tangent to the flight path; and (d) the atmosphere is at rest with respect to the Earth, and its properties are known functions of the altitude. In the light of these hypotheses and of Eq. (7–6), Eqs. (4–42) are rewritten as

$$
\begin{aligned}
\dot{X} - V \cos \gamma &= 0 \\
\dot{h} - V \sin \gamma &= 0 \\
T - D - W \sin \gamma &= 0 \\
L - W \cos \gamma &= 0 \\
\dot{W} + cT &= 0
\end{aligned}
\tag{1}
$$

where X denotes the horizontal distance, h the altitude, V the velocity, γ the path inclination, W the weight, D the drag, L the lift, T the thrust, c the specific fuel consumption, and the dot sign a derivative with respect to time. The first two equations are the kinematical relationships in the horizontal and vertical directions, the third and the fourth are the dy-namical relationships on the tangent and the normal to the flight path, and the last is the definition of weight flow of fuel for the engine. Inci-dentally, the dynamical equations indicate that the drag and the weight component on the tangent to the flight path are balanced by the thrust, while the weight component on the normal to the flight path is balanced by the lift.

According to Chapter 6, the drag of an aircraft can be expressed in the functional form

$$
D = D(h, V, L)
\tag{2}
$$

even when compressibility and viscosity effects are considered. Furthermore, according to Chapter 7, the characteristics of the powerplant are represented by the relationships

$$T = T(h, V, \pi), \qquad c = c(h, V, \pi) \tag{3}$$

where π is the control parameter of the engine.

2.1 Point performance. After the functional relationships (2) and (3) are considered, the dynamical equations on the tangent and the normal to the flight path can be rewritten in the form

$$
\begin{aligned}
T(h, V, \pi) - D(h, V, L) - W \sin \gamma = 0 \\
L - W \cos \gamma = 0
\end{aligned}
\tag{4}
$$

These equations involve the six variables

$$h, V, \gamma, W, L, \pi$$

and, hence, admit a four-parameter family of solutions. If these parameters are chosen to be the altitude, the velocity, the weight, and the power setting, functional solutions of the form

$$
\begin{aligned}
\gamma = f_1(h, V, W, \pi) \\
L = f_2(h, V, W, \pi)
\end{aligned}
\tag{5}
$$

must be expected. Once the dynamical equations have been solved, several other quantities can be determined, for example, the velocity components and the fuel consumed per unit time. In this connection, after the kinematical relations are combined with the first of Eqs. (5) and the definition of weight flow of fuel is combined with Eqs. (3), the following functional relationships are obtained:

$$\frac{dX}{dt} = f_3(h, V, W, \pi)$$

$$\frac{dh}{dt} = f_4(h, V, W, \pi) \tag{6}$$

$$\frac{dW}{dt} = f_5(h, V, \pi)$$

where t is the time. Hence, the velocity components and the fuel consumed per unit time depend on, at most, the four chosen parameters: the altitude, the velocity, the weight, and the power setting.

2.2 Integral performance. After the point performance has been investigated, certain quantities depending on the flight path as a whole (the range, the endurance, and the fuel consumed) must be calculated.

To do this, it is necessary to integrate the differential system composed of Eqs. (6), which involves one independent variable (the time t), five dependent variables (X, h, V, W, π), and two degrees of freedom. This means that, for a given set of initial conditions for X, h, W, infinite trajectories exist which are physically and mathematically possible, more specifically, one trajectory for each arbitrarily specified pair of functions $V(t)$, $\pi(t)$ or equivalent conditions. In view of the dissipative nature of the aerodynamic forces, no first integral can be written for the general case and, consequently, the study of particular flight conditions is of great interest from an engineering standpoint.

3. GLIDING FLIGHT

For the class of gliding paths, the condition $T = 0$ must be introduced into the equations of motion, which are rewritten as

$$\dot{X} - V \cos \gamma = 0$$
$$\dot{h} - V \sin \gamma = 0$$
$$D(h, V, L) + W \sin \gamma = 0 \qquad (7)$$
$$L - W \cos \gamma = 0$$
$$\dot{W} = 0$$

Hence, the weight is constant; furthermore, the drag is balanced by the weight component on the tangent to the flight path, while the lift is balanced by the weight component on the normal to the flight path. For the sake of simplicity, the discussion of Eqs. (7) is now carried out for the class of *shallow glide paths*, that is, trajectories whose inclination with respect to the horizon is so small that

$$\sin \gamma \cong \gamma, \qquad \cos \gamma \cong 1 \qquad (8)$$

Consequently, the following simplified set is obtained:

$$\dot{X} - V = 0$$
$$\dot{h} - V\gamma = 0$$
$$D(h, V, L) + W\gamma = 0 \qquad (9)$$
$$L - W = 0$$
$$\dot{W} = 0$$

3.1 Glide angle and sinking speed. After the expression for the drag is combined with the equation of motion on the normal to the flight path and the lift is eliminated, the drag function can be written in the form $D = D(h, V, W)$. Consequently, the equation of motion on the tangent

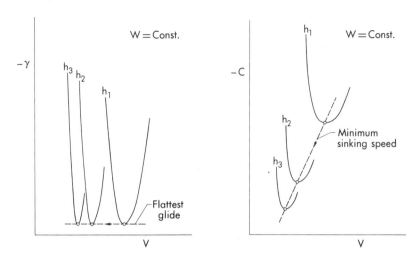

FIG. 1. Glide angle and sinking speed.

to the flight path yields the relationship

$$-\gamma = \frac{D(h,\ V,\ W)}{W} \qquad (10)$$

which means that the glide angle* is equal to the drag per unit weight. Furthermore, the sinking speed† is given by

$$-C = -V\gamma = \frac{D(h,\ V,\ W)V}{W} \qquad (11)$$

and, therefore, is equal to the power per unit weight expended in order to maintain the aerodynamic field around the aircraft.

The glide angle and the sinking speed predicted with Eqs. (10) and (11) are plotted in Fig. 1 versus the velocity for several values of the altitude. For each given altitude, there exists one velocity such that the glide angle is a minimum and another such that the sinking speed is a minimum. The first condition is called the *flattest glide* and occurs when

$$\frac{\partial D}{\partial V} = 0 \qquad (12)$$

---

* In gliding flight, the path inclination is negative, and its absolute value is called the *glide angle*.

† Generally speaking, the vertical component of the velocity or *rate of climb* is defined as $C = V \sin \gamma$ and simplifies to $C = V\gamma$ for a shallow path. For the particular case of gliding flight, the rate of climb is negative, and its absolute value $-C$ is called the *sinking speed*.

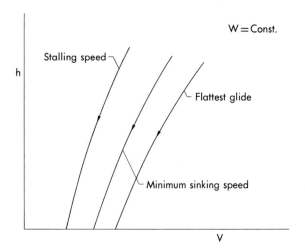

FIG. 2. Characteristic velocities for gliding flight.

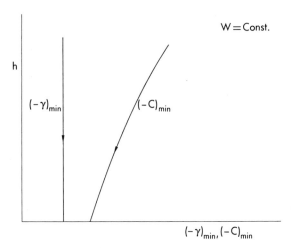

FIG. 3. Optimum glide performance.

that is, when the aerodynamic drag is a minimum. The second condition
is called the *glide with minimum sinking speed* and occurs when

$$\frac{\partial (DV)}{\partial V} = 0 \tag{13}$$

that is, when the power required to overcome the aerodynamic drag DV
is a minimum. Generally speaking, the velocity for flattest glide is higher
than the velocity for minimum sinking speed; furthermore, the latter is

higher than the *stalling velocity* (minimum velocity in quasi-steady glide), which is achieved when flying at the maximum lift coefficient; finally, these velocities depend on the altitude, decreasing as the aircraft progresses toward the lower layers of the atmosphere. For the particular case of a subsonic glider, the characteristic glide velocities can be shown to be inversely proportional to the square root of the atmospheric density (Fig. 2); the minimum glide angle is independent of the altitude (Fig. 3); and, finally, the minimum sinking speed is inversely proportional to the square root of the density, thereby decreasing as the glider approaches the lower layers of the atmosphere (Fig. 3).

3.2 Instantaneous range and endurance. After the altitude is selected as the new independent variable, the kinematical relationships on the horizontal and vertical directions can be rewritten in the form

$$\frac{dX}{dh} = \frac{1}{\gamma}, \qquad \frac{dt}{dh} = \frac{1}{C} \tag{14}$$

Consequently, the range flown per unit decrease in altitude is maximized when the glide angle is a minimum, while the endurance per unit decrease in altitude is maximized when the sinking speed is a minimum.

3.3 Integration process. While the general problem in a vertical plane is characterized by two degrees of freedom, gliding flight involves only one degree of freedom, owing to the fact that the thrust is zero. In this connection, after Eqs. (10) and (11) are accounted for, the differential set (14) can be rewritten in the functional form*

$$-\frac{dX}{dh} = f_1(h, V, W), \qquad -\frac{dt}{dh} = f_2(h, V, W) \tag{15}$$

and, for given initial values of X and t, admits infinite solutions, more specifically, one solution for each arbitrarily specified flight program $V(h)$. Among the possible flight programs, the following are of particular interest: (a) the constant velocity program; (b) the constant Mach number program; (c) the constant dynamic pressure program; (d) the constant angle of attack program; (e) the best range program, in which the function $V(h)$ is chosen so as to minimize the glide angle; and (f) the best endurance program, in which the function $V(h)$ is chosen so as to minimize the sinking speed. Under particular hypotheses, some of these

---

* The functional symbol f_i ($i = 1, 2, \ldots$) is repeated in every section of this chapter, even though its meaning changes from one flight condition to another.

programs may become identical. For example, if compressibility and viscosity effects are neglected, the constant dynamic pressure program is identical with the constant angle of attack program; furthermore, the best range and the best endurance programs become particular cases of the constant angle of attack program.

4. LEVEL FLIGHT

For the category of level paths, the inclination of the trajectory with respect to the horizon is $\gamma = 0$, so that the equations of motion are rewritten in the form

$$\dot{X} - V = 0$$
$$\dot{h} = 0$$
$$T(h, V, \pi) - D(h, V, L) = 0 \qquad (16)$$
$$L - W = 0$$
$$\dot{W} + c(h, V, \pi)T(h, V, \pi) = 0$$

Hence, the drag is balanced by the thrust, while the weight is balanced by the lift.

4.1 Instantaneous velocity. After the lift is eliminated from the dynamical equations, the following functional relationship is obtained:

$$T(h, V, \pi) - D(h, V, W) = 0 \qquad (17)$$

which involves the four variables h, V, W, π, so that a three-parameter

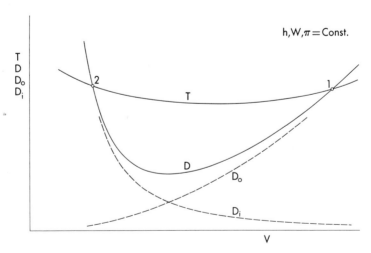

FIG. 4. Graphical determination of the level flight velocity.

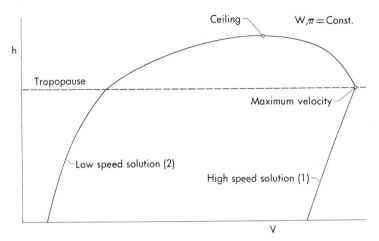

FIG. 5. Level flight solutions in the velocity-altitude domain.

family of solutions exists. This means that, if the altitude, the weight, and the power setting are specified, the only unknown is the velocity; it can be determined by plotting the thrust and the drag versus the velocity and finding the points where these curves intersect (Fig. 4). As an example, for a turbojet aircraft operating subsonically, there are two solutions for the velocity and their existence can be justified in the following manner. While the zero-lift drag D_o increases monotonically with the velocity, the induced drag D_i decreases, so that the total drag has a minimum with respect to the velocity. Since the thrust is almost invariant with respect to the velocity, the thrust-velocity curve and the drag-velocity curve admit two intersections: a high-speed solution 1 corresponding to flight with low angle of attack and a low-speed solution 2 corresponding to flight with high angle of attack.

If the velocity is calculated for different values of the altitude but for constant weight and power setting, the diagram indicated in Fig. 5 can be obtained. This diagram is the locus of the level flight solutions in the velocity-altitude domain and exhibits two characteristic points, one where the altitude is a maximum and another where the velocity is a maximum. The first point is called the *theoretical ceiling* and has the following property: at this altitude, the thrust-velocity curve and the drag-velocity curve become tangent; at any altitude above the theoretical ceiling, the thrust and the drag no longer intersect, meaning that quasi-steady level flight is physically impossible. The second point is also of considerable interest for flight operations, even though maximum velocity does not necessarily imply maximum range. Generally speaking, the maximum velocity of turbojet and turbofan aircraft operating subsonically occurs in the troposphere or at the tropopause; the associated altitude depends to a large degree on the thrust-to-weight ratio, increasing as the thrust-to-weight ratio increases.

4.2 Instantaneous range and endurance. After the instantaneous weight is selected as the new independent variable, the first and the fifth of Eqs. (16) can be rewritten in the form

$$-\frac{dX}{dW} = \frac{V}{c(h, V, \pi)T(h, V, \pi)}$$

$$-\frac{dt}{dW} = \frac{1}{c(h, V, \pi)T(h, V, \pi)} \tag{18}$$

Consequently, the range and the endurance per unit fuel consumed are functions of the altitude, the velocity, and the power setting. However, these variables are not independent but, for each instantaneous weight, must satisfy the level flight equation (17). This means that, if the power setting is eliminated from Eqs. (17) and (18), functional expressions of the form

$$-\frac{dX}{dW} = f_1(h, V, W)$$

$$-\frac{dt}{dW} = f_2(h, V, W) \tag{19}$$

are obtained and are plotted in Fig. 6 versus the velocity for a given

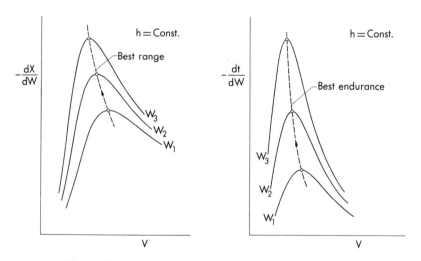

FIG. 6. Instantaneous range and endurance in level flight.

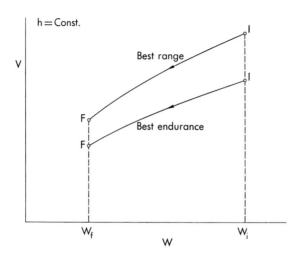

FIG. 7. Velocities for best range and best endurance in level flight.

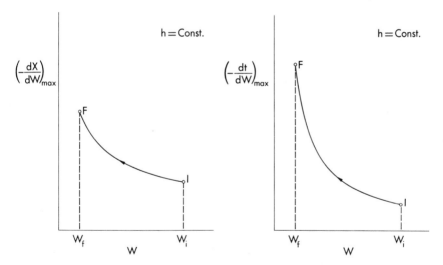

FIG. 8. Maximum instantaneous range and endurance in level flight.

altitude and for several values of the weight. For each given weight, there exists one velocity which maximizes the instantaneous range and another which maximizes the instantaneous endurance. The first condition is called *best range,* and the second, *best endurance.* Generally speaking, the velocity for best range is higher than that for best endurance; furthermore, both velocities decrease as fuel is being consumed (Fig. 7). The corresponding maximum values for the instantaneous range and the instantaneous endurance increase along the flight path as the aircraft becomes lighter because of fuel consumption (Fig. 8) ; more specifically, the maximum instantaneous range of a turbojet aircraft operating subsonically is inversely proportional to the square root of the weight, while the maximum instantaneous endurance is inversely proportional to the weight.

4.3 Integration process. While the general problem in a vertical plane is characterized by two degrees of freedom, level flight involves only one degree of freedom, since the path inclination is zero. Hence, for a given set of initial conditions for X and t, Eqs. (19) admit infinite solutions, more specifically, one solution for each arbitrarily specified flight program $V(W)$. Among these programs, the following are investigated in the subsequent chapters: (a) the constant power setting program; (b) the constant velocity program; (c) the best range program, in which the function $V(W)$ is chosen so as to maximize the instantaneous range; and (d) the best endurance program, in which the function $V(W)$ is chosen so as to maximize the instantaneous endurance.

5. QUASI-LEVEL FLIGHT

In the previous section, level paths were investigated; in this section, quasi-level paths are considered. While the former are defined by the condition $\gamma = 0$, the latter are flown with $\gamma \neq 0$ (that is, with variable altitude) but at such small inclination with respect to the horizon that the following hypotheses are satisfied:

$$\cos \gamma \cong 1, \qquad \sin \gamma \cong \gamma, \qquad W \sin \gamma \ll D \qquad (20)$$

Consequently, the equations of motion are rewritten in the form

$$\dot{X} - V = 0$$
$$\dot{h} - V\gamma = 0$$
$$T(h, V, \pi) - D(h, V, L) = 0 \qquad (21)$$
$$L - W = 0$$
$$\dot{W} + c(h, V, \pi)T(h, V, \pi) = 0$$

Comparison of Eqs. (16) and (21) shows that level paths and quasi-level paths are governed by the same set of equations except for the kinematical relationship in the vertical direction. Furthermore, quasi-level paths reduce to level paths if the condition $\gamma = 0$ is introduced into the second of Eqs. (21).

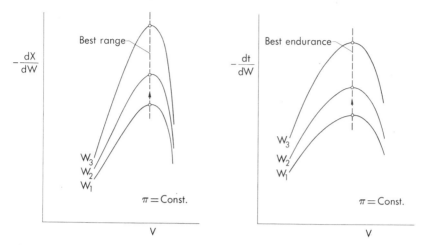

FIG. 9. Instantaneous range and endurance in quasi-level flight with constant power setting.

5.1 Instantaneous range and endurance. Since the kinematic relationship in the horizontal direction, the dynamical equations on the tangent and the normal to the flight path, and the definition of weight flow of fuel are identical for level and quasi-level paths, Eqs. (17) and (18) are valid for the present problem. This means that, if the altitude is eliminated from these equations, the following relationships can be derived:

$$- \frac{dX}{dW} = f_1(V, \pi, W), \qquad - \frac{dt}{dW} = f_2(V, \pi, W) \qquad (22)$$

On the other hand, if the velocity is eliminated from Eqs. (17) and (18), one obtains the result

$$- \frac{dX}{dW} = f_3(h, \pi, W), \qquad - \frac{dt}{dW} = f_4(h, \pi, W) \qquad (23)$$

These two differential sets are equivalent and can be employed with equal generality when studying range and endurance problems.

If Eqs. (22) are employed, the instantaneous range and endurance can be represented as functions of the velocity for a constant power setting and for several values of the weight (Fig. 9). For each given weight, there exists one velocity which maximizes the instantaneous range and another which maximizes the instantaneous endurance. The first condition is called *best range,* and the second, *best endurance.* Generally speaking, the velocity for best instantaneous range is higher than that for best endurance; furthermore, both velocities remain constant in the stratospheric flight of turbojet and turbofan aircraft (Fig. 10). The corresponding maximum values for the instantaneous range and the en-

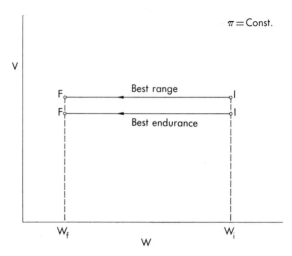

FIG. 10. Velocities for best range and best endurance in quasi-level flight with constant power setting.

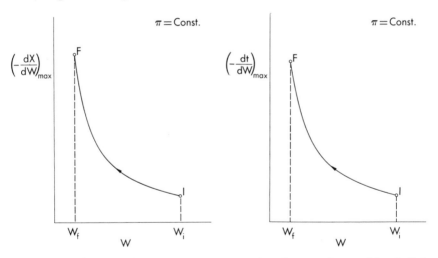

FIG. 11. Maximum instantaneous range and endurance in quasi-level flight with constant power setting.

durance increase along the flight path as the aircraft becomes lighter because of fuel consumption (Fig. 11); more specifically, the maximum instantaneous range and the maximum instantaneous endurance of turbojet and turbofan aircraft operating in the stratosphere are inversely proportional to the weight.

Further insight into the problem of the range and the endurance can be obtained by employing Eqs. (23) and plotting the instantaneous range

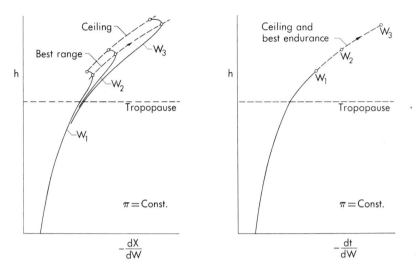

F ɪ ɢ. 12. Instantaneous range and endurance in quasi-level flight with constant power setting.

and endurance versus the altitude for a constant power setting and for several values of the weight (Fig. 12). For each given weight, there exists one altitude at which the instantaneous range is a maximum and another at which the instantaneous endurance is a maximum. In particular, for turbojet and turbofan aircraft flying subsonically in the stratosphere, the best instantaneous endurance is obtained when operating at the ceiling, while the best instantaneous range is achieved when cruising a few thousand feet below the ceiling.

5.2 Integration process. While level paths are characterized by one degree of freedom, quasi-level paths are characterized by two degrees of freedom. Consequently, if Eqs. (22) are employed and if the initial values of X and t are prescribed, infinite solutions exist, more specifically, one solution for each arbitrarily specified pair of functions $\pi(W)$ and $V(W)$. Among all the possible flight programs, the following are investigated in the subsequent chapters: (a) the constant power setting program flown with the velocity distribution corresponding to the best instantaneous range and (b) the constant power setting program flown with the velocity distribution corresponding to the best instantaneous endurance. Concerning the stratospheric flight of turbojet and turbofan aircraft, it can be shown that these two programs are characterized by a constant lift coefficient, a constant velocity, and a continuously increasing flight altitude. Hence, this technique of flight is also called the *cruise-climb*.

6. CLIMBING FLIGHT

Climbing flight is now considered, and the equations of motion are rewritten in the form

$$\dot{X} - V \cos \gamma = 0$$
$$\dot{h} - V \sin \gamma = 0$$
$$T(h, V, \pi) - D(h, V, L) - W \sin \gamma = 0 \tag{24}$$
$$L - W \cos \gamma = 0$$
$$\dot{W} + c(h, V, \pi)T(h, V, \pi) = 0$$

While point performance and integral performance relevant to these equations have been discussed in general in Section 2, attention is now focused on the particular case where the drag function is replaced by a somewhat simplified expression.

6.1 Simplified drag function. From Chapter 6, it is known that the over-all drag of an aircraft is the sum of the zero-lift drag and the induced drag. While the zero-lift drag depends on the velocity and the altitude only, the induced drag depends also on the lift, so that the following functional relationship holds:

$$D = D_o(h, V) + D_i(h, V, L) \tag{25}$$

After the equation of motion on the normal to the flight path is accounted for and the lift is eliminated, Eq. (25) can be rewritten as

$$D = D_o(h, V) + D_i(h, V, W \cos \gamma) \tag{26}$$

which is equivalent to

$$D = [D_o(h, V) + D_i(h, V, W)]\left[1 - \frac{D_i(h, V, W) - D_i(h, V, W \cos \gamma)}{D_o(h, V) + D_i(h, V, W)}\right] \tag{27}$$

Hence, if the approximation

$$\frac{D_i(h, V, W) - D_i(h, V, W \cos \gamma)}{D_o(h, V) + D_i(h, V, W)} \ll 1 \tag{28}$$

is employed, the drag function can be reduced to the form

$$D \cong D_o(h, V) + D_i(h, V, W) \tag{29}$$

which simplifies the study of the climbing problem to a considerable degree. Obviously, the use of Eq. (29) is always permissible for flight with small path inclination. However, it is also permissible for large path inclinations as long as $D_i/D_o \ll 1$. The reason is that any error in evaluating $\cos \gamma$ causes an error in the computation of the induced drag; but, if the flight condition is such that the induced drag is negligible with respect to the zero-lift drag, only a small error is introduced into the computation of the total drag and, hence, of quantities which depend on the total drag, such as the sine of the path inclination, the rate of climb, and the fuel consumed per unit increase in altitude.

6.2 Path inclination, rate of climb, and fuel consumed per unit increase in altitude. Since the drag function (29) has the form $D = D(h, V, W)$, the equation of motion on the tangent to the flight path yields the following solution for the sine of the path inclination:

$$\sin \gamma = \frac{T(h, V, \pi) - D(h, V, W)}{W} \tag{30}$$

so that the rate of climb and the fuel consumed per unit increase in altitude become

$$C = \frac{[T(h, V, \pi) - D(h, V, W)]V}{W}$$

$$-\frac{dW}{dh} = \frac{q(h, V, \pi)W}{[T(h, V, \pi) - D(h, V, W)]V} \tag{31}$$

where $q = cT$ is the fuel consumed per unit time. If the difference $T - D$ is defined as the *excess thrust*, the sine of the path inclination is equal to the excess thrust per unit weight. Furthermore, if the difference $TV - DV$ is defined as the *excess power* (power available for flight operations minus power dissipated in overcoming the aerodynamic drag), the rate of climb is equal to the excess power per unit weight. Finally, the fuel consumed per unit increase in altitude is equal to the fuel consumed per unit time divided by the excess power per unit weight.

The path inclination, the rate of climb, and the fuel consumed per unit increase of altitude predicted with Eqs. (30) and (31) are plotted in Fig. 13 versus the velocity for a constant weight, a constant power setting, and several values of the altitude. For each given altitude, there exists one velocity which maximizes the path inclination, another which maximizes the rate of climb, and a third which minimizes the fuel consumed per unit increase in altitude. The first condition is called the *steepest climb* and occurs when

$$\frac{\partial(T - D)}{\partial V} = 0 \tag{32}$$

that is, when the excess thrust is a maximum. The second condition is

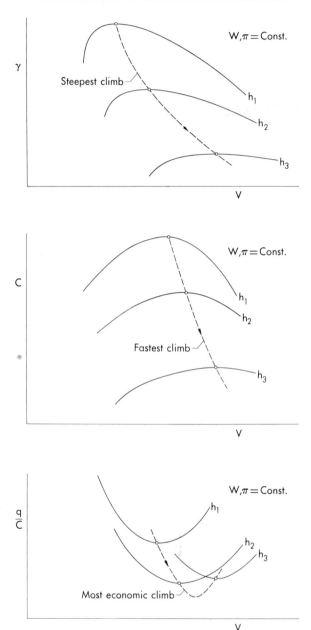

FIG. 13. Path inclination, rate of climb, and fuel consumed per unit increase of altitude.

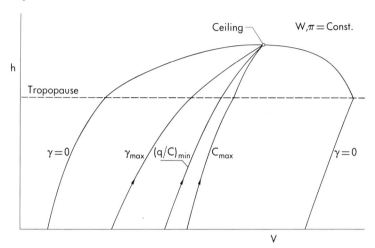

FIG. 14. Characteristic velocities for powered flight in a vertical plane.

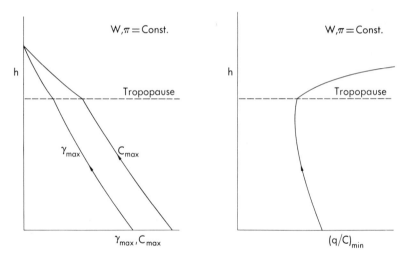

FIG. 15. Optimum climbing performance.

called the *fastest climb* and occurs when

$$\frac{\partial(TV - DV)}{\partial V} = 0 \tag{33}$$

that is, when the excess power is a maximum. Finally, the third condition is called the *most economic climb* and occurs when

$$\frac{\partial}{\partial V}\left(\frac{TV - DV}{cT}\right) = 0 \tag{34}$$

that is, when the ratio of the fuel consumed per unit time to the excess power is a minimum.

In connection with the above results, Figs. 14 and 15 summarize the climbing performance of a typical turbojet-powered aircraft for a given weight and power setting. As Fig. 14 indicates, the velocity for fastest climb is higher than that for most economic climb, while the latter is higher than the velocity for steepest climb; furthermore, these velocities are always bounded by two limiting values, that is, the level flight solutions which are attainable with the given power setting; incidentally, all of these velocities become identical at the theoretical ceiling of the aircraft. Also, Fig. 15 shows the maximum rate of climb, the maximum path inclination, and the minimum fuel consumed per unit increase in altitude as functions of the altitude. Both the maximum rate of climb and the maximum path inclination decrease with the altitude, becoming zero at the ceiling. On the other hand, the minimum fuel consumed per unit increase in altitude has a stationary point with respect to the altitude; beyond this point, the ratio q/C increases with the altitude, becoming infinitely large at the ceiling.

6.3 Instantaneous range, endurance, and fuel consumed per unit increase in altitude. After the altitude is selected as the new independent variable, the first, second, and fifth of Eqs. (24) are rewritten in the form

$$\frac{dX}{dh} = \frac{1}{\tan \gamma}, \qquad \frac{dt}{dh} = \frac{1}{C}, \qquad -\frac{dW}{dh} = \frac{q}{C} \tag{35}$$

Consequently, the distance flown per unit increase in altitude is minimized when the path inclination is a maximum; the time elapsed per unit increase in altitude is minimized when the rate of climb is a maximum; and finally, the fuel consumed per unit increase in altitude is minimized when the ratio of the fuel consumed per unit time to the rate of climb is a minimum.

6.4 Integration process. The next step in the analysis is to evaluate the distance, the time, and the fuel consumed in a climbing maneuver. After Eqs. (30) and (31) are accounted for, the differential set (35) is rewritten in the functional form

$$\frac{dX}{dh} = f_1(h,\ V,\ \pi,\ W)$$

$$\frac{dt}{dh} = f_2(h,\ V,\ \pi,\ W) \tag{36}$$

$$-\frac{dW}{dh} = f_3(h,\ V,\ \pi,\ W)$$

which, for given initial values for X, t, W, admits infinite solutions, more specifically, one solution for each arbitrarily specified pair of functions $\pi(h)$ and $V(h)$.

Among all the possible flight programs, the following have a particular interest: (a) the steepest climb program, which is flown with constant power setting and with the velocity distribution corresponding to the maximum path inclination; (b) the fastest climb program, which is flown with constant power setting and with the velocity distribution corresponding to the maximum rate of climb; and (c) the most economic program, which is flown with constant power setting and with the velocity distribution corresponding to the minimum fuel consumed per unit increase in altitude. For example, consider the second of these flight programs, and disregard the changes in the path inclination, the rate of climb, and the fuel consumed per unit time caused by changes in the weight.* Under these assumptions, the right-hand sides of Eqs. (36) become functions of the altitude only. Consequently, the integration process reduces to that of simple quadratures, even though analytical solutions must be generally ruled out.

7. KINETIC ENERGY CORRECTION

In the previous section, climbing performance was analyzed from a quasi-steady point of view, that is, the inertia terms appearing in the dynamical equations were neglected. This is the same as disregarding the kinetic energy in the energy balance or assuming that the energy developed by the powerplant is entirely employed to maintain the aerodynamic field and to increase the potential energy of the aircraft. Thus, an error is introduced into the rate of climb and, consequently, into the time to climb and the fuel consumed. Since this error can be quite important for some types of jet-propelled aircraft, this section presents an approximate method for correcting it (Ref. 2).

If the tangential acceleration is considered, but the centripetal acceleration is disregarded,† the nonsteady climb is still described by the equations of the previous section, except that the equation of motion on the tangent to the flight path is replaced by

$$T(h, V, \pi) - D(h, V, W) - W \sin \gamma - \frac{W}{g} \dot{V} = 0 \qquad (37)$$

---

* This hypothesis is justified in most climbing maneuvers, since the variation in the weight due to the fuel consumed is less than 6–7% of the initial weight. However, if a more precise analysis is desired, iterative procedures must be employed.

† The curvature of the trajectory is negligible along a major part of the climbing path.

After the kinematic relationship in the vertical direction is accounted for, Eq. (37) can be rewritten as

$$T(h, V, \pi) - D(h, V, W) - W \sin \gamma \left(1 + \frac{V}{g} \frac{dV}{dh}\right) = 0 \qquad (38)$$

and implies that

$$C = V \sin \gamma = \frac{[T(h, V, \pi) - D(h, V, W)]V}{W\left(1 + \dfrac{V}{g} \dfrac{dV}{dh}\right)} \qquad (39)$$

Comparison of Eq. (39) and the first of Eqs. (31) shows that, for the same altitude, velocity, and power setting, the ratio of the accelerated rate of climb (subscript a) to the quasi-steady rate of climb (subscript s) is given by

$$\frac{C_a}{C_s} = \frac{1}{1 + \dfrac{V}{g} \dfrac{dV}{dh}} = \frac{1}{1 + \dfrac{d(V^2/2)}{d(gh)}} \qquad (40)$$

This important ratio can be called the *acceleration factor* and is a measure of the error involved when computing climb (or descent) performance from a quasi-steady standpoint. Clearly, this error depends on the rate of variation of the kinetic energy with respect to the potential energy. Hence, its importance is negligible for propeller-driven aircraft, appreciable for turbojet or turbofan aircraft operating subsonically, and fundamental for turbojet, turboramjet, or ramjet aircraft which attain supersonic speeds at the end of the climb. As an example, if an aircraft climbs with constant dynamic pressure, the acceleration factor is 0.85 at $M = 0.5$, meaning that the actual rate of climb is 85% of that predicted with the quasi-steady approach; as the Mach number increases, the acceleration factor decreases rapidly, becoming 0.59 at $M = 1$ and 0.26 at $M = 2$.

7.1 Remark. The method previously indicated is extremely useful in the approximate prediction of the accelerated climbing performance of subsonic aircraft. Briefly, the method consists of calculating first the quasi-steady rate of climb, then the acceleration factor, and finally the nonsteady rate of climb by multiplication of the two component items. However, truly optimum trajectories cannot be obtained in this way, since the velocity distribution employed in evaluating the acceleration factor is that which was calculated with the quasi-steady approach. The exact formulation of the problem of the optimum ascent or descent with acceleration terms included belongs to the realm of the Calculus of Variations and is discussed in Volume 2.

8. FLIGHT IN A HORIZONTAL PLANE

In this section, a trajectory flown in a horizontal plane is considered, and the following assumptions are employed: (a) the Earth is flat, and the acceleration of gravity is constant; (b) the inertia term is negligible in the equation of motion on the tangent to the flight path but not in the equation of motion on the normal; (c) the thrust is tangent to the flight path; (d) the atmosphere is at rest with respect to the Earth, and its properties are known functions of the altitude; and (e) the sideslip angle is zero. In particular, hypothesis (e) means that both the velocity and the resultant aerodynamic force are contained in the plane of symmetry of the aircraft, as is the case with a properly banked turn.

In the light of these hypotheses and of Eq. (7–6), Eqs. (4–46) and (4–48) are rewritten in the form

$$\dot{X} - V \cos \chi = 0$$

$$\dot{Y} - V \sin \chi = 0$$

$$T - D = 0$$

$$L \sin \mu - \frac{W}{g} V \dot{\chi} = 0$$

$$L \cos \mu - W = 0$$

$$\dot{W} + cT = 0$$

(41)

where X and Y denote Cartesian coordinates measured in the horizontal plane, μ is the velocity roll angle, and χ is the velocity yaw angle.* The first two equations are the kinematical relationships in the X and Y-directions; the third, the fourth, and the fifth are the dynamical relationships on the principal axes (tangent, principal normal, and binormal); and the last is the definition of the weight flow of fuel for the engine. Incidentally, the dynamical equations indicate that the drag is balanced by the thrust, the centrifugal force is balanced by the horizontal component of the lift, and the weight is balanced by the vertical component of the lift.

8.1 Point performance. After the functional relationships (2) and (3) are accounted for, the dynamical equations on the tangent, the principal

---

* Within the context of Part II, the velocity roll angle μ is referred to as the *angle of bank*, since it is identical with the angle of inclination of the plane of symmetry of the aircraft with respect to the vertical; also, the time derivative of the velocity yaw angle $\dot{\chi}$ is called the *evolutory velocity* or *turn rate*.

normal, and the binormal can be rewritten in the form

$$T(h, V, \pi) - D(h, V, L) = 0$$

$$L \sin \mu - \frac{W}{g} V\dot{\chi} = 0 \qquad (42)$$

$$L \cos \mu - W = 0$$

These equations involve the seven variables

$$h, V, \dot{\chi}, \mu, W, L, \pi$$

and, hence, admit a four-parameter family of solutions. If these parameters are chosen to be the altitude, the velocity, the weight, and the power setting, functional solutions of the form

$$\mu = f_1(h, V, W, \pi)$$

$$L = f_2(h, V, W, \pi) \qquad (43)$$

$$\dot{\chi} = f_3(h, V, W, \pi)$$

must be expected. Once the dynamical equations have been solved, several other derived quantities can be calculated, for instance, the *load factor*

$$n = \frac{L}{W} \qquad (44)$$

and the *radius of curvature* of the flight path. If, for simplicity, a right turn is considered, the radius of curvature is given by

$$r = \frac{V}{\dot{\chi}} \qquad (45)$$

In consideration of the previous solutions, both the load factor and the radius of curvature can be functionally written as

$$n = f_4(h, V, W, \pi)$$

$$r = f_5(h, V, W, \pi) \qquad (46)$$

and, consequently, depend on the four chosen parameters: the altitude, the velocity, the weight, and the power setting. Hence, if the weight and the power setting are given, the right-hand sides of Eqs. (43) and (46) become functions of the altitude and the velocity only and are plotted in Figs. 16 and 17 for a typical turbojet aircraft.

    Among the infinite number of properly banked horizontal turns which the aircraft can execute, there are some special turns which are particularly significant, since they supply an indication of the maneuverability of the aircraft in a horizontal plane. These special maneuvers are the turns with maximum angle of bank, maximum load factor, maximum

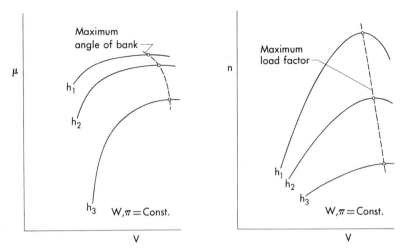

FIG. 16. Angle of bank and load factor.

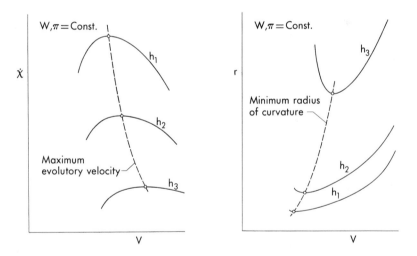

FIG. 17. Evolutory velocity and radius of curvature.

evolutory velocity, and minimum radius of curvature and are indicated by the dashed lines in Figs. 16 and 17. Generally speaking, the velocity for maximum angle of bank is identical with the velocity for maximum load factor and higher than the velocity for maximum $\dot{\chi}$ which, in turn, is higher than the velocity for minimum radius of curvature. Furthermore, these characteristic velocities increase with the altitude, even though they are always bounded by two limiting values, which are represented by the rectilinear flight solutions with the given power setting

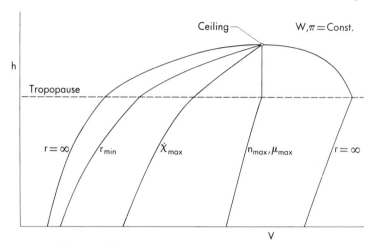

Fig. 18. Characteristic velocities for turning flight.

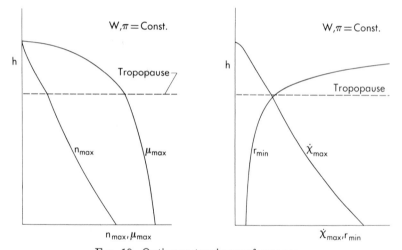

Fig. 19. Optimum turning performance.

(Fig. 18). Finally, the maximum load factor, the maximum angle of bank, and the maximum evolutory velocity decrease with the altitude, becoming zero at the ceiling, while the minimum radius of curvature increases with the altitude, becoming infinitely large at the ceiling (Fig. 19).

8.2 Integral performance. After the point performance has been investigated, certain quantities which depend on the flight path as a whole (the Cartesian coordinates, the velocity yaw angle, and the fuel consumed) must be calculated. In consideration of Eqs. (3), (41), and (43), the differential set to be integrated can be represented as

$$\frac{dX}{dt} = f_6(V, \chi)$$

$$\frac{dY}{dt} = f_7(V, \chi)$$

$$\frac{d\chi}{dt} = f_8(h, V, W, \pi)$$ \hfill (47)

$$\frac{dW}{dt} = f_9(h, V, \pi)$$

and involves one independent variable (the time t), six dependent variables (X, Y, V, χ, W, π), and two degrees of freedom. Thus, for a given set of initial conditions for X, Y, χ, W, infinite trajectories exist which are physically and mathematically possible, more specifically, one trajectory for each arbitrarily specified pair of functions $V(t), \pi(t)$ or equivalent conditions. Among all the possible flight programs, the following have a particular interest: (a) the constant power setting program flown with the velocity distribution corresponding to the maximum load factor (or the maximum angle of bank); (b) the constant power setting program flown with the velocity distribution corresponding to the maximum evolutory velocity; and (c) the constant power setting program flown with the velocity distribution corresponding to the minimum radius of curvature. If the change in the weight due to the fuel consumed is neglected, each of these special trajectories can be shown to be a circular arc flown with constant values of the velocity, the angle of bank, and the evolutory velocity. In particular, the radius of the turn with the maximum load factor is greater than that of the turn with maximum evolutory velocity, which is obviously greater than the minimum radius of curvature.

9. FLIGHT LIMITATIONS

In the previous sections, the performance of an aircraft was analyzed in a functional form. With particular reference to powered flight in a vertical plane and to the velocity-altitude domain, the characteristic velocities were summarized in Fig. 14. These theoretical solutions can be unrestrictedly employed for flight operation only if no limitations are imposed on the aircraft. In practice, however, several limitations of an aerodynamic or a structural nature must be considered; hence, the usable portion of the velocity-altitude domain is reduced somewhat, depending on the type of aircraft (Ref. 1). Among these limitations, those associated with the phenomena of stall, buffeting, gust load, sonic boom, and aerodynamic heating are now discussed.

9.1 Stalling limit. Because of stability and control considerations, it is desirable that the angle of attack in flight be smaller than that for which stalling occurs. With reference to level flight, the *stalling boundary* is obtained by introducing the condition $C_L = C_{LS}$ (where C_{LS} is the stalling lift coefficient) into the equation of motion on the normal to the flight path. For a given atmospheric model, this operation yields a functional relationship of the form

$$f_1(h, V, W) = 0 \qquad (48)$$

which, for each given weight, separates the region of the velocity-altitude domain where stalling occurs from that in which it does not occur.

9.2 Buffet limit. For some types of aircraft, it is desirable that the angle of attack in flight be smaller than that for which buffeting occurs. With reference to level flight, the *buffet boundary* is obtained by introducing the condition $C_L = C_{LB}$ (where C_{LB} is the buffeting lift coefficient) into the equation of motion on the normal to the flight path. Once more, this operation yields a functional relationship of the form

$$f_2(h, V, W) = 0 \qquad (49)$$

which, for each given weight, separates the region of the velocity-altitude domain where buffeting occurs from that in which it does not occur.

9.3 Gust load limit. Consider an aircraft in level flight, and assume that such a vehicle is subjected to a vertically ascending gust whose speed is a known function of the altitude. Because of the gust, the angle of attack increases, the lift increases, and the load factor becomes larger than one. If the load factor is assumed to be equal to the maximum value for which the aircraft is designed, the functional relationship

$$f_3(h, V, W) = 0 \qquad (50)$$

is obtained. This relationship defines the *gust load boundary* or *structural placard* and can impose severe limitations on both the maximum speed and the speed for best climb.

9.4 Sonic boom limit. If an aircraft flies at supersonic speeds, a system of shock waves is produced and propagates through the atmosphere. The shock wave reaching the ground carries an overpressure which, for a given aircraft configuration, is a function of the Mach number, the flight altitude, and the angle of attack. If this overpressure is assumed to be equal to the maximum value which is permissible for the comfort of the population on the ground (a few pounds per square foot), the functional relationship

$$f_4(h, V, W) = 0 \tag{51}$$

is obtained. This relationship defines the *sonic boom boundary* and can impose severe limitations on both the maximum speed and the speed for best climb.

9.5 Aerodynamic heating limit. At moderate or high supersonic speeds, important heat transfer phenomena occur between the surrounding medium and the aircraft. The time rate of heat transfer from the boundary layer to either the entire wetted area or some specific region (e.g., the leading edge of the wing and the nose of the fuselage) depends mainly on the Mach number, the Reynolds number, and the angle of attack (see Chapter 14). If this heating rate is assumed to be equal to the limiting value which is permissible in order to prevent excessive thermal stresses and/or deterioration of the surface (this depends on the engineering precautions employed in order to protect and cool the surfaces), the functional relationship

$$f_5(h, V, W) = 0 \tag{52}$$

can be found and is called the *aerodynamic heating boundary*. In practice, this boundary can impose severe limitations on the maximum speed and the speed for best climb.

9.6 Remark. While the above limitations are characteristic of the aircraft, several other limitations characteristic of the engine must be considered (see Chapter 7). As an example, the combustion chamber pressure of a turbojet or a ramjet is bounded by a lower limit (the flame-out pressure) and an upper limit (the maximum allowable pressure for which the engine is designed). As another example, the temperatures at the compressor outlet and at the turbine inlet must be less than the maximum allowable values for which these turbojet components are designed. If the analysis of the engine cycle is carried out, these limiting conditions can be shown to have the form

$$f(h, V, \pi) = 0 \tag{53}$$

where π is the control parameter of the engine. Incidentally, the boundary curves defined functionally by Eq. (53) are known to impose severe limitations on the ceiling, the maximum speed, and the speed for best climb of turbojet or ramjet vehicles designed to attain supersonic velocities.

10. CONCLUSION AND INTRODUCTION TO THE FOLLOWING CHAPTERS

In this chapter, quasi-steady flight in a vertical plane and a horizontal plane has been analyzed in connection with both the point performance problem and the integral performance problem. By representing the drag, the thrust, and the specific fuel consumption in a functional form, it has been possible to predict the functional nature of the solutions, even though these solutions have not been explicitly stated. In particular, the point performance problem in a vertical plane and that in a horizontal plane have been shown to yield a four-parameter family of solutions for each given aircraft.

If particular hypotheses are employed in the representation of the characteristics of the aircraft and the engine, considerable simplifications are possible. In the first place, a large section of the performance problem becomes amenable to analytical methods and yields closed form solutions. In the second place, the introduction of appropriate dimensionless groups allows the number of parameters characterizing each problem to be reduced.

In connection with the above discussion, the performance problem will be treated in the following chapters for three types of aircraft: (a) a low-speed aircraft whose drag polar is parabolic with constant coefficients and whose engine characteristics are ideally independent of the Mach number; (b) a low-speed aircraft whose drag polar is nonparabolic and whose engine characteristics are ideally independent of the Mach number; and (c) a high-speed aircraft whose aerodynamic and engine characteristics are arbitrarily dependent on the Mach number.

For problems of type (a) and (b), the point performance problem is no longer governed by a four-parameter family of solutions but, after appropriate similarity parameters are introduced, by a two-parameter family. On the other hand, for problems of type (c), the point performance problem reduces to a three-parameter family. These statements emphasize the advantages which are inherent in the use of dimensionless variables and explain why they are consistently employed throughout the following chapters.

EXERCISES

1. In connection with level flight with a given weight and power setting, show that the following condition must be satisfied at the ceiling:

$$\frac{\partial(T - D)}{\partial V} = 0 \qquad (54)$$

Hence, the ceiling occurs when the excess thrust is a maximum with respect to the velocity for constant values of the altitude, the power setting, and the weight.

2. In connection with level flight with a given weight and power setting, show that the following condition must be satisfied at the altitude where the velocity is maximum:

$$\frac{\partial(T - D)}{\partial h} = 0 \tag{55}$$

Thus, the maximum speed occurs when the excess thrust is a maximum with respect to the altitude for constant values of the velocity, the power setting, and the weight.

3. Consider the fastest climb of an aircraft with a constant power setting, and disregard the effects due to weight changes in the dynamical equations. Approximating the tangent of the path inclination, the rate of climb, and the fuel consumed per unit time with linear functions of the altitude (for intervals of about 5000 ft), show that the following analytical solutions hold:

$$\Delta X = \frac{\Delta h}{\Delta(\tan \gamma)} \log \frac{\tan \gamma_2}{\tan \gamma_1}$$

$$\Delta t = \frac{\Delta h}{\Delta C} \log \frac{C_2}{C_1} \tag{56}$$

$$-\Delta W = \frac{\Delta q}{\Delta C} \Delta h + \frac{q_1 C_2 - C_1 q_2}{\Delta C} \Delta t$$

where the subscripts 1 and 2 refer to the endpoints of each interval of integration. Consequently, by adding the above increments, the distance, the time, and the fuel consumed between any given initial and final altitudes can be determined.

4. In connection with turning flight in a horizontal plane, show that the load factor and the angle of bank are related by

$$n = \frac{1}{\cos \mu} \tag{57}$$

Hence, turning flight with maximum angle of bank is identical with turning flight with maximum load factor.

5. In connection with turning flight in a horizontal plane, show that the evolutory velocity and the radius of curvature satisfy the following relationships:

$$\dot{\chi} = g \frac{\sqrt{n^2 - 1}}{V}, \qquad r = \frac{V^2}{g\sqrt{n^2 - 1}} \tag{58}$$

where n is the load factor. Notice that straight and level flight can be regarded as the limiting case of turning flight for $r \to \infty$. Hence, this limiting case occurs for $n = 1$, which implies that $\dot{x} = 0$ and $\mu = 0$.

6. Consider a constant altitude turn executed with constant power setting and constant velocity. Neglecting the changes in the weight of the aircraft due to fuel consumption, show that the load factor, the angle of bank, the evolutory velocity, and the radius of curvature are simultaneously constant. Furthermore, assuming the initial conditions

$$t_i = 0, \qquad X_i = Y_i = 0, \qquad \chi_i = 0 \qquad (59)$$

show that the geometry of the trajectory is described by the parametric equations

$$X = \frac{V}{\dot{\chi}} \sin (\dot{\chi}t), \qquad Y = \frac{V}{\dot{\chi}} [1 - \cos (\dot{\chi}t)] \qquad (60)$$

References

1. ANONYMOUS, *Jet Transport Performance Methods*, The Boeing Company, Document No. D6-1420, 1959.

2. PHILLIPS, F. C., *A Kinetic Energy Correction to Predicted Rate of Climb*, Journal of the Aerospace Sciences, Vol. 9, No. 5, 1942.

3. MIELE, A., *Some Recent Advances in the Mechanics of Terrestrial Flight*, ARS Journal, Vol. 28, No. 9, 1958.

4. MIELE, A., *Interrelationship of Calculus of Variations and Ordinary Theory of Maxima and Minima for Flight Mechanics Applications*, ARS Journal, Vol. 29, No. 1, 1959.

CHAPTER 9

PERFORMANCE OF AN AIRCRAFT
WITH A PARABOLIC POLAR

1. INTRODUCTION

In the previous chapter, the performance problem was considered in general with the assumption that the characteristics of the aircraft and the engine are arbitrary. In particular, attention was devoted to both flight in a vertical plane and flight in a horizontal plane. In this chapter, the entire performance problem is reconsidered for the particular case of an aircraft satisfying the following assumptions: (a) the drag polar is parabolic with constant coefficients; and (b) the characteristics of the powerplant are independent of the speed and proportional to some power of the atmospheric density. Obviously, because of these hypotheses, considerable limitations are imposed on the resulting theory; yet, its merit is that simple analytical relationships can be obtained, from which the essential features of the performance problem of turbojet and turbofan aircraft operating subsonically can be readily understood (Ref. 1).

2. FLIGHT IN A VERTICAL PLANE

If all the hypotheses of Section 8–2 are retained, quasi-steady flight in a vertical plane is represented by the equations

$$\dot{X} - V \cos \gamma = 0$$
$$\dot{h} - V \sin \gamma = 0$$
$$T - D - W \sin \gamma = 0 \qquad (1)$$
$$L - W \cos \gamma = 0$$
$$\dot{W} + cT = 0$$

where X denotes the horizontal distance, h the altitude, V the velocity, γ the path inclination, W the weight, D the drag, L the lift, T the thrust, c the specific fuel consumption, and the dot sign a derivative with respect to time.

2.1 Aerodynamic characteristics. In accordance with Chapter 6, the aerodynamic forces are defined as

$$D = \tfrac{1}{2}C_D\rho S V^2, \qquad L = \tfrac{1}{2}C_L\rho S V^2 \qquad (2)$$

149

where ρ is the air density, S a reference area, C_D the drag coefficient, and C_L the lift coefficient. In turn, because of hypotheses (a), these coefficients satisfy the relationship

$$C_D = C_{DO} + KC_L^2 \tag{3}$$

where C_{DO} is the zero-lift drag coefficient and K the induced drag factor. Consequently, after Eqs. (2) and (3) are combined and the lift coefficient is eliminated, the following relation is obtained for the drag function:

$$D = \frac{1}{2}C_{DO}\rho S V^2 + \frac{2KL^2}{\rho S V^2} \tag{4}$$

2.2 Engine characteristics. Because of hypothesis (b) and in accordance with Chapter 7, an idealized jet engine is considered, and its main performance characteristics, the thrust and the specific fuel consumption, obey the laws

$$\frac{T}{T_*} = \left(\frac{\rho}{\rho_*}\right)^x, \quad \frac{c}{c_*} = \left(\frac{\rho}{\rho_*}\right)^y \tag{5}$$

where x and y are dimensionless exponents (typical values: $x = 0.7$ and $y = 0.2$ for tropospheric flight; $x = 1$ and $y = 0$ for stratospheric flight) and the asterisk denotes quantities evaluated at the tropopause. The quantity c_* is regarded as a characteristic constant of the engine; on the other hand, T_* is identified with the power setting and can be controlled in flight between a lower bound, assumed zero, and an upper bound which depends on the characteristics of the powerplant.

2.3 Dimensionless parameters. The solution of the dynamical equations can be simplified substantially, if certain dimensionless parameters are introduced. They are the *load factor* (lift-to-weight ratio), the *dimensionless thrust,* and the *dimensionless velocity.* These parameters are defined as (Ref. 11)

$$n = \frac{L}{W}, \quad z = \frac{TE_{\max}}{W}, \quad u = \frac{V}{V_R} \tag{6}$$

where

$$E_{\max} = \frac{1}{2\sqrt{KC_{DO}}} \tag{7}$$

is the maximum aerodynamic efficiency (maximum lift-to-drag ratio) and where

$$V_R = \sqrt{\frac{2W}{\rho S}} \sqrt[4]{\frac{K}{C_{DO}}} \tag{8}$$

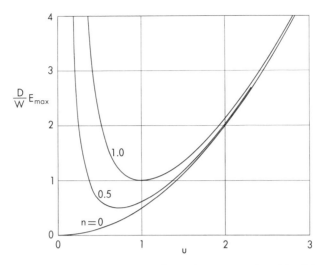

FIG. 1. Dimensionless drag versus dimensionless speed and load factor.

is a reference velocity. The physical meaning of these parameters can be clarified by rewriting the drag function (4) in the form

$$D = \frac{W}{2E_{max}}\left(u^2 + \frac{n^2}{u^2}\right) \tag{9}$$

which is plotted in Fig. 1 versus the dimensionless speed for several values of the load factor.* While the zero-lift drag increases monotonically with the velocity, the induced drag decreases. Consequently, for a given load factor, the over-all drag has the minimum value

$$D = \frac{W}{E_{max}}n \tag{10}$$

which occurs for

$$u = \sqrt{n} \tag{11}$$

In particular, if the load factor is $n = 1$, these equations become

$$D = \frac{W}{E_{max}}, \qquad u = 1 \tag{12}$$

This means that the dimensionless speed is the ratio of the actual flight speed to that speed for which the over-all drag is a minimum in level flight; furthermore, the dimensionless thrust is the ratio of the actual

---

* For quasi-steady flight in a vertical plane, the load factor is always less than or equal to one.

thrust to the minimum drag in level flight. To conclude this section, several remarks are appropriate:

(a) Since the dimensionless speed is proportional to the square root of the dynamic pressure, the existence of an optimum dimensionless speed is equivalent to the existence of an optimum dynamic pressure. This consideration has a twofold implication. If the altitude and the load factor are prescribed, there exists a velocity which minimizes the drag; conversely, if the velocity and the load factor are given, there exists an altitude for which the drag is a minimum (see Figs. 6–19 through 6–21).

(b) Once the dimensionless speed and the load factor are given, not only can the drag per unit weight be calculated but also several other related quantities. One of these is the ratio of the induced drag to the zero-lift drag

$$R = \frac{KC_L^2}{C_{DO}} = \frac{n^2}{u^4} \tag{13}$$

which will be referred to in the remainder of the text as the *drag ratio*. Another is the ratio of the actual aerodynamic efficiency to its maximum value

$$\frac{E}{E_{\max}} = \frac{2\sqrt{R}}{1 + R} = \frac{2nu^2}{n^2 + u^4} \tag{14}$$

which will be referred to as the *aerodynamic efficiency ratio*.

(c) As Fig. 1 indicates, the drag per unit weight is almost independent of the load factor for flight speeds such that $u > 2$. This means that, should the drag function (9) be replaced by a simplified relationship in which $n = 1$, no great loss of accuracy would be incurred in the computation of the total drag as well as of any quantity which is related to the total drag, such as the path inclination and the rate of climb.

3. GLIDING FLIGHT

The class of shallow glide paths is now considered. After hypotheses (8–8) are employed and the condition of zero thrust is introduced into the equations of motion, the following differential set is obtained:

$$\dot{X} - V = 0$$
$$\dot{h} - V\gamma = 0$$
$$D + W\gamma = 0 \tag{15}$$
$$L - W = 0$$
$$\dot{W} = 0$$

Its properties are now investigated from both a local point of view (point performance) and an over-all point of view (integral performance).

3.1 Glide angle and sinking speed. Since the load factor is $n = 1$, the aerodynamic drag is written in the form

$$D = \frac{W}{2E_{max}}\left(u^2 + \frac{1}{u^2}\right) \tag{16}$$

Consequently, the equation of motion on the tangent to the flight path yields the following solution for the glide angle (modulus of the path inclination):

$$-\gamma = \frac{D}{W} = \frac{1}{2E_{max}}\left(u^2 + \frac{1}{u^2}\right) \tag{17}$$

so that the sinking speed (modulus of the rate of climb) becomes

$$-\frac{C}{V_R} = -u\gamma = \frac{1}{2E_{max}}\left(u^3 + \frac{1}{u}\right) \tag{18}$$

Among all the possible glide conditions, there are two which have particular interest for flight operations: the flattest glide and the glide with minimum sinking speed. If the derivative of the right-hand side of Eq. (17) with respect to the dimensionless speed is calculated and set equal to zero, it is seen that the flattest glide occurs when

$$u = 1 \tag{19}$$

which implies that $R = 1$ and

$$-\gamma = \frac{1}{E_{max}} \tag{20}$$

Analogously, if the derivative of the right-hand side of Eq. (18) with respect to the dimensionless speed is calculated and set equal to zero, it is seen that the minimum sinking speed occurs for

$$u = \frac{1}{\sqrt[4]{3}} \tag{21}$$

which implies that $R = 3$ and

$$-\frac{C}{V_R} = \frac{2}{3}\frac{\sqrt[4]{3}}{E_{max}} \tag{22}$$

From these results, it is concluded that the velocity for flattest glide is about 32% higher than that which yields the glide with minimum sinking speed; furthermore, the induced drag is equal to the zero-lift drag for flattest glide but is three times the zero-lift drag for minimum sinking speed; also, the aerodynamic efficiency is equal to the maximum for flattest glide but is 87% of the maximum for minimum sinking speed. In closing, the following remarks are pertinent:

(a) The existence of optimum flight conditions depends on the inter-play of the induced drag and the zero-lift drag. Both extremes of the velocity scale must be avoided in quasi-steady flight. In fact, low velocities cause a heavy performance penalty because of large induced drag; conversely, high velocities cause a heavy performance penalty because of large zero-lift drag.

(b) According to Chapter 6, the induced drag factor of a subsonic aircraft is inversely proportional to the aspect ratio $Æ$. Hence, the glide angle and the sinking speed obey the proportionality relationships

$$-\gamma \sim \sqrt{\frac{C_{DO}}{Æ}}, \qquad -C \sim \sqrt[4]{\frac{C_{DO}}{Æ^3}} \tag{23}$$

This means that a 10% decrease in the zero-lift drag coefficient causes a 5% decrease in the glide angle and a 2.5% decrease in the sinking speed. Conversely, a 10% increase in the aspect ratio causes a 5% decrease in the glide angle and a 7.5% decrease in the sinking speed. Thus, the glide angle is more sensitive than the sinking speed to changes in the zero-lift drag coefficient, while the opposite is true with regard to changes in the aspect ratio.

3.2 Range and endurance. After the altitude is selected as the new independent variable, the kinematical relationships on the horizontal and vertical directions are rewritten in the form

$$\frac{dX}{dh} = \frac{1}{\gamma} = -\frac{2u^2}{1+u^4} E_{\max}$$

$$\frac{dt}{dh} = \frac{1}{C} = -\frac{2u}{1+u^4} \frac{E_{\max}}{V_{RO}} \sqrt{\sigma} \tag{24}$$

where V_{RO} is the reference velocity evaluated at sea level and $\sigma = \rho/\rho_o$ the relative density. In order to integrate these differential equations, the relationship $u(h)$ must be specified. In this connection, two particular flight programs are now discussed, that is, the constant angle of attack program and the constant velocity program.

3.2.1 *Constant Angle of Attack*. If the angle of attack is constant, the lift coefficient is constant; since both the actual velocity and the reference velocity are inversely proportional to the square root of the density, the dimensionless speed is constant. Hence, after the end-conditions

$$X_i = 0, \qquad t_i = 0, \qquad X_f = X, \qquad t_f = t \tag{25}$$

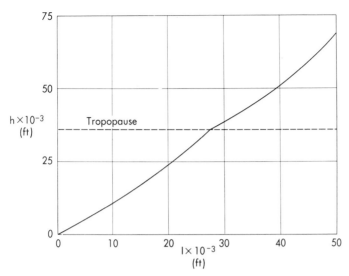

FIG. 2. The function $I(h)$.

are considered, one obtains the definite integrals

$$X = \frac{2u^2}{1 + u^4} E_{\max} (h_i - h_f)$$

$$t = \frac{2u}{1 + u^4} \frac{E_{\max}}{V_{RO}} [I(h_i) - I(h_f)]$$

(26)

where the function $I(h)$ is defined as

$$I(h) = \int_0^h \sqrt{\sigma} \, dh$$

(27)

and is plotted in Fig. 2 with reference to the 1959 ARDC Model Atmosphere. From these relationships, it is clear that the maximum range is achieved for $u = 1$ and is given by

$$X = E_{\max} (h_i - h_f)$$

(28)

while the maximum endurance is achieved for $u = \sqrt[4]{1/3}$ and is given by

$$t = \frac{3}{2\sqrt[4]{3}} \frac{E_{\max}}{V_{RO}} [I(h_i) - I(h_f)]$$

(29)

In particular, Eq. (28) indicates that the glider is capable of converting potential energy into the work necessary to achieve range in a resisting medium. Since the transformation factor is the lift-to-drag ratio, it is concluded that this quantity is an important parameter in the aerodynamic design of gliders.

3.2.2 *Constant Velocity.* If the velocity is constant, the dimensionless speed continuously increases along the flight path according to the law

$$u = v\sqrt{\sigma} \tag{30}$$

where $v = V/V_{RO}$ is a constant. If an exponential atmosphere is assumed, the density-altitude relationship is represented by

$$\sigma = \exp\left(-\frac{h}{\lambda}\right) \tag{31}$$

where λ is a constant (see Appendix), and the differential equations for the range and the endurance become

$$\frac{dX}{d\sigma} = \frac{2\lambda E_{\max} v^2}{1 + v^4 \sigma^2}$$
$$\frac{dt}{d\sigma} = \frac{2\lambda E_{\max} v}{V_{RO}(1 + v^4 \sigma^2)} \tag{32}$$

Hence, after the end-conditions (25) are accounted for, the following definite integrals are obtained:

$$X = 2\lambda E_{\max} \arctan\left[\frac{v^2(\sigma_f - \sigma_i)}{1 + v^4 \sigma_f \sigma_i}\right]$$
$$t = \frac{2\lambda E_{\max}}{v V_{RO}} \arctan\left[\frac{v^2(\sigma_f - \sigma_i)}{1 + v^4 \sigma_f \sigma_i}\right] \tag{33}$$

and show that the range and the endurance depend on the velocity maintained along the flight path.

If the initial and final altitudes are given, the range is maximized when the dimensionless velocity has the value

$$v = \frac{1}{\sqrt[4]{\sigma_i \sigma_f}} = \exp\left(\frac{h_i + h_f}{4\lambda}\right) \tag{34}$$

which implies that

$$X = 2\lambda E_{\max} \arctan\left(\sinh \frac{h_i - h_f}{2\lambda}\right) \tag{35}$$

On the other hand, the endurance is maximized when the dimensionless velocity satisfies the transcendental equation

$$2v^2\left[\frac{\sigma_i}{1 + v^4 \sigma_i^2} - \frac{\sigma_f}{1 + v^4 \sigma_f^2}\right] + \arctan\left[\frac{v^2(\sigma_f - \sigma_i)}{1 + v^4 \sigma_i \sigma_f}\right] = 0 \tag{36}$$

which can only be solved by graphical methods.

3.2.3 *Comparison of Different Flight Techniques.* In the previous sections, two flight programs were investigated, that is, constant angle of attack and constant velocity. A comparison of these programs shows that, for the same end-altitudes, the former is superior to the latter from both the range and the endurance standpoints. As an example, for a jet vehicle flying with the engine shut off from an initial altitude of 40,000 ft to sea level, the best constant angle of attack program yields 11% more range and 8% more endurance than the best constant velocity program.

4. LEVEL FLIGHT

For the category of level paths, the condition of zero path inclination is to be introduced into the equations of motion, which simplify to

$$\dot{X} - V = 0$$
$$\dot{h} = 0$$
$$T - D = 0 \qquad (37)$$
$$L - W = 0$$
$$\dot{W} + cT = 0$$

These equations are now investigated both locally (point performance) and integrally (integral performance).

4.1 Flight velocity. Since the load factor is $n = 1$, the aerodynamic drag is represented by Eq. (16). Consequently, the equation of motion on the tangent to the flight path becomes

$$T - \frac{W}{2E_{\max}}\left(u^2 + \frac{1}{u^2}\right) = 0 \qquad (38)$$

and leads to

$$u^4 - 2zu^2 + 1 = 0 \qquad (39)$$

where z is the dimensionless thrust. The solutions of this biquadratic equation are given by (Fig. 3)

$$u_1 = \sqrt{z + \sqrt{z^2 - 1}}, \qquad u_2 = \sqrt{z - \sqrt{z^2 - 1}} \qquad (40)$$

and imply that

$$u_1 u_2 = 1 \qquad (41)$$

Thus, of the two velocities which are physically possible in level flight, one is always greater and the other always less than the speed for minimum drag. Notice that, for large values of the dimensionless thrust, the high-speed solution and the low-speed solution may no longer hold. More

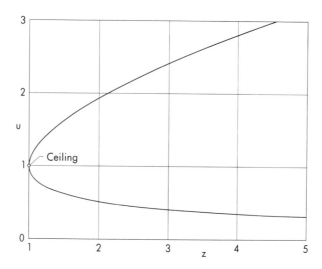

FIG. 3. Level flight solutions.

specifically, the high-speed solution may be invalidated by the occurrence of severe compressibility effects; in turn, the low-speed solution may be invalidated by the circumstance that the angle of attack is so large that the parabolic approximation no longer holds for the drag polar.

4.1.1 *Ceiling.* By definition, the ceiling is the highest altitude at which unaccelerated level flight is physically possible for a given weight and power setting. From Eqs. (40), it appears that real solutions to the level flight equation exist for $z \geq 1$ only. Hence, the ceiling is defined by

$$z = 1 \qquad (42)$$

which implies that $u = 1$.

For the particular case of stratospheric flight, the dimensionless thrust satisfies the relationship

$$z = z_* \delta \qquad (43)$$

where z_* is the dimensionless thrust at the tropopause and $\delta = \rho/\rho_*$ the density ratio, that is, the density at any altitude divided by the density at the tropopause. Consequently, the density ratio at the ceiling is given by (Ref. 3)

$$\delta = \frac{1}{z_*} \qquad (44)$$

Notice that, for an atmosphere in which the acceleration of gravity, the composition of the air, and the temperature are constant, the density

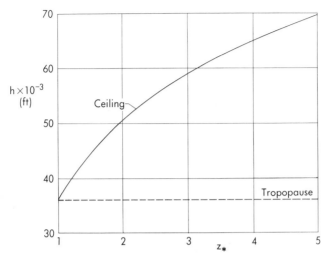

FIG. 4. Ceiling.

ratio and the altitude satisfy the relationship (see Appendix)

$$\delta = \exp\left[-\frac{kg}{a^2}(h - h_*)\right] \tag{45}$$

where k is the ratio of the specific heats and a the speed of sound. Thus, if Eqs. (44) and (45) are combined, the following expression is obtained for the ceiling (Fig. 4):

$$h = h_* + \frac{a^2}{kg}\log z_* \tag{46}$$

4.2 Range and endurance. If the first and the fifth of Eqs. (37) are employed and the weight is selected as the new independent variable, the following differential relationships are obtained:

$$-\frac{dX}{dW} = \frac{V}{cT} = \frac{V}{cD}$$
$$-\frac{dt}{dW} = \frac{1}{cT} = \frac{1}{cD} \tag{47}$$

and, after the drag function (16) is accounted for, can be rewritten in the form

$$-\frac{dX}{dW} = \frac{E_{max}V_R}{cW}\frac{2u^3}{1+u^4}$$
$$-\frac{dt}{dW} = \frac{E_{max}}{cW}\frac{2u^2}{1+u^4} \tag{48}$$

If the subscript i denotes quantities evaluated at the initial point and the dimensionless variables

$$\xi = \frac{Xc}{V_{Ri}E_{\max}}, \qquad \theta = \frac{tc}{E_{\max}}, \qquad \mu = \frac{W}{W_i} \tag{49}$$

are introduced, the differential expressions for the range and the endurance become

$$-\frac{d\xi}{d\mu} = \frac{2u^3}{1+u^4}\frac{1}{\sqrt{\mu}}$$
$$\tag{50}$$
$$-\frac{d\theta}{d\mu} = \frac{2u^2}{1+u^4}\frac{1}{\mu}$$

Since the maximum instantaneous range occurs for

$$u = \sqrt[4]{3} \tag{51}$$

while the maximum instantaneous endurance occurs for

$$u = 1 \tag{52}$$

the following conclusions are obtained: (a) the velocity for best instantaneous range is about 32% higher than that which yields the best instantaneous endurance; (b) the induced drag is one-third of the zero-lift drag for best range but equals the zero-lift drag for best endurance; and (c) the aerodynamic efficiency is 87% of the maximum for best range but equals the maximum for best endurance.

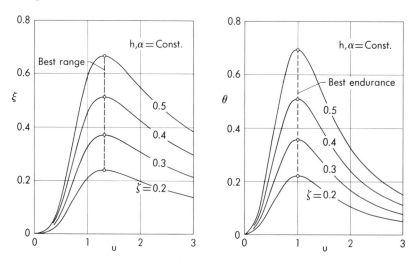

FIG. 5. Range and endurance in constant altitude-constant angle of attack flight.

In order to integrate differential equations (50), the relationship $u(\mu)$ must be specified. In this connection, several flight programs are now discussed, that is, constant angle of attack, constant velocity, and constant thrust (Refs. 3 through 5).

4.2.1 *Constant Angle of Attack.* If the angle of attack is held constant, the lift coefficient is constant; since both the flight velocity and the reference velocity are proportional to $\sqrt{\mu}$, the dimensionless speed is constant. Hence, after the fuel-to-weight ratio (ratio of the fuel weight to the weight of the aircraft at the initial point) is denoted by ζ and after the end-conditions

$$\xi_i = 0, \qquad \theta_i = 0, \qquad \mu_i = 1$$
$$\xi_f = \xi, \qquad \theta_f = \theta, \qquad \mu_f = 1 - \zeta \tag{53}$$

are assumed, one obtains the definite integrals (Fig. 5)

$$\xi = 4\,\frac{u^3}{1+u^4}\,(1 - \sqrt{1-\zeta})$$

$$\theta = 2\,\frac{u^2}{1+u^4}\,\log\frac{1}{1-\zeta} \tag{54}$$

Consequently, the maximum range is achieved for

$$u = \sqrt[4]{3} \tag{55}$$

and is given by

$$\xi = \sqrt{3}\,\sqrt[4]{3}(1 - \sqrt{1-\zeta}) \tag{56}$$

while the maximum endurance is achieved for

$$u = 1 \tag{57}$$

and is given by

$$\theta = \log\frac{1}{1-\zeta} \tag{58}$$

Incidentally, when this flight technique is employed, the thrust required is proportional to the instantaneous weight; hence, the engine must be throttled so as to produce a continuously decreasing thrust along the flight path.

4.2.2 *Constant Velocity.* If the flight velocity is held constant, the dimensionless speed continuously increases along the flight path according

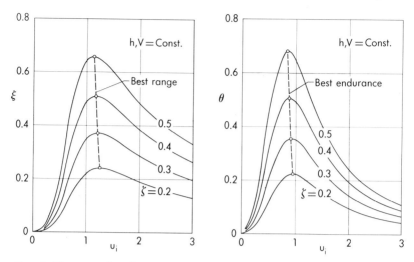

FIG. 6. Range and endurance in constant altitude-constant velocity flight.

to the law

$$u = \frac{u_i}{\sqrt{\mu}} \tag{59}$$

where u_i is the dimensionless speed at the initial point. Hence, the differential relationships (50) are rewritten as

$$-\frac{d\xi}{d\mu} = \frac{2u_i^3}{u_i^4 + \mu^2}$$

$$\tag{60}$$

$$-\frac{d\theta}{d\mu} = \frac{2u_i^2}{u_i^4 + \mu^2}$$

and, after the end-conditions (53) are considered, lead to the definite integrals (Fig. 6)

$$\xi = 2u_i \arctan \frac{\zeta u_i^2}{1 - \zeta + u_i^4}$$

$$\tag{61}$$

$$\theta = 2 \arctan \frac{\zeta u_i^2}{1 - \zeta + u_i^4}$$

Thus, the dimensionless range and endurance depend on both the fuel-to-weight ratio and the dimensionless speed at the initial point. In particular, for each given ζ, there exists one initial dimensionless speed which maximizes the range and another which maximizes the endurance. While the former can be calculated by approximate methods only, the latter can

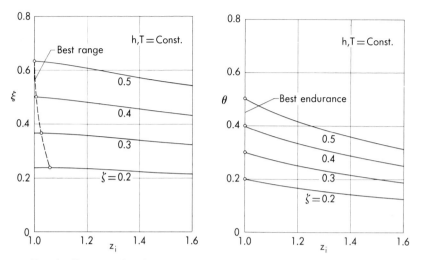

FIG. 7. Range and endurance in constant altitude-constant thrust flight.

be determined analytically and is given by

$$u_i = \sqrt[4]{1 - \zeta} \tag{62}$$

Incidentally, when this flight technique is employed, the zero-lift drag is constant along the trajectory; however, owing to the decrease in the lift coefficient, the induced drag decreases, so that the over-all drag decreases. This means that the engine must be controlled so as to produce a continuously decreasing thrust along the flight path.

4.2.3 *Constant Thrust.* If the thrust of the engine is held constant, the dimensionless thrust can be rewritten as

$$z = \frac{z_i}{\mu} \tag{63}$$

where z_i is the dimensionless thrust at the initial point. Hence, after the first of Eqs. (40) is employed, the dimensionless speed becomes

$$u = \sqrt{\frac{z_i}{\mu} + \sqrt{\left(\frac{z_i}{\mu}\right)^2 - 1}} \tag{64}$$

and Eqs. (50) are transformed into

$$-\frac{d\xi}{d\mu} = \frac{1}{z_i} \sqrt{z_i + \sqrt{z_i^2 - \mu^2}}, \qquad -\frac{d\theta}{d\mu} = \frac{1}{z_i} \tag{65}$$

Thus, for the end-conditions (53), the following definite integrals are obtained (Fig. 7):

$$\xi = \frac{2}{3}\left[\left(2 + \sqrt{1 - \left(\frac{\mu}{z_i}\right)^2}\right)\sqrt{z_i - \sqrt{z_i^2 - \mu^2}}\right]_{\mu=1-\zeta}^{\mu=1}$$

$$\theta = \frac{\zeta}{z_i} \tag{66}$$

and indicate that the dimensionless range and endurance depend on both the fuel-to-weight ratio and the dimensionless thrust at the initial point. In particular, for each given ζ, there exists one value of z_i which maximizes the range and another which maximizes the endurance. While the former can be determined by numerical methods only, the latter is given by

$$z_i = 1 \tag{67}$$

which is logical, since the endurance is a monotonically decreasing function of z_i and real solutions for the velocity exist for $z_i \geq 1$ only. Incidentally, when this flight technique is employed, both the dimensionless speed and the actual speed increase along the flight path, while the lift coefficient and the angle of attack decrease.

4.2.4 *Comparison of Different Flight Techniques.* In the previous sections, three flight programs were investigated, that is, constant angle of attack, constant velocity, and constant thrust. A comparison of these programs is given in Figs. 8 and 9 where the subscripts h, α, V, T denote the constant altitude, constant angle of attack, constant velocity, and constant thrust conditions, respectively. It is clear that the best constant angle of attack program is superior from both the range and the endurance standpoint. As an example, for $\zeta = 0.5$, the best constant angle of attack program yields 5% more range and 39% more endurance than the best constant thrust program.

4.2.5 *Altitude Effects.* In this section, the effect of the altitude on the range and the endurance in the stratosphere is investigated. It is observed that the reference velocity is inversely proportional to the square root of the density and that the specific fuel consumption is constant. Consequently, if the angle of attack is assumed to have the same constant value at every altitude, the range ratio is given by

$$\frac{X}{X_*} = \frac{1}{\sqrt{\delta}} \tag{68}$$

and the endurance ratio by

$$\frac{t}{t_*} = 1 \tag{69}$$

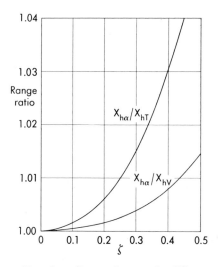

FIG. 8. Comparison of different flight techniques from the range standpoint.

FIG. 9. Comparison of different flight techniques from the endurance standpoint.

While the endurance is independent of the altitude, the range is influenced considerably by it, being inversely proportional to the square root of the density. Thus, the range at 50,000 ft is about 40% greater than the range at the tropopause. In conclusion, jet-propelled aircraft must cruise at high altitudes, that is, in the neighborhood of the ceiling.

4.2.6 *Case Where the Thrust Is Limited.** The previous conclusions are unrestrictedly valid if, and only if, the thrust is unbounded. If an upper limit of the form

$$T < T_{\max} \tag{70}$$

is considered, the following question arises: If it is assumed that the maximum available thrust in the stratosphere varies with the altitude according to the law

$$T_{\max} = T_{*\max} \, \delta \tag{71}$$

what is the new solution of the maximum range problem?

In order to answer this question, the thrust required along the best constant angle of attack trajectory must be determined and plotted as a function of the instantaneous weight (Fig. 10). Clearly, two possible situations may arise: (a) if inequality (70) is satisfied everywhere, then no modification is to be introduced in the flight program; (b) if inequality

---

* For the sake of brevity, the results of this section are presented without proof.

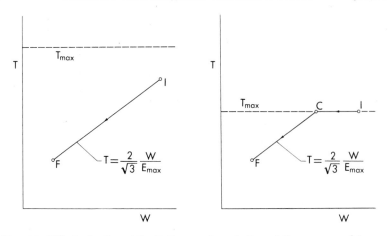

Fig. 10. Effect of a thrust limitation on the solution of the range problem.

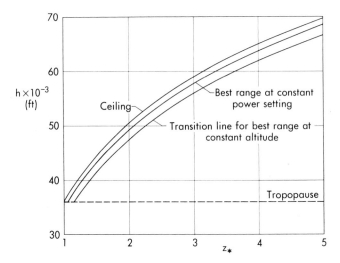

Fig. 11. Ceiling, transition line for best range at constant altitude, and characteristic line for best range at constant power setting.

(70) is not satisfied along some portion of the optimum path, then, for that portion, the constant angle of attack program must be replaced by a maximum thrust program. In the latter case, the transition from the constant thrust program to the constant angle of attack program is governed by the parameter

$$z_* = \frac{T_{*\max}E_{\max}}{W} \tag{72}$$

and occurs when (Fig. 11)

$$\delta = \frac{2}{\sqrt{3}z_*} \tag{73}$$

that is, when the difference between the ceiling associated with the instantaneous weight and the actual flight altitude is given by

$$\Delta h = \frac{a^2}{kg} \log \frac{2}{\sqrt{3}} \cong 3000 \text{ ft} \tag{74}$$

where a is the speed of sound and k the ratio of the specific heats.

5. QUASI-LEVEL FLIGHT

In the previous section, level paths were investigated; in this section, quasi-level paths are considered. Hence, after hypotheses (8–20) are employed, the equations of motion are rewritten in the form

$$\dot{X} - V = 0$$
$$\dot{h} - V\gamma = 0$$
$$T - D = 0 \tag{75}$$
$$L - W = 0$$
$$\dot{W} + cT = 0$$

and are now investigated with the assumptions that the power setting is given and that the flight takes place in the stratosphere. This means that the variation of the thrust with the altitude is represented by the first of Eqs. (5), where $x = 1$ and where the thrust at the tropopause is regarded as a constant. The analytical treatment is simplified substantially, if one introduces the dimensionless variables

$$\xi = \frac{X c_*}{V_{R*i} E_{\max}}, \qquad \theta = \frac{t c_*}{E_{\max}}, \qquad \mu = \frac{W}{W_i} \tag{76}$$

where

$$V_{R*i} = \sqrt{\frac{2W_i}{\rho_* S}} \sqrt[4]{\frac{K}{C_{DO}}} \tag{77}$$

is the reference velocity evaluated at the tropopause and at the initial weight.

If these dimensionless groups are employed, Eqs. (48) become

$$-\frac{d\xi}{d\mu} = \frac{2u^3}{1 + u^4} \frac{1}{\sqrt{\mu\delta}}, \qquad -\frac{d\theta}{d\mu} = \frac{2u^2}{1 + u^4} \frac{1}{\mu} \tag{78}$$

Since the power setting is specified, the dimensionless speed, the weight ratio, and the density ratio are not independent but must be consistent with the level flight equation (39), which is rewritten here in the form

$$\delta = \frac{1 + u^4}{2u^2} \frac{\mu}{z_{*i}} \tag{79}$$

where

$$z_{*i} = \frac{T_* E_{\max}}{W_i} \tag{80}$$

is the dimensionless thrust evaluated at the tropopause and at the initial weight. Consequently, after the density ratio is eliminated from Eqs. (78) and (79), the differential expressions for the range and the endurance become

$$\begin{aligned}
-\frac{d\xi}{d\mu} &= \frac{2u^4}{(1 + u^4)^{3/2}} \frac{\sqrt{2z_{*i}}}{\mu} \\
-\frac{d\theta}{d\mu} &= \frac{2u^2}{1 + u^4} \frac{1}{\mu}
\end{aligned} \tag{81}$$

Thus, the maximum instantaneous range occurs for

$$u = \sqrt[4]{2} \tag{82}$$

which implies that (Fig. 11)

$$\delta = \frac{3}{2\sqrt{2}z_*} \tag{83}$$

On the other hand, the maximum instantaneous endurance occurs for

$$u = 1 \tag{84}$$

which implies that

$$\delta = \frac{1}{z_*} \tag{85}$$

From these results, it appears that the dimensionless speed for best instantaneous range is about 19% higher than that which yields the best instantaneous endurance; clearly, the operating altitudes are not the same, since the best endurance occurs at the ceiling while the best range occurs when the difference between the instantaneous ceiling and the actual flight altitude is given by

$$\Delta h = \frac{a^2}{kg} \log \frac{3}{2\sqrt{2}} \cong 1230 \text{ ft} \tag{86}$$

Hence, the actual speed for best range is only 15% higher than that for best endurance. Furthermore, the induced drag is one-half of the zero-lift drag for best range but equals the zero-lift drag for best endurance; finally, the aerodynamic efficiency is 94% of the maximum for best range but equals the maximum for best endurance.

5.1 Constant angle of attack. In order to integrate the differential equations (81), the relationship $u(\mu)$ must be specified. In this connection, the particular case where the angle of attack is constant is now considered; this means that the lift coefficient and the dimensionless speed are constant. After the end-conditions (53) are considered, the following definite integrals are obtained:

$$\xi = \frac{2u^4}{(1+u^4)^{3/2}} \sqrt{2z_{*i}} \log \frac{1}{1-\zeta}$$
$$\theta = \frac{2u^2}{1+u^4} \log \frac{1}{1-\zeta} \tag{87}$$

Hence, the maximum range is achieved for $u = \sqrt[4]{2}$ and is given by

$$\xi = \frac{4}{3} \sqrt{\frac{2z_{*i}}{3}} \log \frac{1}{1-\zeta} \tag{88}$$

while the maximum endurance is achieved for $u = 1$ and is given by

$$\theta = \log \frac{1}{1-\zeta} \tag{89}$$

5.2 Altitude increase. The constant power setting-constant angle of attack program has one dominant characteristic. Owing to the fact that the dimensionless speed is constant, both the velocity V and the ratio δ/μ are constant along the flight path. Hence, the altitude increases as fuel is being consumed (*cruise-climb*); in particular, the ratio of the final to the initial density is given by

$$\frac{\delta_f}{\delta_i} = 1 - \zeta \tag{90}$$

and implies that

$$h_f - h_i = \frac{a^2}{kg} \log \frac{1}{1-\zeta} \tag{91}$$

For example, if the fuel-to-weight ratio is 0.5, the increase in altitude between the endpoints of the trajectory is about 14,400 ft.

In closing, it is worth noting that the inclination of the trajectory with respect to the horizon is given by

$$\gamma = \frac{3}{4} \sqrt{\frac{3}{2z_{*i}}} \frac{a^2 c_*}{kg V_{R*i} E_{\max}} \tag{92}$$

and its order of magnitude is 10^{-3} radians. Since the weight component on the tangent to the flight path is in the order of 1% of either the thrust or the drag, the hypothesis of quasi-level flight is more than justified from an engineering point of view.

5.3 Comparison of different flight techniques. It is of interest to compare the constant angle of attack-constant power setting program with the constant angle of attack-constant altitude program. If the subscripts α, π, h denote the constant angle of attack, constant power setting, and constant altitude conditions, respectively, and if identical initial conditions are assumed, laborious manipulations lead to the results (Ref. 7)

$$\frac{X_{\alpha\pi}}{X_{\alpha h}} = \frac{1}{2} \frac{\log\left[1/(1-\zeta)\right]}{1 - \sqrt{1-\zeta}}$$

$$\frac{t_{\alpha\pi}}{t_{\alpha h}} = 1$$

(93)

the first of which is plotted in Fig. 12. For relatively long ranges, the advantages of variable altitude flight are impressive; for example, if the fuel-to-weight ratio is 0.5, the cruise-climb technique yields 18% more range than the constant altitude technique.

5.4 Design considerations. In the previous sections, the performance of a given aircraft was considered, and the optimum flight conditions were determined. In this section, the effect of the zero-lift drag coefficient C_{DO}, the aspect ratio $\mathcal{R}$, the wing surface S, and the design thrust T_* on the

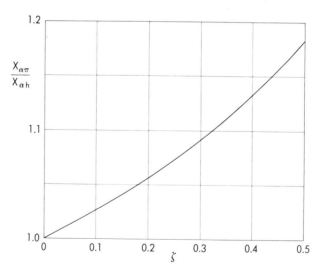

FIG. 12. Comparison of different flight techniques from the range standpoint.

range is considered. For simplicity, the variation in the weight of the aircraft caused by variations of these parameters is neglected. Owing to the fact that the induced drag factor of a subsonic aircraft is inversely proportional to the aspect ratio, the stratospheric range at constant power setting and constant angle of attack can be shown to obey the proportionality relationship

$$X \sim \frac{1}{C_{DO}} \sqrt{\frac{\mathcal{R} T_*}{S}} \tag{94}$$

Consequently, a 10% increase in either the aspect ratio or the thrust at the tropopause causes a 5% increase in the range; on the other hand, a 10% decrease in the drag coefficient causes a 10% increase in the range.

With regard to the wing surface, an interesting minimal problem is now formulated: "Assuming that the frontal area of the fuselage-nacelle group S_F is given, find the wing surface S which maximizes the range." This problem is equivalent to finding the wing surface which minimizes the function $C_{DO}\sqrt{S}$. After the over-all drag coefficient is written in the form

$$C_{DO} = C_{DOW} + C_{DOF} \frac{S_F}{S} \tag{95}$$

and it is assumed that the zero-lift drag coefficient of the wing-empennage group C_{DOW} and the zero-lift drag coefficient of the fuselage-nacelle group C_{DOF} are constant, it is clear that the function in question is minimized when the following condition is satisfied (Ref. 7):

$$\frac{C_{DOF} S_F}{C_{DOW} S} = 1 \tag{96}$$

Hence, the optimum design is achieved when the parasite drag of the nonlifting surfaces equals the parasite drag of the lifting surfaces. In closing, it is emphasized that the variation in the weight of the aircraft has been neglected in this analysis and that a design is a compromise between many contrasting requirements; consequently, the aforementioned optimum configuration must be considered *cum grano salis*.

6. CLIMBING FLIGHT

For didactic purposes, the discussion of the climbing flight is divided into two parts. In the first part, the approximation $n = 1$ is employed in the evaluation of the drag function; in the second part, the exact expression for the load factor is used. The solution obtained with the first approach is called the *simplified solution*; that obtained with the second approach is called, within the framework of quasi-steady flight, the *exact solution* (Ref. 10).

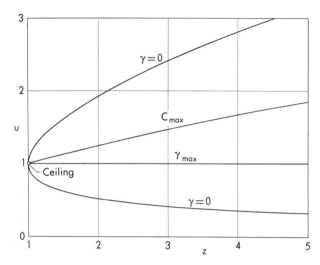

Fig. 13. Characteristic velocities for powered flight in a vertical plane.

6.1 Simplified analysis. After the approximation $n = 1$ is introduced into Eq. (9) and the thrust-to-weight ratio is denoted by $\tau = T/W$, the dynamical equation on the tangent to the flight path yields the following solution for the path inclination:

$$\sin \gamma = \frac{T - D}{W} = \tau - \frac{1}{2E_{\max}}\left(u^2 + \frac{1}{u^2}\right) \qquad (97)$$

so that the rate of climb becomes

$$\frac{C}{V_R} = u \sin \gamma = \tau u - \frac{1}{2E_{\max}}\left(u^3 + \frac{1}{u}\right) \qquad (98)$$

After these two equations are multiplied by the maximum aerodynamic efficiency, the following results are obtained:

$$E_{\max} \sin \gamma = z - \frac{1}{2}\left(u^2 + \frac{1}{u^2}\right)$$

$$E_{\max} \frac{C}{V_R} = zu - \frac{1}{2}\left(u^3 + \frac{1}{u}\right) \qquad (99)$$

and show that the climbing performance can be expressed in terms of a two-parameter family of solutions (the parameters being the dimensionless thrust and the dimensionless velocity) which are independent of the particular aircraft, that is, independent of the particular value of $E_{\max}$.

Among all the possible climbing conditions, the following have a particular interest for flight operations: the steepest climb, the fastest climb, and the most economic climb. If the derivative of the path inclina-

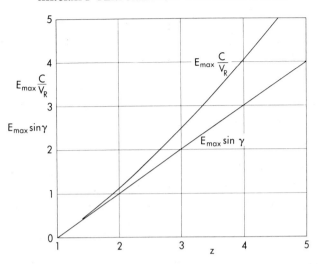

FIG. 14. Maximum values of the path inclination and the rate of climb.

tion with respect to the dimensionless speed is calculated and set equal to zero, it is seen that the steepest climb occurs when

$$u = 1 \tag{100}$$

which implies that

$$E_{\max} \sin \gamma = z - 1 \tag{101}$$

Furthermore, the condition for fastest climb is represented by the biquadratic equation

$$3u^4 - 2zu^2 - 1 = 0 \tag{102}$$

whose solution is

$$u = \frac{1}{\sqrt{3}} \sqrt{z + \sqrt{z^2 + 3}} \tag{103}$$

and implies that

$$E_{\max} \frac{C}{V_R} = \frac{2}{3\sqrt{3}} \sqrt{z + \sqrt{z^2 + 3}} \, [2z - \sqrt{z^2 + 3}] \tag{104}$$

Finally, since it is assumed that both the thrust and the specific fuel consumption are independent of the velocity, the fuel consumed per unit increase in altitude becomes inversely proportional to the rate of climb. Consequently, the most economic climb and the fastest climb of an idealized turbojet aircraft are identical.

Relationships (100) through (104) are plotted in Figs. 13 and 14 and yield several interesting conclusions:

(a) Since $z > 1$ for climbing flight, the velocity for fastest ascent is greater than that for steepest ascent; furthermore, both these velocities are bounded by the level flight solutions which are obtainable with the given thrust.

(b) For large values of the thrust, the ratio of the velocity for fastest ascent to the level flight velocity tends to $\sqrt{1/3}$. Thus, the speed for fastest ascent is 58% of that attainable in level flight with the same thrust.

(c) For large values of the thrust, the maximum rate of climb becomes proportional to $T^{3/2}$. Hence, a high thrust is necessary in order to obtain high rates of climb and, therefore, low climbing times.

(d) For large values of the thrust, the fuel consumed per unit increase in altitude becomes inversely proportional to $\sqrt{T}$. Therefore, the use of a large thrust favors fuel economy in climbing maneuvers.

6.2 Exact analysis. Climbing flight is now investigated by considering the exact expression (9) for the drag function, where $n \neq 1$. By simple algebraic manipulations, the dynamical equations on the tangent and the normal to the flight path can be rewritten as

$$z - \frac{1}{2}\left(u^2 + \frac{n^2}{u^2}\right) - E_{\max} \sin \gamma = 0$$

$$n - \cos \gamma = 0 \tag{105}$$

Hence, after the load factor is eliminated, the following relationship is obtained:

$$z - \frac{1}{2}\left(u^2 + \frac{\cos^2 \gamma}{u^2}\right) - E_{\max} \sin \gamma = 0 \tag{106}$$

and can be rewritten in the form

$$\sin^2 \gamma - 2E_{\max} u^2 \sin \gamma + 2zu^2 - 1 - u^4 = 0 \tag{107}$$

Consequently, the sine of the path inclination and the dimensionless rate of climb are given by

$$\sin \gamma = E_{\max} u^2 \left[1 \overset{(\pm)}{} \sqrt{1 - \frac{2zu^2 - 1 - u^4}{E_{\max}^2 u^4}}\right]$$

$$\frac{C}{V_R} = E_{\max} u^3 \left[1 \overset{(\pm)}{} \sqrt{1 - \frac{2zu^2 - 1 - u^4}{E_{\max}^2 u^4}}\right] \tag{108}$$

where the lower sign is to be exclusively employed for $\tau < 1$, while both signs may yield physically possible solutions for $\tau > 1$.

With reference to the case where $\tau < 1$, the steepest climb occurs when the dimensionless speed satisfies the biquadratic equation

$$(1 + E_{max}^2)u^4 - 2zu^2 + (z^2 - E_{max}^2) = 0 \qquad (109)$$

whose solution is

$$u = \sqrt{\frac{z + E_{max}\sqrt{1 + E_{max}^2} - z^2}{1 + E_{max}^2}} \qquad (110)$$

and implies that

$$\sin \gamma = \frac{zE_{max} - \sqrt{1 + E_{max}^2} - z^2}{1 + E_{max}^2} \qquad (111)$$

Analogously, the fastest climb occurs when the dimensionless speed satisfies the equation

$$9(1 + E_{max}^2)u^8 - 6z(4 + E_{max}^2)u^6$$
$$+ (6 - 3E_{max}^2 + 16z^2)u^4 - 8zu^2 + 1 = 0 \quad (112)$$

which must be generally solved by approximate methods. The associated maximum rate of climb is to be calculated with the second of Eqs. (108).

6.3 Relationships between exact and simplified solutions. After the climbing problem has been solved in both an approximate and an exact form, the following questions arise: What is the relationship between these solutions? What is the error involved in the use of the simplified solutions?

Concerning the first question, denote by x the quantity

$$x = \frac{2zu^2 - 1 - u^4}{E_{max}^2 u^4} \qquad (113)$$

and assume that

$$x \ll 1 \qquad (114)$$

If the Maclaurin expansion

$$\sqrt{1 - x} \cong 1 - \frac{x}{2} \qquad (115)$$

is employed, the exact solutions (108) reduce to the simplified solutions represented by Eqs. (99).

Concerning the second question, denote by the subscripts s and e quantities associated with the simplified solution and the exact solu-

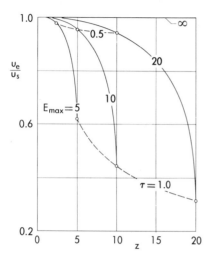

FIG. 15. Relationship between exact and simplified solutions (steepest climb).

FIG. 16. Relationship between exact and simplified solutions (steepest climb).

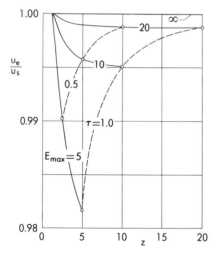

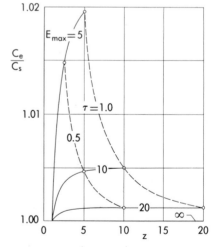

FIG. 17. Relationship between exact and simplified solutions (fastest climb).

FIG. 18. Relationship between exact and simplified solutions (fastest climb).

tion, respectively. Since the simplified optimum conditions depend on the parameter z only, while the exact optimum conditions depend also on E_{max}, the following functional relationships hold for the steepest climb:

$$\frac{u_e}{u_s} = f_1(z, E_{max}), \qquad \frac{\sin \gamma_e}{\sin \gamma_s} = f_2(z, E_{max}) \qquad (116)$$

and the fastest climb:

$$\frac{u_e}{u_s} = f_3(z, E_{max}), \qquad \frac{C_e}{C_s} = f_4(z, E_{max}) \qquad (117)$$

These relationships are plotted in Figs. 15 through 18, from which the following conclusions are derived:

(a) Concerning the fastest climb, the relative errors which the simplified solutions introduce into the computation of the optimum velocity and the rate of climb are negligible from an engineering point of view. For an aircraft whose maximum aerodynamic efficiency is 20, their order of magnitude is 0.1%, even for thrust-to-weight ratios approaching unity.

(b) Regarding the steepest climb, the relative errors involved in the use of the simplified solutions are small as far as the path inclination is concerned but may become significant as far as the optimum velocity is concerned. However, for an aircraft whose maximum aerodynamic efficiency is 20, the velocity error is less than 5% while the path inclination error is less than 1%, as long as the thrust-to-weight ratio is less than 0.5.

(c) From the previous discussion, it follows that the simplified solutions are acceptable for most engineering applications. Also, they are more valuable for fastest climb analyses than for steepest climb analyses. The reason is that the fastest climb is characterized by a higher velocity and, therefore, by a smaller induced drag than the steepest climb.

7. KINETIC ENERGY CORRECTION

In the previous chapter, the effect of the unsteadiness of the motion on the climb and descent performance was analyzed. It was shown that, if the aircraft is accelerating or decelerating, the quasi-steady rate of climb must be corrected according to the multiplying factor

$$\frac{C_a}{C_s} = \frac{1}{1 + \dfrac{d(V^2/2)}{d(gh)}} \qquad (118)$$

which is called the *acceleration factor*. It depends on the rate of variation of the kinetic energy with respect to the potential energy and is now evaluated for a number of typical maneuvers (Ref. 12).

7.1 Flight with constant dynamic pressure. Consider a climbing path flown with constant dynamic pressure, that is, a trajectory flown in such a way that

$$\frac{\rho V^2}{2} = \text{Const} \tag{119}$$

The derivative of the kinetic energy per unit mass with respect to the density is given by

$$\frac{d(V^2/2)}{d\rho} = -\frac{V^2}{2\rho} \tag{120}$$

Furthermore, for an atmosphere in which the acceleration of gravity and the composition of the air are constant, the aerostatic equation and the equation of state yield the following derivative of the density with respect to the potential energy per unit mass (see Appendix):

$$\frac{d\rho}{d(gh)} = -\frac{k\rho}{a^2}\left(1 + \frac{\alpha R}{g}\right) \tag{121}$$

where k is the ratio of the specific heats, a the speed of sound, R the air constant, and α the derivative of the air temperature with respect to the altitude. Consequently, if $M = V/a$ denotes the Mach number and Eqs. (118) through (121) are combined, the acceleration factor becomes

$$\frac{C_a}{C_s} = \frac{1}{1 + \dfrac{k}{2}\left(1 + \dfrac{\alpha R}{g}\right)M^2} \tag{122}$$

and is plotted in Fig. 19 for both tropospheric and stratospheric flight.

The above result applies to the flattest glide, the glide with minimum sinking speed, and the steepest climb, since each of these maneuvers is flown with a constant dimensionless speed and, therefore, with a constant dynamic pressure. Notice that the acceleration factor is less than one. Hence, the actual value of the glide angle and the sinking speed are smaller than those predicted with the quasi-steady approach. Also, the actual value of the path inclination associated with the steepest climb is smaller than that which was predicted with the quasi-steady approach.

7.2 Fastest stratospheric ascent. For a turbojet aircraft which climbs with the maximum quasi-steady rate of climb at every altitude, the optimum dimensionless speed is represented by Eq. (103). Consequently, with reference to stratospheric flight, the optimum kinetic energy per unit mass and the local density satisfy the relationship

$$\frac{V^2}{2} = \frac{W}{3\rho S}\sqrt{\frac{K}{C_{DO}}}\left[\frac{T_* E_{\max}}{W}\frac{\rho}{\rho_*} + \sqrt{\left(\frac{T_* E_{\max}}{W}\frac{\rho}{\rho_*}\right)^2 + 3}\right] \tag{123}$$

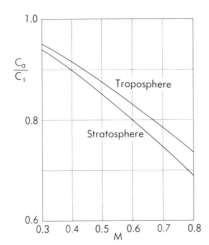

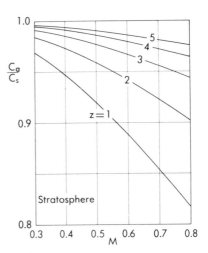

FIG. 19. Acceleration factor for flight with constant dynamic pressure.

FIG. 20. Acceleration factor for fastest stratospheric climb.

Since the derivative of the kinetic energy per unit mass with respect to the density is given by

$$\frac{d(V^2/2)}{d\rho} = -\frac{V^2}{2\rho}\left(1 - \frac{z}{\sqrt{z^2 + 3}}\right) \tag{124}$$

the acceleration factor becomes (Fig. 20)

$$\frac{C_a}{C_s} = \frac{1}{1 + \dfrac{k}{2}\left(1 - \dfrac{z}{\sqrt{z^2 + 3}}\right)M^2} \tag{125}$$

8. FLIGHT IN A HORIZONTAL PLANE

In this section, curvilinear flight in a horizontal plane is investigated. If all the hypotheses of Section 8–8 are retained, the equations of motion are written in the form

$$\dot{X} - V\cos\chi = 0$$
$$\dot{Y} - V\sin\chi = 0$$
$$T - D = 0$$
$$L\sin\mu - \frac{W}{g}V\dot\chi = 0 \tag{126}$$
$$L\cos\mu - W = 0$$
$$\dot{W} + cT = 0$$

where X and Y denote Cartesian coordinates measured in a horizontal plane, χ is the velocity yaw angle, and μ is the velocity roll angle. Because of the dynamical equation in the vertical direction, the load factor is always larger than one, a result which is opposite to that valid for flight in a vertical plane, where the load factor is always less than one.

8.1 Solution of the dynamical equations. If the similarity parameters defined in Section 2 and the drag function (9) are employed, the dynamical equations can be reduced to the dimensionless set (Ref. 11)

$$2z - u^2 - \frac{n^2}{u^2} = 0$$

$$n \sin \mu - u \frac{\dot{\chi} V_R}{g} = 0 \qquad (127)$$

$$n \cos \mu - 1 = 0$$

Consequently, the following expressions are obtained for the load factor:

$$n = u\sqrt{2z - u^2} \qquad (128)$$

the angle of bank:

$$\cos \mu = \frac{1}{u\sqrt{2z - u^2}} \qquad (129)$$

and the evolutory velocity:

$$\frac{\dot{\chi} V_R}{g} = \sqrt{2z - u^2 - \frac{1}{u^2}} \qquad (130)$$

After the dimensionless radius of curvature is written in the form

$$\frac{rg}{V_R^2} = \frac{u}{\dfrac{\dot{\chi} V_R}{g}} = \frac{1}{\sqrt{\dfrac{2z}{u^2} - 1 - \dfrac{1}{u^4}}} \qquad (131)$$

it is concluded that the turning performance can be expressed in terms of a two-parameter family of solutions, the parameters being the dimensionless speed and the dimensionless thrust. The main comments on these solutions are as follows:

(a) In order to execute a turn with a finite radius of curvature, the following inequality must be satisfied:

$$z > \frac{1}{2}\left(u^2 + \frac{1}{u^2}\right) \qquad (132)$$

which means that the thrust must be greater than the drag of the aircraft in unaccelerated straight level flight. After this relationship is combined with Eqs. (128) and (129), the following additional inequalities are derived:

$$n > 1, \quad \mu > 0 \tag{133}$$

(b) Straight and level flight can be regarded as the limiting case of turning flight for $r \to \infty$. This limiting case occurs for

$$z = \frac{1}{2}\left(u^2 + \frac{1}{u^2}\right) \tag{134}$$

which implies that $n = 1$ and $\mu = 0$ in accordance with the results of Section 4.

(c) While the load factor and the angle of bank depend on the dimensionless speed and the dimensionless thrust only, the evolutory velocity and the radius of curvature depend also on the wing loading. More specifically, a low wing loading yields good turning performance, that is, a high evolutory velocity and a small radius of curvature.

8.2 Special maneuvers. Among the infinite number of properly banked horizontal turns which an aircraft can execute, there are some special turns which have a particular significance, since they supply an indication of the maneuverability of the aircraft in a horizontal plane. These special maneuvers are the turns with the maximum load factor, the maximum angle of bank, the maximum evolutory velocity, and the minimum radius of curvature.

Because of Eqs. (128) and (129), the turn with the maximum load factor is identical with the turn with the maximum angle of bank and occurs when the dimensionless speed has the value

$$u = \sqrt{z} \tag{135}$$

which implies that

$$n = z \tag{136}$$

and that

$$\cos \mu = \frac{1}{z} \tag{137}$$

Furthermore, the turn with the maximum evolutory velocity occurs for

$$u = 1 \tag{138}$$

which implies that

$$\frac{\dot{\chi} V_R}{g} = \sqrt{2(z - 1)} \tag{139}$$

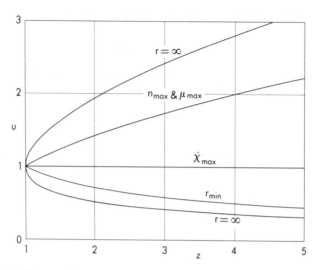

FIG. 21. Characteristic velocities for powered flight in a horizontal plane.

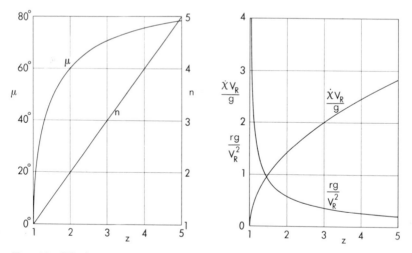

FIG. 22. Maximum values of the load factor, the angle of bank, and the evolutory velocity; minimum radius of curvature.

Finally, the turn with the minimum radius of curvature occurs when

$$u = \frac{1}{\sqrt{z}} \tag{140}$$

implying that

$$\frac{rg}{V_R^2} = \frac{1}{\sqrt{z^2 - 1}} \tag{141}$$

These results are summarized in Figs. 21 and 22, from which the following conclusions are derived:

(a) Since $z > 1$ at any altitude below the ceiling, the speed for maximum load factor is higher than that for maximum evolutory velocity; furthermore, the latter is higher than the speed for minimum radius of curvature. At any rate, all of these velocities are bounded by the level flight solutions which are obtainable with the given thrust.

(b) The turning performance improves as the parameter z increases. Therefore, an increase in the thrust favors good turning performance; furthermore, for a given weight and power setting, the turning performance is considerably better at low altitudes than in the neighborhood of the ceiling.

(c) As the parameter z increases, the load factor required for any of the optimum turns increases. While the load factor for minimum radius of curvature is always less than $\sqrt{2}$, the load factor for maximum evolutory velocity or maximum angle of bank can be so large that the optimum turning maneuver may become impossible because of structural considerations.

(d) The turn with the maximum load factor is executed at the lift coefficient for which the aerodynamic efficiency is a maximum. On the other hand, the turns with the maximum evolutory velocity and the minimum radius of curvature require higher lift coefficients. Since these lift coefficients increase with the dimensionless thrust, the turning performance calculated with the parabolic polar may become unrealistic for large values of the thrust. In such a case, the semianalytical method outlined in Chapter 10 must be employed.

9. PERFORMANCE IN A SPECIFIED ATMOSPHERE

In the preceding sections, flight performance was investigated in a dimensionless form independently of the distribution of the atmospheric properties versus the altitude. The next step is to determine the behavior of the aircraft in a specified atmosphere. For example, consider the level flight equation (40) and rewrite it in the functional form

$$u = f_1(z) \tag{142}$$

which, with reference to stratospheric flight, is equivalent to

$$V\sqrt{\frac{\rho S}{2W}}\sqrt[4]{\frac{C_{DO}}{K}} = f_1\left[\frac{T_*E_{\max}}{W}\frac{\rho}{\rho_*}\right] \tag{143}$$

Observe that, for a given atmospheric model (for instance, the 1959 ARDC Model Atmosphere), the density is a known function of the altitude, that is,

$$\rho = \rho(h) \tag{144}$$

Consequently, if the previous equations are combined, the following functional relationship is obtained for a given aircraft:

$$V = f_2(h, W, T_*) \tag{145}$$

This means that if the thrust at the tropopause and the weight are specified, Eq. (145) reduces to the form

$$V = f_2(h) \tag{146}$$

which is represented in Fig. 8–5. If this procedure is repeated for the remaining flight conditions, it is possible to pass from the results presented in this chapter to the corresponding results indicated in Chapter 8 by a simple transformation of coordinates.

10. COMPARISON OF CONSTANT THRUST AND CONSTANT POWER AIRCRAFT

In the previous sections, the performance of a constant thrust aircraft was calculated; if a similar technique is employed, the performance of a constant power aircraft can be determined. If the propeller efficiency is denoted by η and the shaft horsepower by P, the thrust developed by a reciprocating engine-propeller combination is given by

$$T = \frac{\eta P}{V} \tag{147}$$

Hence, while the performance of turbojet aircraft can be expressed in terms of the parameters u and z, the performance of piston-engined aircraft can be represented in terms of the variables u and ψ, where

$$\psi = \frac{\eta P E_{\max}}{W V_R} \tag{148}$$

is the thrust-to-drag ratio evaluated at the speed for minimum drag in level flight. In this connection, simple computations lead to the comparative data summarized in Table 1.

Concerning the optimum flight conditions, some important conclusions can be readily derived, if it is assumed that (a) the propeller efficiency

TABLE 1

COMPARATIVE NONOPTIMUM PERFORMANCE OF
CONSTANT THRUST AND CONSTANT POWER AIRCRAFT

Flight condition	Physical magnitude	Turbojet aircraft	Piston-engined aircraft
Level flight	u	$\sqrt{z \pm \sqrt{z^2 - 1}}$	$u^4 - 2\psi u + 1 = 0$
Climbing flight	$E_{\max} \sin \gamma$	$z - \dfrac{1}{2}\left(u^2 + \dfrac{1}{u^2}\right)$	$\dfrac{\psi}{u} - \dfrac{1}{2}\left(u^2 + \dfrac{1}{u^2}\right)$
	$E_{\max} \dfrac{C}{V_R}$	$zu - \dfrac{1}{2}\left(u^3 + \dfrac{1}{u}\right)$	$\psi - \dfrac{1}{2}\left(u^3 + \dfrac{1}{u}\right)$
Turning flight	$n^2 = \dfrac{1}{\cos^2 \mu}$	$u^2(2z - u^2)$	$u(2\psi - u^3)$
	$\left(\dfrac{\dot{\chi} V_R}{g}\right)^2$	$2z - u^2 - \dfrac{1}{u^2}$	$2\dfrac{\psi}{u} - u^2 - \dfrac{1}{u^2}$
	$\left(\dfrac{V_R^2}{rg}\right)^2$	$\dfrac{2z}{u^2} - 1 - \dfrac{1}{u^4}$	$2\dfrac{\psi}{u^3} - 1 - \dfrac{1}{u^4}$

and the shaft horsepower are independent of the velocity and (b) the specific fuel consumption of the piston-engined aircraft is proportional to the velocity when referred to the unit time and the unit thrust.* Simple manipulations lead to the results summarized in Table 2, where the subscript j refers to the jet aircraft and the subscript p to the piston-engined aircraft. The interesting result of the analysis is that, regardless of the flight condition, the following inequality holds:

$$\frac{u_j}{u_p} \geqq \sqrt[4]{3} \qquad (149)$$

Hence, the dimensionless velocities characteristic of jet-propelled aircraft are at least 32% greater than the corresponding velocities for piston-engined aircraft.† In the derivation of this important result, it was

---

* This means that the specific fuel consumption referred to the unit time and the unit power is independent of the velocity.

† Concerning level flight, the difference in the operating altitudes of jet aircraft and piston-engined aircraft is such that the actual velocities of jet aircraft are at least 50% greater than the corresponding velocities of piston-engined aircraft.

TABLE 2

COMPARATIVE OPTIMUM PERFORMANCE OF
CONSTANT THRUST AND CONSTANT POWER AIRCRAFT

Flight condition	Type of optimum	u_j	u_p	$\dfrac{u_j}{u_p}$
Level flight	Ceiling	1	$\dfrac{1}{\sqrt[4]{3}}$	$\sqrt[4]{3}$
	Maximum range	$\sqrt[4]{3}$	1	$\sqrt[4]{3}$
	Maximum endurance	1	$\dfrac{1}{\sqrt[4]{3}}$	$\sqrt[4]{3}$
Climbing flight	Steepest climb	1	$u^4 + \psi u - 1 = 0$	$\geq \sqrt[4]{3}$
	Fastest climb and most economic climb	$\dfrac{1}{\sqrt{3}}\sqrt{z + \sqrt{z^2 + 3}}$	$\dfrac{1}{\sqrt[4]{3}}$	$\geq \sqrt[4]{3}$
Turning flight	Maximum angle of bank and maximum load factor	$\sqrt{z}$	$\sqrt[3]{\dfrac{\psi}{2}}$	$\sqrt[4]{3}$
	Maximum evolutory velocity	1	$u^4 + \psi u - 1 = 0$	$\geq \sqrt[4]{3}$
	Minimum radius of curvature	$\dfrac{1}{\sqrt{z}}$	$\dfrac{2}{3\psi}$	$\sqrt[4]{3}$

observed that jet-propelled vehicles satisfy the inequality

$$z \geqq 1 \tag{150}$$

at any altitude below the ceiling, while piston-engined aircraft are characterized by the inequality

$$\psi \geqq \tfrac{2}{3}\sqrt[4]{3} \tag{151}$$

Furthermore, the statements relative to flight with the maximum angle of bank and to flight with the minimum radius of curvature are subordinated to the equal performance condition; more specifically, the maximum angle of bank and the minimum radius of curvature are assumed to have equal values for the jet aircraft and the piston-engined aircraft.

EXERCISES

1. With reference to gliding flight, consider the exact form of the dynamical equations. Show that the flattest glide occurs for

$$u = \sqrt[4]{\frac{E_{max}^2}{1 + E_{max}^2}} \qquad (152)$$

which, following a Maclaurin expansion, can be rewritten as

$$u \cong 1 - \frac{1}{4E_{max}^2} \qquad (153)$$

Consequently, the relative error involved in the approximate solution (19) is $0.25/E^2_{max}$, that is, negligible from an engineering point of view.

Furthermore, show that the glide with the minimum sinking speed occurs for

$$u = \sqrt[4]{\frac{E_{max}^2 - 2 + E_{max}\sqrt{E_{max}^2 - 8}}{6(1 + E_{max}^2)}} \qquad (154)$$

which, following a Maclaurin expansion, can be rewritten as

$$u \cong \frac{1}{\sqrt[4]{3}}\left(1 - \frac{1}{E_{max}^2}\right) \qquad (155)$$

Consequently, the relative error involved in the approximate solution (21) is $1/E^2_{max}$, that is, negligible from an engineering point of view.

2. Consider level flight for a given weight and power setting. Concerning stratospheric flight, show that the velocity is a monotonically decreasing function of the altitude. Concerning tropospheric flight, show that, for $0.6 < z_* < 1.4$, the velocity is a maximum at the altitude where the dimensionless speed satisfies the relation

$$u = \sqrt[4]{17/3} \qquad (156)$$

Otherwise, the highest velocity (not an analytical maximum) occurs at sea level for $z_* < 0.6$ and at the tropopause for $z_* > 1.4$.

3. Consider an aircraft in constant altitude-constant velocity flight. Under the assumption that

$$\frac{\varsigma u_i^2}{1 - \varsigma + u_i^4} \ll 1 \qquad (157)$$

show that the range is maximized when the dimensionless speed at the initial point satisfies the relationship

$$u_i = \sqrt[4]{3(1 - \varsigma)} \qquad (158)$$

4. Consider a turbojet aircraft flying in the stratosphere. Employing the equations of the standard atmosphere (see Appendix) and assuming a constant acceleration of gravity, prove the results expressed by Eqs. (74), (86), and (91).

5. Consider a turbojet aircraft in tropospheric quasi-level flight with constant power setting and constant angle of attack. Show that the maximum range is given by

$$\xi = \frac{15}{8} \sqrt[4]{\frac{5}{3}} z_{*i} \left(\frac{1}{\sqrt{1 - \zeta}} - 1 \right) \tag{159}$$

and occurs when the dimensionless speed is $u = \sqrt[4]{5/3}$. Also, prove that the maximum endurance is given by

$$\theta = \frac{7}{2} (z_{*i})^{2/7} \left[\frac{1}{(1 - \zeta)^{2/7}} - 1 \right] \tag{160}$$

and occurs for $u = 1$.

6. Compare constant power setting and constant altitude tropospheric flight, assuming that the angle of attack is constant and that the initial conditions are identical. Prove that

$$\frac{X_{\alpha\pi}}{X_{\alpha h}} = \frac{1}{\sqrt{1 - \zeta}}$$

$$\frac{t_{\alpha\pi}}{t_{\alpha h}} = \frac{7}{2} \frac{[1/(1 - \zeta)^{2/7}] - 1}{\log [1/(1 - \zeta)]} \tag{161}$$

7. For a jet-propelled aircraft, prove that the aerodynamic efficiency ratio $E/E_{\max}$ assumes the following values: $\sqrt{3/4}$ for best range at constant altitude; $\sqrt{15/16}$ for best tropospheric range at constant power setting; and $\sqrt{8/9}$ for best stratospheric range at constant power setting. Show that the drag ratio R takes the following values: $1/3$ for best range at constant altitude, $3/5$ for best tropospheric range at constant power setting, and $1/2$ for best stratospheric range at constant power setting.

8. With reference to tropospheric flight at constant power setting and constant angle of attack, prove that the wing surface maximizing the range is given by

$$\frac{C_{DOF}S_F}{C_{DOW}S} = \frac{2}{3} \tag{162}$$

9. Consider the steepest climb, and make use of the approximation

$$\frac{z^2 - 1}{E_{\max}^2} \ll 1 \tag{163}$$

Show that Eq. (110) admits the linearized solution

$$u = 1 - \left(\frac{z-1}{2E_{\max}}\right)^2 \tag{164}$$

Hence, for an aircraft whose maximum aerodynamic efficiency is 20, the relative error involved in the approximate solution (100) is 1% for $z = 5$ and about 5% for $z = 10$.

10. Analyze the variation of the optimum turning performance with the altitude, assuming that the weight and the power setting are given. Show that the optimum velocities increase with the altitude with one exception: the velocity for maximum load factor, which is a constant in the stratosphere.

11. In connection with the previous exercise, show that the maximum load factor, angle of bank, and evolutory velocity decrease with the altitude, while the minimum radius of curvature increases.

12. Compare the performance of a jet aircraft and a piston-engined aircraft, and prove the comparative data summarized in Tables 1 and 2.

REFERENCES

1. LIPPISCH, A., *Performance Theory of Airplanes with Jet Propulsion*, Headquarters, Air Matériel Command, Translation Report No. F-TS-685-RE, 1946.

2. FREEMAN, H. B., *Simple Analytical Equations for the Velocity of an Airplane in Unaccelerated Level, Climbing, and Diving Flight*, Journal of the Aerospace Sciences, Vol. 14, No. 3, 1947.

3. PAGE, R. K., *Performance Calculations for Jet-Propelled Aircraft*, Journal of the Royal Aeronautical Society, Vol. 51, No. 437, 1947.

4. SANTANGELO, G., *Sulle Caratteristiche di Volo degli Aeroplani con Turboreattore*, L'Aerotecnica, Vol. 27, No. 5, 1947.

5. EDWARDS, A. D., *Performance Estimation of Civil Jet Aircraft*, Aircraft Engineering, Vol. 22, Nos. 253–254–255, 1950.

6. LAUSETTI, A., *Caratteristiche di Volo degli Aerei a Reazione a Velocità Iposonica*, L'Aerotecnica, Vol. 28, No. 6, 1948.

7. ASHKENAS, I. L., *Range Performance of Turbojet Airplanes*, Journal of the Aerospace Sciences, Vol. 15, No. 2, 1948.

8. SANTANGELO, G., *Dal Volo Simmetrico al Volo a Coltello*, Rivista Aeronautica, Vol. 21, No. 11, 1945.

9. SANTANGELO, G., *La Virata Corretta Non Stazionaria e Stazionaria degli Aeroplani con Gruppo Propulsore di Qualsiasi Tipo*, L'Aerotecnica, Vol. 34, No. 1, 1954.

10. MIELE, A., *Il Calcolo delle Caratteristiche di Salita e della Quota di Tangenza degli Aeroplani Azionati da Turboreattori*, L'Aerotecnica, Vol. 30, No. 2, 1950.

11. MIELE, A., *Steady Properly Banked Turns of Turbojet-Propelled Airplanes*, NACA TM No. 1382, 1955.

12. MIELE, A., *Gráficos para el Cálculo Rápido de las Características de Vuelos de Trepada Acelerados*, Ciencia y Técnica, Vol. 119, No. 602, 1952.

CHAPTER 10

PERFORMANCE OF AN AIRCRAFT WITH AN ARBITRARY POLAR

1. INTRODUCTION

In the previous chapter, the performance of a jet-propelled aircraft was investigated under the assumption of a parabolic drag polar with constant coefficients. In this chapter, the parabolic approximation is removed, and the entire performance problem in both a vertical plane and a horizontal plane is re-examined with the aid of the following hypotheses: (a) the drag polar is arbitrary but independent of the Mach number and the Reynolds number; and (b) the characteristics of the powerplant are independent of the speed and proportional to some power of the atmospheric density.

Because the relevant physical concepts have already been discussed in Chapter 9, this chapter is mainly concerned with analytical techniques. While the fundamental variables of the parabolic case are the dimensionless thrust and the dimensionless speed, the fundamental variables of the nonparabolic case are the thrust-to-weight ratio and the lift coefficient. In particular, by investigating the optimum flight conditions from the lift coefficient point of view, it is possible to predict the operating points in the polar diagram of the aircraft; the general conclusion is that, while powered flight in a vertical plane is characterized by lift coefficients below or equal to that for maximum aerodynamic efficiency, the opposite occurs for gliding flight in a vertical plane as well as for powered flight in a horizontal plane (Refs. 1 through 5).

2. FLIGHT IN A VERTICAL PLANE

If all the hypotheses employed in Section 8–2 are retained, quasi-steady flight in a vertical plane is represented by the equations

$$\dot{X} - V \cos \gamma = 0$$
$$\dot{h} - V \sin \gamma = 0$$
$$T - D - W \sin \gamma = 0 \qquad (1)$$
$$L - W \cos \gamma = 0$$
$$\dot{W} + cT = 0$$

190

where X denotes the horizontal distance, h the altitude, V the velocity, γ the path inclination, W the weight, D the drag, L the lift, T the thrust, c the specific fuel consumption, and the dot sign a derivative with respect to time.

In accordance with Chapter 6, the aerodynamic forces are defined as

$$D = \tfrac{1}{2}C_D\rho SV^2, \qquad L = \tfrac{1}{2}C_L\rho SV^2 \tag{2}$$

where ρ is the atmospheric density, S a reference area, C_D the drag coefficient, and C_L the lift coefficient. In turn, because of hypothesis (a), these coefficients satisfy the relationship

$$C_D = C_D(C_L) \tag{3}$$

which is called the drag polar. Furthermore, in accordance with Chapter 7 and because of hypothesis (b), the characteristics of the powerplant are represented by the relationships

$$\frac{T}{T_*} = \left(\frac{\rho}{\rho_*}\right)^x$$
$$\frac{c}{c_*} = \left(\frac{\rho}{\rho_*}\right)^y \tag{4}$$

where the asterisk denotes quantities evaluated at the tropopause. The symbols x and y denote dimensionless exponents (typical values: $x = 0.7$ and $y = 0.2$ for tropospheric flight; $x = 1$ and $y = 0$ for stratospheric flight), c_* is a characteristic constant of the engine, and T_* is the thrust at the tropopause or power setting.

2.1 Dimensionless parameters. As the following analysis shows, the solution of the equations of motion can be simplified substantially, if one introduces the dimensionless parameters

$$\tau = \frac{T}{W}, \qquad u = \frac{V}{V_R} \tag{5}$$

The first of these is called the *thrust-to-weight ratio,* and the second, the *dimensionless speed,* that is, the ratio of the flight velocity to the reference velocity

$$V_R = \sqrt{\frac{2W}{\rho S}} \tag{6}$$

which is identical with the speed in level flight at the angle of attack corresponding to $C_L = 1$.

3. GLIDING FLIGHT

The class of shallow glide paths is now considered with the aid of assumptions (8–8). Consequently, the equations of motion are given by

$$\dot{X} - V = 0$$
$$\dot{h} - V\gamma = 0$$
$$D + W\gamma = 0 \tag{7}$$
$$L - W = 0$$
$$\dot{W} = 0$$

and are now investigated from both a local point of view (point performance) and an over-all point of view (integral performance).

3.1 Glide angle and sinking speed. After the definitions (2) are introduced and the dynamical equations are divided by the weight, the following results are obtained:

$$C_D u^2 + \gamma = 0, \qquad C_L u^2 - 1 = 0 \tag{8}$$

and imply that

$$-\gamma = \frac{1}{E}$$
$$-\frac{C}{V_R} = \frac{1}{E\sqrt{C_L}} \tag{9}$$
$$u = \frac{1}{\sqrt{C_L}}$$

where E is the aerodynamic efficiency or lift-to-drag ratio and $-C$ the sinking speed (modulus of the rate of climb). These equations represent the glide performance in terms of a one-parameter family of solutions, the parameter being the lift coefficient. After eliminating the lift coefficient, one obtains functional relationships of the form

$$-\gamma = f_1(u), \qquad -\frac{C}{V_R} = f_2(u) \tag{10}$$

which are plotted in Fig. 1 for a subsonic jet aircraft having a maximum lift-to-drag ratio of 20 and a stalling lift coefficient of 1.5.

Among the infinite number of glide conditions which are physically possible, the following are of particular importance for engineering applications: the flattest glide, the glide with minimum sinking speed, and the glide with minimum velocity. These special glides occur when the quantities

$$E, \qquad E\sqrt{C_L}, \qquad C_L$$

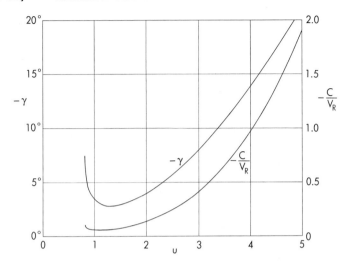

FIG. 1. Glide performance.

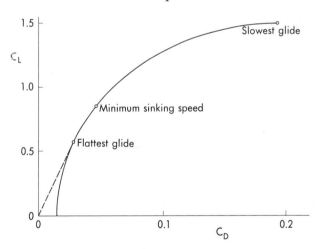

FIG. 2. Optimum glide conditions in the polar diagram.

are, respectively, maximum. After the *logarithmic derivative of the lift coefficient with respect to the drag coefficient**

$$\lambda = \frac{d \log C_L}{d \log C_D} = \frac{C_D}{C_L} \frac{dC_L}{dC_D} \tag{11}$$

---

* For the region of the polar between the minimum drag point and the stalling point, the logarithmic derivative λ is positive and is a monotonically decreasing function of the lift coefficient.

is introduced, it can be shown that $\lambda = 1$ for the flattest glide, $\lambda = 2/3$ for the minimum sinking speed, and $\lambda = 0$ for the slowest glide. Consequently, flattest glide occurs for a lift coefficient smaller than that for minimum sinking speed; furthermore, the latter is smaller than the lift coefficient for minimum velocity (Fig. 2). Incidentally, this *minimum* or *stalling velocity* is given by

$$V_S = \sqrt{\frac{2W}{C_{LS}\rho S}} = \frac{V_R}{\sqrt{C_{LS}}} \tag{12}$$

where C_{LS} is the *stalling lift coefficient*.

3.2 Range and endurance. After the altitude is selected as the new independent variable, the kinematical relationships in the horizontal and vertical directions are rewritten in the form

$$\frac{dX}{dh} = \frac{1}{\gamma} = -E$$

$$\frac{dt}{dh} = \frac{1}{C} = -\frac{E\sqrt{C_L \sigma}}{V_{RO}} \tag{13}$$

where V_{RO} is the reference velocity evaluated at sea level and $\sigma = \rho/\rho_o$ the relative density. These differential equations are now integrated under the assumption that the angle of attack is constant along the flight path; hence, the lift coefficient, the drag coefficient, and the aerodynamic efficiency are simultaneously constant. If the end-conditions

$$X_i = 0, \qquad t_i = 0$$

$$X_f = X, \qquad t_f = t \tag{14}$$

are considered, the following definite integrals are obtained:

$$X = E(h_i - h_f)$$

$$t = \frac{E\sqrt{C_L}}{V_{RO}}[I(h_i) - I(h_f)] \tag{15}$$

where the function $I(h)$ is defined by (see Fig. 9-2)

$$I(h) = \int_0^h \sqrt{\sigma}\, dh \tag{16}$$

As the first of Eqs. (15) indicates, the glider is capable of converting potential energy into the work necessary to achieve range in a resisting medium; since the transformation factor is the lift-to-drag ratio, the best range is achieved by flying at the angle of attack which maximizes the lift-to-drag dratio. Also, from the second of Eqs. (15) it is clear that the best endurance is achieved by flying at a higher angle of attack, that which maximizes the function $E\sqrt{C_L}$.

4. LEVEL FLIGHT

For the category of level paths, the dynamical equations simplify to

$$\dot{X} - V = 0$$
$$\dot{h} = 0$$
$$T - D = 0 \qquad (17)$$
$$L - W = 0$$
$$\dot{W} + cT = 0$$

and are now investigated both locally (point performance) and integrally (integral performance).

4.1 Equilibrium lift coefficient. After the dynamical equations are divided by the weight, the following results are obtained:

$$\tau - C_D u^2 = 0$$
$$C_L u^2 - 1 = 0 \qquad (18)$$

and imply that

$$\tau = \frac{1}{E}, \qquad u = \frac{1}{\sqrt{C_L}} \qquad (19)$$

These equations represent the level flight performance in terms of a one-parameter family of solutions, the parameter being the lift coefficient. After eliminating the lift coefficient, one obtains the functional relationship

$$u = f_1(\tau) \qquad (20)$$

which is plotted in Fig. 3. Since the lift coefficient is a double-valued function of the aerodynamic efficiency, there exist two possible solutions for each thrust-to-weight ratio (Fig. 4): a high-speed solution 1 characterized by a lift coefficient below that for maximum aerodynamic efficiency and a low-speed solution 2 characterized by a lift coefficient beyond that for maximum aerodynamic efficiency. As the altitude increases, the thrust-to-weight ratio obtainable for a given power setting

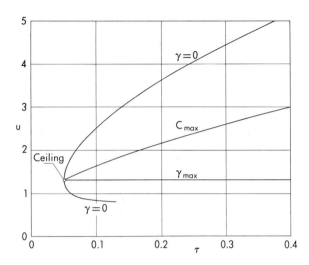

FIG. 3. Characteristic velocities for powered flight in a vertical plane.

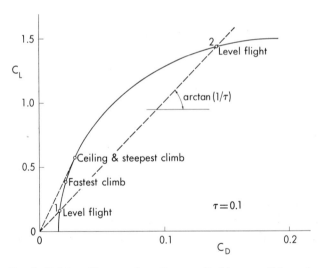

FIG. 4. Level flight, ceiling, and optimum climbing conditions in the polar diagram.

decreases, and the aerodynamic efficiency which is required for level flight increases. At the ceiling, the required aerodynamic efficiency becomes identical with the maximum value which is available because of the characteristics of the aircraft. At any altitude above the ceiling, un-accelerated level flight is physically impossible, since the required aerodynamic efficiency exceeds the maximum available value.

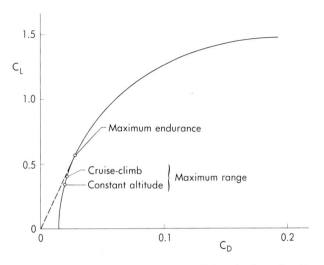

FIG. 5. Optimum range and endurance conditions in the polar diagram.

4.2 Instantaneous range and endurance. After the weight is selected as the new independent variable, the first and the fifth of Eqs. (17) are rewritten in the form

$$-\frac{dX}{dW} = \frac{V}{cT} = \frac{EV}{cW}$$

$$-\frac{dt}{dW} = \frac{1}{cT} = \frac{E}{cW}$$

$$(21)$$

If the subscript i denotes quantities evaluated at the initial point, if the dimensionless coordinates

$$\xi = \frac{Xc}{V_{Ri}}, \qquad \theta = tc, \qquad \mu = \frac{W}{W_i} \qquad (22)$$

are introduced, and if it is observed that the instantaneous velocity is given by

$$V = \sqrt{\frac{2W}{C_L \rho S}} = V_{Ri}\sqrt{\frac{\mu}{C_L}} \qquad (23)$$

the differential expressions for the range and the endurance can be rewritten in the form

$$-\frac{d\xi}{d\mu} = \frac{E}{\sqrt{C_L \mu}}, \qquad -\frac{d\theta}{d\mu} = \frac{E}{\mu} \qquad (24)$$

This means that, for each given weight, the maximum instantaneous range and the maximum instantaneous endurance occur when the functions

$$\frac{E}{\sqrt{C_L}}, \quad E$$

are, respectively, maximum. If the logarithmic derivative of the lift coefficient with respect to the drag coefficient is introduced, the following results can be shown to hold at the stationary points under consideration: $\lambda = 2$ for best range and $\lambda = 1$ for best endurance. Hence, the best range occurs for a lift coefficient smaller, and therefore for a flight velocity higher, than that associated with the best endurance (Fig. 5).

4.3 Integration process. The next step is to integrate the differential equations (24). If the angle of attack is assumed to be constant and the end-conditions

$$\begin{aligned} \xi_i &= 0, & \theta_i &= 0, & \mu_i &= 1 \\ \xi_f &= \xi, & \theta_f &= \theta, & \mu_f &= 1 - \zeta \end{aligned} \tag{25}$$

are considered (the symbol ζ denotes the fuel-to-weight ratio), the following results are derived:

$$\begin{aligned} \xi &= 2\,\frac{E}{\sqrt{C_L}}\,(1 - \sqrt{1 - \zeta}) \\ \theta &= E \log \frac{1}{1 - \zeta} \end{aligned} \tag{26}$$

Incidentally, this flight technique is characterized by a continuously decreasing velocity and, consequently, by a continuously decreasing thrust.

5. QUASI-LEVEL FLIGHT

In the previous section, level paths were investigated; in this section, quasi-level paths are considered. Hence, after hypotheses (8–20) are employed, the equations of motion are rewritten in the form

$$\begin{aligned} \dot{X} - V &= 0 \\ \dot{h} - V\gamma &= 0 \\ T - D &= 0 \\ L - W &= 0 \\ \dot{W} + cT &= 0 \end{aligned} \tag{27}$$

and are now investigated with the assumptions that the power setting is given and that the flight takes place in the stratosphere. For this problem, it is appropriate to define the quantities

$$V_{R*i} = \sqrt{\frac{2W_i}{\rho_* S}}, \qquad \tau_{*i} = \frac{T_*}{W_i} \tag{28}$$

and introduce the dimensionless variables

$$\xi = \frac{Xc_*}{V_{R*i}}, \qquad \theta = tc_*, \qquad \mu = \frac{W}{W_i} \tag{29}$$

After it is observed that the instantaneous velocity is given by

$$V = \sqrt{\frac{2T_*}{C_D \rho_* S}} = V_{R*i} \sqrt{\frac{\tau_{*i}}{C_D}} \tag{30}$$

the differential equations for the range and the endurance (21) can be rewritten as

$$-\frac{d\xi}{d\mu} = \frac{E}{\mu} \sqrt{\frac{\tau_{*i}}{C_D}}, \qquad -\frac{d\theta}{d\mu} = \frac{E}{\mu} \tag{31}$$

Thus, for each given weight, the best instantaneous range and the best instantaneous endurance occur when the functions

$$\frac{E}{\sqrt{C_D}}, \qquad E$$

are, respectively, maximum. Since $\lambda = 3/2$ for best range and $\lambda = 1$ for best endurance, the maximum instantaneous range occurs for a lift coefficient smaller, and therefore for a flight velocity higher, than that associated with the maximum instantaneous endurance (Fig. 5). Incidentally, the flight altitude is not specified in the present problem and must be determined from the relationship

$$\delta = \frac{W}{T_* E} \tag{32}$$

where $\delta = \rho/\rho_*$ is the density ratio.

The next step is to integrate the differential equations (31). If a constant angle of attack is assumed and the end-conditions (25) are considered, the following results are obtained (Ref. 4):

$$\xi = E\sqrt{\frac{\tau_{*i}}{C_D}} \log \frac{1}{1-\zeta}, \qquad \theta = E \log \frac{1}{1-\zeta} \tag{33}$$

Incidentally, this flight technique is characterized by a constant velocity as can be seen from Eq. (30) and by a cruise-climb as can be seen from Eq. (32). The increase in altitude between the endpoints is still governed by Eq. (9–91); furthermore, the relative advantage of the cruise-climb with respect to the constant altitude flight can still be computed with Eq. (9–93).

6. CLIMBING FLIGHT

Climbing flight is now considered and, for didactic purposes, the discussion is divided into two parts. In the first part, the analysis is restricted to small path inclinations; in the second part, an exact analysis is presented.

6.1 Simplified analysis. If the square of the path inclination is assumed to be negligible with respect to one, the equations of motion are rewritten as

$$\dot{X} - V = 0$$
$$\dot{h} - V\gamma = 0$$
$$T - D - W\gamma = 0 \tag{34}$$
$$L - W = 0$$
$$\dot{W} + cT = 0$$

Furthermore, after the dynamical equations are divided by the weight, the following results are obtained:

$$\tau - C_D u^2 - \gamma = 0, \qquad C_L u^2 - 1 = 0 \tag{35}$$

and imply that

$$\gamma = \tau - \frac{1}{E}$$

$$\frac{C}{V_R} = \frac{1}{\sqrt{C_L}}\left(\tau - \frac{1}{E}\right) \tag{36}$$

$$u = \frac{1}{\sqrt{C_L}}$$

These equations express the climbing performance in terms of a two-parameter family of solutions, the parameters being the lift coefficient and the thrust-to-weight ratio. After eliminating the lift coefficient, one obtains the functional relationships (Fig. 6)

$$\gamma = f_1(u, \tau), \qquad \frac{C}{V_R} = f_2(u, \tau) \tag{37}$$

Thus, for each given τ, infinite climbing conditions exist; among these, the steepest climb and the fastest climb are analyzed here. Because of the first of Eqs. (36), the steepest climb occurs when the aerodynamic efficiency is a maximum, which implies that $\lambda = 1$. On the other hand, because of the second of Eqs. (36), the fastest climb occurs when

$$\lambda = \frac{2}{3 - \tau E} \tag{38}$$

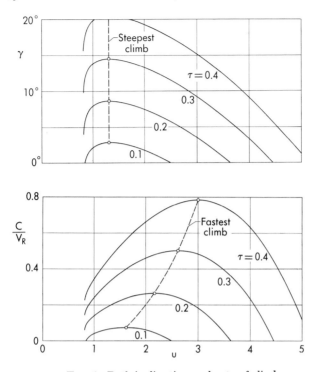

FIG. 6. Path inclination and rate of climb.

Since $\tau > 1/E$ for ascending flight, the logarithmic derivative of the lift coefficient with respect to the drag coefficient satisfies the inequality $\lambda > 1$; thus, the fastest climb occurs for a lift coefficient smaller, and therefore for a flight velocity higher, than that associated with the steepest climb (Figs. 3 and 4).

6.2 Exact analysis. Climbing flight is now investigated by considering the exact form (1) for the equations of motion. In particular, after the dynamical equations are divided by the weight, the following results are obtained:

$$\tau - C_D u^2 - \sin \gamma = 0, \qquad C_L u^2 - \cos \gamma = 0 \qquad (39)$$

and imply that

$$\tau - \frac{\cos \gamma}{E} - \sin \gamma = 0 \qquad (40)$$

where E is the lift-to-drag ratio. After this equation is rearranged in the form

$$(1 + E^2) \sin^2 \gamma - 2\tau E^2 \sin \gamma + \tau^2 E^2 - 1 = 0 \qquad (41)$$

the sine of the path inclination is given by

$$\sin \gamma = \frac{\tau E^2 \overset{(+)}{-} \sqrt{1 + E^2(1 - \tau^2)}}{1 + E^2} \tag{42}$$

where the lower sign is to be exclusively employed for $\tau < 1$, while both signs may yield physically possible solutions for $\tau > 1$. Furthermore, the dimensionless rate of climb and the dimensionless velocity become

$$\frac{C}{V_R} = \frac{1}{\sqrt{C_L}} \sqrt{\frac{E}{(1 + E^2)^3}} \sqrt{\tau \overset{(-)}{\mp} \sqrt{1 + E^2(1 - \tau^2)}}$$

$$\times \left[\tau E^2 \overset{(+)}{-} \sqrt{1 + E^2(1 - \tau^2)} \right] \tag{43}$$

$$u = \frac{1}{\sqrt{C_L}} \sqrt{E \frac{\tau \overset{(-)}{\mp} \sqrt{1 + E^2(1 - \tau^2)}}{1 + E^2}}$$

Relationships (42) and (43) supply the most general solution of the dynamical equations in a vertical plane in terms of the lift coefficient and the thrust-to-weight ratio. In particular, if the approximation

$$\tau^2 \ll 1 \ll E^2 \tag{44}$$

is employed, they lead once more to the simplified solutions represented by Eqs. (36).

7. FLIGHT IN A HORIZONTAL PLANE

In this section, curvilinear flight in a horizontal plane is investigated employing all the hypotheses of Section 8–8. Consequently, the equations of motion are written in the form

$$\dot{X} - V \cos \chi = 0$$
$$\dot{Y} - V \sin \chi = 0$$
$$T - D = 0 \tag{45}$$
$$L \sin \mu - \frac{W}{g} V \dot{\chi} = 0$$
$$L \cos \mu - W = 0$$
$$\dot{W} + cT = 0$$

where X and Y denote Cartesian coordinates measured in the horizontal plane, χ is the velocity yaw angle, and μ is the velocity roll angle.

7.1 Solution of the dynamical equations. After the dynamical equations are divided by the weight, the following relationships are obtained:

$$\tau - C_D u^2 = 0$$

$$C_L u \sin \mu - \frac{\dot{\chi} V_R}{g} = 0 \tag{46}$$

$$C_L u^2 \cos \mu - 1 = 0$$

and can be solved explicitly in terms of the lift coefficient and the thrust-to-weight ratio. Once the dynamical equations have been solved, the load factor and the radius of curvature of the flight path can be determined from the relationships

$$n = C_L u^2, \qquad \frac{rg}{V_R^2} = \frac{u}{\dot{\chi} V_R / g} \tag{47}$$

In this connection, simple manipulations lead to the results (Ref. 5)

$$u = \sqrt{\frac{\tau}{C_D}}$$

$$n = \tau E$$

$$\cos \mu = \frac{1}{\tau E} \tag{48}$$

$$\frac{\dot{\chi} V_R}{g} = \sqrt{C_L^2 \frac{\tau}{C_D} - \frac{C_D}{\tau}}$$

$$\frac{rg}{V_R^2} = \frac{1}{\sqrt{C_L^2 - (C_D/\tau)^2}}$$

which, after the lift coefficient is eliminated, yield the functional relationships (Figs. 7 through 10)

$$n = f_1(u, \tau), \qquad \mu = f_2(u, \tau)$$
$$\frac{\dot{\chi} V_R}{g} = f_3(u, \tau), \qquad \frac{rg}{V_R^2} = f_4(u, \tau) \tag{49}$$

Incidentally, for large values of the thrust-to-weight ratio, that is, for

$$(\tau E)^2 \gg 1 \tag{50}$$

the evolutory velocity and the radius of curvature can be approximated by

$$\frac{\dot{\chi} V_R}{g} = C_L \sqrt{\frac{\tau}{C_D}}, \qquad \frac{rg}{V_R^2} = \frac{1}{C_L} \tag{51}$$

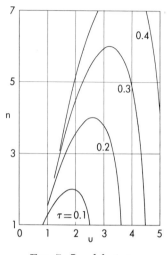

FIG. 7. Load factor.

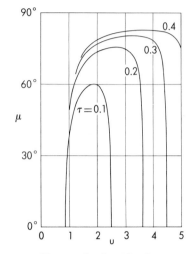

FIG. 8. Angle of bank.

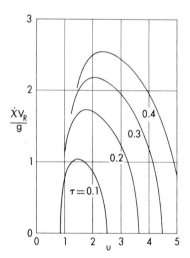

FIG. 9. Evolutory velocity.

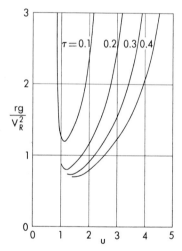

FIG. 10. Radius of curvature.

7.2 Particular cases. Among the infinite number of properly banked horizontal turns which the aircraft can execute for a given thrust-to-weight ratio, three special maneuvers are now analyzed: the turn with the maximum load factor (or the maximum angle of bank), the turn with the maximum evolutory velocity, and the turn with the minimum radius of curvature. These maneuvers occur when the functions

$$E, \qquad \tau \frac{C_L^2}{C_D} - \frac{C_D}{\tau}, \qquad C_L^2 - \left(\frac{C_D}{\tau}\right)^2$$

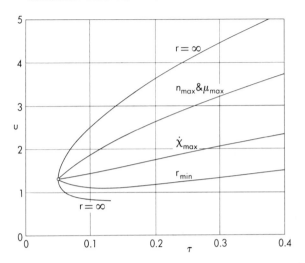

FIG. 11. Characteristic velocities for powered flight in a horizontal plane.

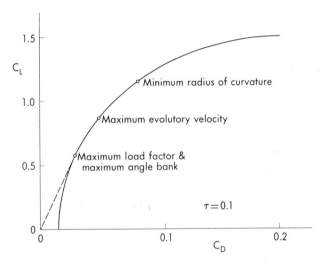

FIG. 12. Optimum turns in the polar diagram.

are, respectively, maximum. If the logarithmic derivative of the lift coefficient with respect to the drag coefficient is introduced, it can be shown
that $\lambda = 1$ in the turn with the maximum load factor or the maximum
angle of bank. On the other hand, the turn with the maximum evolutory
velocity occurs when

$$\lambda = \frac{1}{2}\left(1 + \frac{1}{\tau^2 E^2}\right) \tag{52}$$

while the turn with the minimum radius of curvature occurs when

$$\lambda = \frac{1}{\tau^2 E^2} \tag{53}$$

Since $\tau > 1/E$ at any altitude below the ceiling, the turning flight with the maximum load factor or the maximum angle of bank is characterized by an angle of attack lower than that associated with the maximum evolutory velocity; furthermore, the maximum evolutory velocity occurs for an angle of attack lower than that associated with the minimum radius of curvature (Figs. 11 and 12).

For the particular case where the approximation (50) is valid, the logarithmic derivative of the lift coefficient with respect to the drag coefficient simplifies to $\lambda = 1/2$ for maximum evolutory velocity and $\lambda = 0$ for minimum radius of curvature. This is equivalent to stating that the maximum evolutory velocity and the minimum radius of curvature are achieved when the functions

$$\frac{C_L}{\sqrt{C_D}}, \quad C_L$$

are, respectively, maximum. Thus, the maneuverability of the aircraft can be increased by the use of high lift devices such as flaps and slots. In particular, the minimum radius of curvature is expressed by

$$r = \frac{V_S^2}{g} \tag{54}$$

and, therefore, equals twice the kinetic energy height corresponding to the stalling velocity of the airplane in straight and level flight.

8. PERFORMANCE IN A SPECIFIED ATMOSPHERE

In the preceding sections, flight performance was investigated in a dimensionless form independently of the distribution of the atmospheric properties versus the altitude. The next step is to determine the behavior of the aircraft in a specified atmosphere. For example, consider level flight in the stratosphere, and rewrite the functional relationship (20) in the form

$$V \sqrt{\frac{\rho S}{2W}} = f_1 \left(\frac{T_*}{W} \frac{\rho}{\rho_*} \right) \tag{55}$$

For a given atmospheric model, the density is a known function of the altitude; hence, Eq. (55) yields the relationship

$$f_2(h, V, W, T_*) = 0 \tag{56}$$

which, if the thrust at the tropopause and the weight are specified, reduces to the form

$$f_2(h, V) = 0 \qquad (57)$$

that is represented in Fig. 8–5. If this procedure is repeated for the remaining flight conditions, it is possible to pass from the results presented in this chapter to the corresponding results indicated in Chapter 8 by a simple transformation of coordinates.

9. PARABOLIC POLAR

Since the parabolic polar has the form

$$C_D = C_{DO} + KC_L^2 \qquad (58)$$

where C_{DO} is the zero-lift drag coefficient and K the induced drag factor, the results indicated in the previous chapter can be derived as a particular case of those presented here. With particular regard to the optimum flight conditions, the transformation is readily performed, if it is observed that the logarithmic derivative of the lift coefficient with respect to the drag coefficient can be written as

$$\lambda = \frac{1 + R}{2R} \qquad (59)$$

and implies that

$$R = \frac{1}{2\lambda - 1} \qquad (60)$$

where $R = KC_L^2/C_{DO}$ is the drag ratio, that is, the ratio of the induced drag to the zero-lift drag.

For example, consider gliding flight, and observe that $\lambda = 1$ for the flattest glide and $\lambda = 2/3$ for the minimum sinking speed. Use of Eq. (60) shows that the optimum values for the drag ratio are $R = 1$ for the flattest glide and $R = 3$ for the minimum sinking speed, in agreement with the results of Section 9–3.

10. COMPARISON OF CONSTANT THRUST AND CONSTANT POWER AIRCRAFT

In the previous sections, the performance of a constant thrust aircraft was determined. If a similar technique is employed, the performance of a constant power aircraft can be calculated. If η denotes the propeller efficiency and P the shaft horsepower, the thrust developed by a recipro-

Table 1

COMPARATIVE NONOPTIMUM PERFORMANCE OF
CONSTANT THRUST AND CONSTANT POWER AIRCRAFT

Flight condition	Physical magnitude	Turbojet aircraft	Piston-engined aircraft
Level flight	u	$\dfrac{1}{\sqrt{C_L}}$	$\dfrac{1}{\sqrt{C_L}}$
	E	$\dfrac{1}{\tau}$	$\dfrac{1}{\pi\sqrt{C_L}}$
Climbing flight	u	$\dfrac{1}{\sqrt{C_L}}$	$\dfrac{1}{\sqrt{C_L}}$
	γ	$\tau - \dfrac{1}{E}$	$\pi\sqrt{C_L} - \dfrac{1}{E}$
	$\dfrac{C}{V_R}$	$\dfrac{1}{\sqrt{C_L}}\left(\tau - \dfrac{1}{E}\right)$	$\pi - \dfrac{1}{E\sqrt{C_L}}$
Turning flight	u	$\sqrt{\dfrac{\tau}{C_D}}$	$\sqrt[3]{\dfrac{\pi}{C_D}}$
	$n = \dfrac{1}{\cos\mu}$	τE	$C_L\left(\dfrac{\pi}{C_D}\right)^{2/3}$
	$\left(\dfrac{\dot{\chi}V_R}{g}\right)^2$	$C_L^2\,\dfrac{\tau}{C_D} - \dfrac{C_D}{\tau}$	$C_L^2\left(\dfrac{\pi}{C_D}\right)^{2/3} - \left(\dfrac{C_D}{\pi}\right)^{2/3}$
	$\left(\dfrac{V_R^2}{rg}\right)^2$	$C_L^2 - \left(\dfrac{C_D}{\tau}\right)^2$	$C_L^2 - \left(\dfrac{C_D}{\pi}\right)^{4/3}$

cating engine-propeller combination is given by

$$T = \frac{\eta P}{V} \tag{61}$$

Hence, while the performance of turbojet aircraft can be expressed in terms of the parameters C_L and τ, the performance of piston-engined aircraft can be represented in terms of the variables C_L and π, where

$$\pi = \frac{\eta P}{W V_R} \tag{62}$$

TABLE 2

COMPARATIVE OPTIMUM PERFORMANCE OF
CONSTANT THRUST AND CONSTANT POWER AIRCRAFT

Flight condition	Type of optimum	λ_j	λ_p	$\dfrac{\lambda_j}{\lambda_p}$
Level flight	Ceiling	1	2/3	3/2
	Maximum range	2	1	2
	Maximum endurance	1	2/3	3/2
Climbing flight	Steepest climb	1	$\dfrac{2}{2 + \pi E\sqrt{C_L}}$	$\geq 3/2$
	Fastest climb and most economic climb	$\dfrac{2}{3 - \tau E}$	2/3	$\geq 3/2$
Turning flight	Maximum angle of bank and maximum load factor	1	2/3	3/2
	Maximum evolutory velocity	$\dfrac{1}{2}\left[1 + \dfrac{1}{(\tau E)^2}\right]$	$\dfrac{1}{3}\left[1 + \dfrac{1}{(\pi E\sqrt{C_L})^{4/3}}\right]$	3/2
	Minimum radius of curvature	$\dfrac{1}{(\tau E)^2}$	$\dfrac{2}{3(\pi E\sqrt{C_L})^{4/3}}$	3/2

is the thrust-to-weight ratio evaluated at the level flight velocity which corresponds to $C_L = 1$. In this connection, simple computations lead to the data summarized in Table 1.

Concerning the optimum flight conditions, some important conclusions can be readily obtained, if it is assumed that (a) the propeller efficiency and the shaft horsepower are independent of the velocity and (b) the specific fuel consumption of the piston-engined aircraft is a linear function of the velocity when referred to the unit time and the unit thrust.* Simple manipulations lead to the comparative results summarized in Table 2, where the subscript j refers to the jet aircraft and the subscript p to the piston-engined aircraft. The conclusions of the analysis are the following:

---

* This means that the specific fuel consumption referred to the unit time and the unit power is independent of the velocity.

(a) For flight in a vertical plane, the optimum conditions of turbojet aircraft occur at lift coefficients below or equal to that for maximum lift-to-drag ratio; the opposite occurs for piston-engined aircraft.

(b) For curvilinear flight in a horizontal plane, the optimum conditions of both turbojet and piston-engined aircraft occur at lift coefficients beyond or equal to that for maximum lift-to-drag ratio.

(c) Regardless of the flight condition, the following inequality holds:

$$\frac{\lambda_j}{\lambda_p} \geq \frac{3}{2} \tag{63}$$

Hence, turbojet aircraft utilize lower angles of attack (and, therefore, higher flight velocities) than piston-engined aircraft.

In the derivation of these important results, it was observed that jet-propelled vehicles satisfy the inequality

$$\tau E \geq 1 \tag{64}$$

at any altitude below the ceiling, while piston-engined aircraft are characterized by the inequality

$$\pi E \sqrt{C_L} \geq 1 \tag{65}$$

Furthermore, the statements relative to flight with the maximum evolutory velocity and to flight with the minimum radius of curvature are subordinated to the following constraint: the load factors pertaining to these conditions are assumed to have equal values for the jet aircraft and the piston-engined aircraft.

EXERCISES

1. With reference to gliding flight, consider the exact form for the dynamical equations. Derive the relationships

$$-\sin \gamma = \frac{1}{\sqrt{1 + E^2}}$$

$$-\frac{C}{V_R} = \frac{1}{E \sqrt{C_L}} \left(\frac{E^2}{1 + E^2} \right)^{3/4} \tag{66}$$

$$u = \frac{1}{\sqrt{C_L}} \sqrt[4]{\frac{E^2}{1 + E^2}}$$

which, for large values of the lift-to-drag ratio, reduce to the simplified solutions represented by Eqs. (9). Furthermore, if the angle of attack is constant and the end-conditions (14) are employed, show that the following particular integrals hold:

$$X = E(h_i - h_f)$$

$$t = \frac{E\sqrt{C_L}}{V_{RO}}\left(\frac{1 + E^2}{E^2}\right)^{3/4}[I(h_i) - I(h_f)] \tag{67}$$

and, for large values of the lift-to-drag ratio, reduce to the simplified solutions represented by Eqs. (15).

2. Prove that the following differential expressions are a mathematical consequence of Eqs. (1):

$$dX + E\left(dh + \frac{V}{c}\frac{dW}{W}\right) = 0$$

$$dt + \frac{E}{\cos\gamma}\left(\frac{dh}{V} + \frac{1}{c}\frac{dW}{W}\right) = 0 \tag{68}$$

For the particular case where both the angle of attack and the velocity are held constant in the stratosphere, derive the relationships

$$X + E\left(h + \frac{V}{c}\log W\right) = \text{Const}$$

$$t + E\left(\frac{h}{V} + \frac{1}{c}\log W\right) = \text{Const} \tag{69}$$

the second of which is subordinated to the hypothesis that $\cos\gamma \cong 1$ (shallow path). Hence, if the variation in potential energy is small with respect to the work dissipated because of the aerodynamic forces, these integrals simplify to

$$X + V\frac{E}{c}\log W = \text{Const}$$

$$t + \frac{E}{c}\log W = \text{Const} \tag{70}$$

By nondimensionalizing Eqs. (70) and applying the proper end-conditions, rederive Eqs. (33).

3. Consider a path flown with constant power setting and constant angle of attack in the stratosphere. Prove that the increase in altitude between the endpoints of the trajectory is given by Eq. (9–91).

4. Consider a turbojet aircraft operating at constant power setting and constant angle of attack in the troposhere. Denoting by ζ the fuel-

to-weight ratio, show that the dimensionless range and endurance are given by

$$\xi = 2\tau_{*i} \frac{E^2}{\sqrt{C_L}} \left(\frac{1}{\sqrt{1 - \varsigma}} - 1 \right)$$
$$\theta = \frac{7}{2} \tau_{*i}^{2/7} E^{9/7} \left[\frac{1}{(1 - \varsigma)^{2/7}} - 1 \right]$$

(71)

5. Compare a constant power setting path and a constant altitude path, assuming that the angle of attack is constant and that the initial conditions are identical. After calculating the range and the endurance, rederive Eqs. (9–93) which are valid for stratospheric flight and Eqs. (9–161) which are valid for tropospheric flight.

6. Consider the exact climbing flight of a constant-thrust aircraft and focus attention on the solutions represented by Eqs. (42) and (43). Assuming that the aerodynamic efficiency is given and defining the following limiting thrust-to-weight ratio:

$$\tau_{\lim} = \sqrt{(E^2 + 1)/E^2}$$

(72)

show that only one set of solutions is possible for $\tau < 1$, while two sets are possible for $1 < \tau < \tau_{\lim}$. Finally, prove that quasi-steady climb is physically impossible if the thrust-to-weight ratio exceeds the above limiting value.

7. The results of the present chapter are valid for a drag polar having the form $C_D = C_D(C_L)$. By specializing this polar into a parabolic one, calculate the results already derived in Chapter 9.

8. Compare the performance of jet aircraft and piston-engined aircraft, and prove the comparative data summarized in Tables 1 and 2.

References

1. LIPPISCH, A., *Performance Theory of Airplanes with Jet Propulsion*, Headquarters, Air Matériel Command, Translation Report No. F-TS-685-RE, 1946.
2. SANTANGELO, G., *Sulle Caratteristiche di Volo degli Aeroplani con Turboreattore*, L'Aerotecnica, Vol. 27, No. 5, 1947.
3. LAUSETTI, A., *Caratteristiche di Volo degli Aerei a Reazione a Velocità Iposonica*, L'Aerotecnica, Vol. 28, No. 6, 1948.
4. ASHKENAS, I. L., *Range Performance of Turbojet Airplanes*, Journal of the Aerospace Sciences, Vol. 15, No. 2, 1948.
5. MIELE, A., *Steady Properly Banked Turns of Turbojet-Propelled Airplanes*, NACA TM No. 1382, 1955.

CHAPTER 11

AIRCRAFT PERFORMANCE
AT HIGH SUBSONIC, TRANSONIC,
AND SUPERSONIC SPEEDS

1. INTRODUCTION

In Chapters 9 and 10, the performance of a jet-propelled aircraft was investigated under the assumption that the characteristics of the aircraft and the engine are independent of the Mach number. In this chapter, the above restriction is removed, and the analysis is extended to cover the case where the coefficients of zero-lift drag, induced drag, thrust, and specific fuel consumption are arbitrarily dependent on the Mach number. For the sake of discussion, the treatment refers to turbojet and turbofan aircraft. However, the method presented here is applicable to turbo-prop aircraft without modification; furthermore, it can be applied to ramjet vehicles, provided that the corrected rotor speed of the turbojet or turbofan engine is replaced by the corrected fuel-to-air ratio of the ramjet engine (Ref. 6).

1.1 Characteristics of the performance problem. A peculiarity of the high-speed performance problem is that the solutions are so strongly influenced by the aircraft and the engine that it is simply impossible to reach general conclusions which are unrestrictedly valid for every case and subcase. For that reason, this chapter is concerned only with the analytical and graphical procedures necessary to determine the performance of a given aircraft powered by a given engine; the design problem is not considered, since it is so complex that it escapes an analytical approach. However, the method presented here is preliminary to design, since the basic design philosophy consists of (a) considering a discrete number of configurations which depend upon certain arbitrary parameters (for instance, the surface area, the aspect ratio, the angle of sweep, and the thickness ratio of the wing), (b) determining the drag polar, the weight, and the flight performance of each of these configurations, and (c) selecting that particular configuration which meets the desired requirements. Incidentally, the design problem may or may not

213

have real solutions, depending upon the specifications imposed; furthermore, when real solutions exist, they are generally not unique.

1.2 Multivalued solutions. For the low-speed performance problem considered in the previous chapters, the level flight equation was found to have one pair of solutions; furthermore, the optimum flight conditions were found to admit unique solutions. This situation is generally unchanged in the high-speed case, as long as the aircraft operates in the high-subsonic, low-transonic domain. On the other hand, if the aircraft is designed to attain supersonic speeds, the level flight equation may have one, two, or several pairs of solutions; furthermore, the optimum flight conditions may be single-valued or multivalued (Refs. 6 through 8). When several solutions exist, they must be studied in detail in order to distinguish relative maximum points from relative minimum points as well as to determine that particular point which yields the absolute maximum or minimum for the function under consideration. For these reasons, it is didactically convenient to separate the discussion of high subsonic–low transonic flight from that of supersonic flight. While the former is considered in the beginning sections of this chapter, the latter is presented at the end in less detail, since the analytical method is the same.

1.3 Organization of the following sections. In the following sections, the performance problem is formulated in a dimensional form and, then, simplified by introducing appropriate similarity parameters. Among these, two are characteristic of the aircraft (the load factor and the dimensionless wing loading), two are characteristic of the engine (the corrected rotor speed and the coefficient of specific fuel consumption), and two are common to both the aircraft and the engine (the Mach number and the modified thrust coefficient). Both nonoptimum and optimum conditions are investigated using either a parabolic or an arbitrary polar. In particular, the optimum conditions are determined with two alternative and complementary methods: a *direct graphical procedure* and an *indirect analytical approach*. In order to illustrate the theory, numerical examples are developed for two particular aircraft configurations: a Mach 0.9, swept-wing transport powered by turbofan engines ($S_R/S = 0.028$) and a Mach 3, delta-wing transport powered by turbojet engines ($S_R/S = 0.050$). For these configurations, the aerodynamic characteristics were presented in Chapter 6, and the engine characteristics, in Chapter 7. At any rate, it must be emphasized that, while the formulas and the procedures of this chapter are general, the majority of the engineering conclusions are particular, since they are based on specific aircraft configurations.

2. FLIGHT IN A VERTICAL PLANE

If all the hypotheses of Section 8–2 are retained, quasi-steady flight in a vertical plane is governed by the equations

$$
\begin{aligned}
\dot{X} - V \cos \gamma &= 0 \\
\dot{h} - V \sin \gamma &= 0 \\
T - D - W \sin \gamma &= 0 \\
L - W \cos \gamma &= 0 \\
\dot{W} + cT &= 0
\end{aligned}
\tag{1}
$$

where X denotes the horizontal distance, h the altitude, V the velocity, γ the path inclination, W the weight, D the drag, L the lift, T the thrust, c the specific fuel consumption, and the dot sign a derivative with respect to time.

2.1 Aerodynamic characteristics. It is known from Chapter 6 that, if Reynolds number effects are neglected, the characteristics of a high-speed configuration can be expressed in terms of the drag coefficient C_D, the lift coefficient C_L, and the Mach number M. These dimensionless groups are defined by

$$
C_D = \frac{2D}{\rho S V^2}, \qquad C_L = \frac{2L}{\rho S V^2}, \qquad M = \frac{V}{a}
\tag{2}
$$

where S is a reference surface, ρ the air density, and a the speed of sound. If p denotes the free-stream pressure and k the ratio of the specific heats, the speed of sound can be written as

$$
a = \sqrt{k \frac{p}{\rho}}
\tag{3}
$$

Consequently, the aerodynamic coefficients become

$$
C_D = \frac{2D}{kpSM^2}, \qquad C_L = \frac{2L}{kpSM^2}
\tag{4}
$$

Notice that these coefficients and the Mach number are not independent but are related by the drag polar. In particular, if the parabolic approximation is employed, the drag polar is expressed by

$$
C_D = C_{DO}(M) + K(M)C_L^2
\tag{5}
$$

where the zero-lift drag coefficient C_{DO} and the induced drag factor K are functions of the Mach number only.

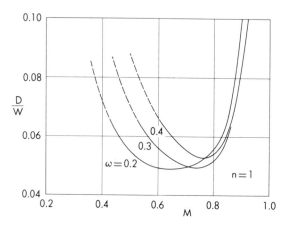

FIG. 1. Drag per unit weight versus Mach number and dimensionless wing loading.

2.1.1 *Drag per Unit Weight.* After Eqs. (4) and (5) are combined and the aerodynamic coefficients are eliminated, the drag function becomes

$$D = \frac{k}{2} C_{DO} pSM^2 + \frac{2KL^2}{kpSM^2} \tag{6}$$

Furthermore, if the *load factor*

$$n = \frac{L}{W} \tag{7}$$

and the *dimensionless wing loading*

$$\omega = \frac{2W}{kpS} \tag{8}$$

are introduced, the drag per unit weight can be written in the form

$$\frac{D}{W} = \frac{C_{DO}M^2}{\omega} + \frac{K\omega}{M^2} n^2 \tag{9}$$

For the particular case where $n = 1$, the drag function becomes

$$\frac{D}{W} = \frac{C_{DO}M^2}{\omega} + \frac{K\omega}{M^2} \tag{10}$$

and, with reference to the subsonic, swept-wing transport under consideration, is plotted in Fig. 1 versus the Mach number for several values of the
dimensionless wing loading. Notice that the $\omega = $ Const curves in Fig. 1
are divided into two parts. The solid portion is that along which the para-

bolic approximation holds. The dashed portion is that along which the parabolic approximation does not hold, even though the trends predicted are qualitatively correct; thus, if a more precise estimation of the drag is desired, the exact expression of the polar must be employed (see Section 9).

2.1.2 *Drag Ratio and Aerodynamic Efficiency Ratio.* Once the Mach number, the dimensionless wing loading, and the load factor are given, not only can the drag per unit weight be calculated but also several other related quantities. One of these is the ratio of the induced drag to the zero-lift drag or *drag ratio*

$$R = \frac{KC_L^2}{C_{DO}} = \frac{K}{C_{DO}}\left(\frac{\omega n}{M^2}\right)^2 \tag{11}$$

Another is the ratio of the actual aerodynamic efficiency to its maximum value or *aerodynamic efficiency ratio**

$$\frac{E}{E_{\max}} = \frac{2\sqrt{R}}{1+R} = \frac{2\sqrt{K/C_{DO}}\,\omega n/M^2}{1+(\sqrt{K/C_{DO}}\,\omega n/M^2)^2} \tag{12}$$

2.1.3 *Minimum Drag Condition.* As Eq. (10) and Fig. 1 indicate, the drag of an aircraft in level flight depends on both the Mach number and the dimensionless wing loading. In particular, for each given Mach number, there exists a dimensionless wing loading (and, hence, a flight altitude) which minimizes the over-all drag; conversely, for each given dimensionless wing loading, there exists a Mach number such that the over-all drag is a minimum.

If the Mach number is held constant, the dimensionless wing loading for minimum drag is given by

$$\omega = M^2\sqrt{\frac{C_{DO}}{K}} \tag{13}$$

which implies that (Fig. 2)

$$\frac{D}{W} = \frac{1}{E_{\max}} \tag{14}$$

On the other hand, if the dimensionless wing loading is held constant, the Mach number for minimum drag is defined by the equation

$$\omega = M^2\sqrt{\frac{C_{DO}}{K}}\sqrt{\frac{2+C_{DOM}}{2-K_M}} \tag{15}$$

---

* It is recalled that the maximum aerodynamic efficiency for a given Mach number is given by $E_{\max} = 1/2\sqrt{KC_{DO}}$

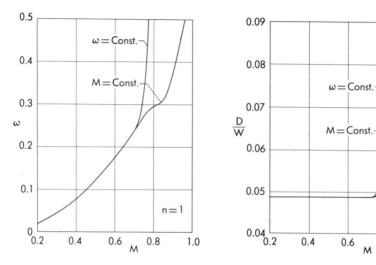

FIG. 2. Minimum drag condition.

in which the subscript M denotes a *logarithmic derivative with respect to the Mach number*, that is,

$$C_{DOM} = \frac{d \log C_{DO}}{d \log M} = \frac{M}{C_{DO}} \frac{dC_{DO}}{dM}$$

$$K_M = \frac{d \log K}{d \log M} = \frac{M}{K} \frac{dK}{dM} \tag{16}$$

The corresponding value for the minimum drag is given by (Fig. 2)

$$\frac{D}{W} = \frac{1}{2E_{max}} \frac{4 + (C_{DO}/K)_M}{\sqrt{(2 + C_{DOM})(2 - K_M)}} \tag{17}$$

In connection with these results, the following conclusions arise: (a) the minimum drag in the transonic region is considerably higher than the minimum drag in the subsonic region; (b) if the Mach number is given, the induced drag associated with the minimum drag condition is equal to the zero-lift drag; on the other hand, if the dimensionless wing loading is given, the induced drag associated with the minimum drag condition can be considerably larger than the zero-lift drag (see Exercises); and (c) in the low subsonic region, differentiation with respect to ω and differentiation with respect to M yield identical results; for this region, both the drag ratio and the aerodynamic efficiency ratio tend to unity, in accordance with the low-speed theory developed in Chapter 9 (see exercises).

2.2 Engine characteristics. It is known from Chapter 7 that, if Reynolds number effects are neglected, the characteristics of a turbojet or turbofan engine can be expressed in terms of the coefficient of thrust K_T, the coefficient of specific fuel consumption K_c, the Mach number M, and the corrected rotor speed N_c. These dimensionless groups are defined by

$$K_T = \frac{T}{pS_R}, \qquad K_c = \frac{ca_*^2}{ga}$$

$$M = \frac{V}{a}, \qquad N_c = \frac{N}{N_{\max}} \frac{a_*}{a} \tag{18}$$

where S_R is a fixed reference area of the engine, g the acceleration of gravity, N the actual rotor speed, $N_{\max}$ the maximum rotor speed, and the asterisk denotes quantities evaluated at the tropopause. Notice that these similarity parameters are not independent but satisfy the expressions

$$K_T = K_T(M, N_c), \qquad K_c = K_c(M, N_c) \tag{19}$$

which fulfill for the engine a function analogous to that of the drag polar for the aircraft.

As the subsequent theory shows, performance analyses can be simplified to some degree if the thrust coefficient is replaced by the *modified thrust coefficient*

$$K_t = \frac{2T}{kpS} = \frac{2}{k} \frac{S_R}{S} K_T \tag{20}$$

and if the dependence of the coefficient of specific fuel consumption on the corrected rotor speed is disregarded (this approximation is always permissible for some interval of the corrected rotor speed). This means that relationships (19) are replaced by the functions

$$K_t = K_t(M, N_c), \qquad K_c = K_c(M) \tag{21}$$

3. GLIDING FLIGHT

The class of shallow glide paths is now considered and, after hypotheses (8–8) are employed, the following differential set is obtained:

$$\dot{X} - V = 0$$
$$\dot{h} - V\gamma = 0$$
$$D + W\gamma = 0 \tag{22}$$
$$L - W = 0$$
$$\dot{W} = 0$$

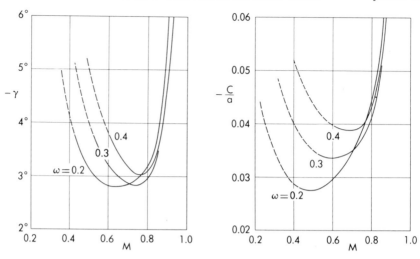

FIG. 3. Glide angle and sinking speed.

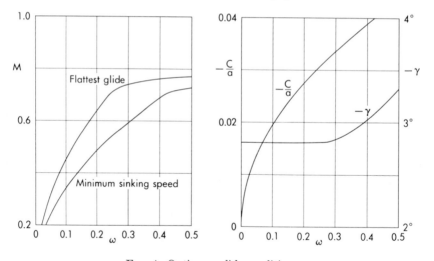

FIG. 4. Optimum glide conditions.

Since the load factor is $n = 1$, the drag function is represented by Eq. (10), so that the glide angle becomes

$$-\gamma = \frac{D}{W} = \frac{C_{DO}M^2}{\omega} + \frac{K\omega}{M^2} \tag{23}$$

while the sinking speed can be written in the form

$$-\frac{C}{a} = -M\gamma = \frac{C_{DO}M^3}{\omega} + \frac{K\omega}{M} \tag{24}$$

After these functions are plotted versus the Mach number for several values of the dimensionless wing loading (Fig. 3), the flattest glide and minimum sinking speed conditions can be found graphically by determining the lowest points of the $\omega = $ Const curves. An alternative procedure consists of differentiating the right-hand sides of Eqs. (23) and (24) with respect to the Mach number and setting the results equal to zero. This operation yields the expressions (Fig. 4-left)

$$\omega = M^2 \sqrt{\frac{C_{DO}}{K}} \sqrt{\frac{2 + C_{DOM}}{2 - K_M}}$$

$$\omega = M^2 \sqrt{\frac{C_{DO}}{K}} \sqrt{\frac{3 + C_{DOM}}{1 - K_M}}$$

(25)

the first of which determines the Mach number for flattest glide, and the second, that for minimum sinking speed. Since these functions have the form $M = M(\omega)$, the minimum glide angle and the minimum sinking speed can be expressed in terms of the dimensionless wing loading only and are indicated in Fig. 4-right. In closing, the following remarks are pertinent:

(a) Since the atmospheric pressure increases as the glider descends toward lower altitudes, the parameter ω decreases along the flight path. Hence, for the subsonic, swept-wing transport under consideration, the Mach number continuously decreases in either a flattest glide or a minimum sinking speed maneuver.

(b) The drag ratios for flattest glide and for minimum sinking speed are given by

$$R = \frac{2 + C_{DOM}}{2 - K_M}$$

$$R = \frac{3 + C_{DOM}}{1 - K_M}$$

(26)

and depend strongly on the instantaneous Mach number. For the particular case of low subsonic flight, the logarithmic derivatives of the aerodynamic coefficients with respect to the Mach number vanish, and the drag ratios reduce to $R = 1$ and $R = 3$, respectively, in accordance with the low-speed theory developed in Chapter 9.

(c) As the previous analysis indicates, there exist two methods for finding the optimum flight conditions, one direct and another indirect. With the *direct method*, a sequence of nonoptimum conditions is calculated prior to determining the optimum point. With the *indirect method*, nonoptimum conditions are bypassed, and the search for the optimum operating point is carried out by employing the analytical expressions for the maximum or minimum under consideration. The main advantage of the first method over the second is that it supplies not only the optimum point but also the behavior of the function in its vicinity; its main disadvantage is that the optimum conditions cannot be determined accurately unless a considerable number of nonoptimum points are calculated for each of the $\omega = $ Const curves. For these reasons, direct and indirect methods must be considered as complementary, rather than competitive; both methods can be of assistance in performance analyses if employed with discrimination and good judgment. Incidentally, the indirect method demands that the logarithmic derivative of the aerodynamic coefficients with respect to the Mach number be evaluated; consequently, either techniques of numerical differentiation must be employed or an analytical expression for the variation of the aerodynamic coefficients with the Mach number must be found.

(d) In order to calculate the range and the endurance along either a flattest descent trajectory or a minimum sinking speed trajectory, Eqs. (8–14) must be integrated subject to either the flattest glide condition or the minimum sinking speed condition (see exercises). For example, consider the flattest glide, and observe that, since ω is a known function of the altitude, the instantaneous Mach number, the glide angle, and the sinking speed can be uniquely related to the altitude. Since the right-hand sides of Eqs. (8–14) become known functions of the altitude, the integration process reduces to that of a simple quadrature. An analogous remark holds for the maneuver of minimum sinking speed.

(e) For some types of gliding paths, the variation in kinetic energy may not be negligible with respect to the variation in potential energy; under such conditions, the quasi-steady approach is no longer justified, and the present results must be corrected in order to account for the unsteadiness of the motion. The correction factor depends on the rate of variation of the kinetic energy with respect to the potential energy and can be calculated with the procedure which was developed in Chapter 8.

4. LEVEL FLIGHT

For the category of level paths, the condition $\gamma = 0$ is to be introduced into the equations of motion which simplify to

$$\dot{X} - V = 0$$
$$\dot{h} = 0$$
$$T - D = 0 \qquad (27)$$
$$L - W = 0$$
$$\dot{W} + cT = 0$$

These equations are now investigated both locally (point performance) and integrally (integral performance).

4.1 Flight velocity. Since the load factor is $n = 1$, the drag is represented by Eq. (10). Consequently, after the equation of motion on the tangent to the flight path is multiplied by the factor $2/kpS$, the following relationship is obtained:

$$K_t = C_{DO}M^2 + K\frac{\omega^2}{M^2} \tag{28}$$

and involves the three variables ω, N_c, M, so that a two-parameter family of solutions exists. This means that, if the dimensionless wing loading and the corrected rotor speed are specified, the only unknown is the Mach number; it can be determined graphically by plotting the thrust available (left-hand side of the level flight equation) and the thrust

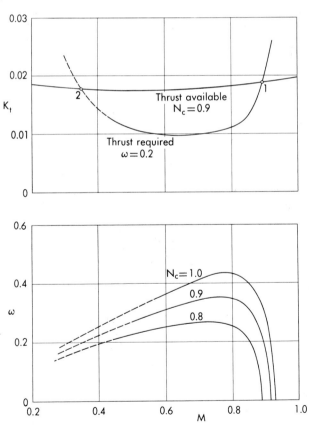

FIG. 5. Solution of the level flight equation.

required (right-hand side of the level flight equation) versus the Mach number and finding the points where these curves intersect. In this connection, a particular example is indicated in Fig. 5-top and shows that, for prescribed values of the corrected rotor speed and the dimensionless wing loading, there exist two solutions for the Mach number, a high-speed solution 1 corresponding to flight with low angle of attack and a low-speed solution 2 corresponding to flight with high angle of attack.

While this graphical procedure is physically intuitive, its utility is limited to the case where only a few particular solutions must be found. On the other hand, if the totality of level flight solutions is desired, a different approach is recommended. Since Eq. (28) is an algebraic relation of the second degree in the dimensionless wing loading, the following explicit solution can be obtained:

$$\omega = M \sqrt{\frac{K_t - C_{DO} M^2}{K}} \tag{29}$$

and is plotted in Fig. 5-bottom for the swept-wing, turbofan transport under consideration.

4.2 Ceiling. The theoretical ceiling is now investigated with the assumption that the corrected rotor speed is prescribed. Since ω is inversely proportional to the static pressure and since the static pressure is a monotonically decreasing function of the altitude, the highest point of each of the $N_c = $ Const curves in Fig. 5-bottom is the ceiling corresponding to the prescribed corrected rotor speed. In addition to this graphical procedure, the ceiling can also be determined by differentiating the right-hand side of Eq. (29) with respect to the Mach number and setting the result equal to zero. Simple manipulations yield the relationship

$$K_t = C_{DO} M^2 \frac{4 + (C_{DO}/K)_M}{2 + (K_t/K)_M} \tag{30}$$

whose left-hand side represents the thrust available, and whose right-hand side, the thrust required at the ceiling; hence, the equilibrium Mach number can be determined with the procedure illustrated in Fig. 6-left. By repeating this procedure for several corrected rotor speeds, the function $M(N_c)$, which is the locus of the ceiling conditions, can be obtained and is plotted in Fig. 6-right. The associated dimensionless wing loading can be obtained by substituting the Mach number at the ceiling into either Eq. (29) or

$$\omega = M^2 \sqrt{\frac{C_{DO}}{K}} \sqrt{\frac{2 + (C_{DO}/K_t)_M}{2 + (K_t/K)_M}} \tag{31}$$

and, in consideration of Eq. (30), can be expressed in terms of the cor-

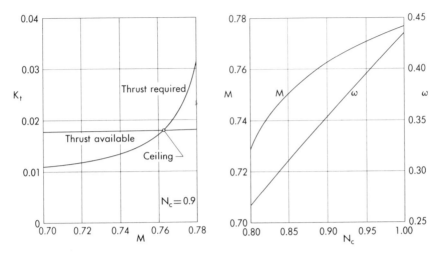

FIG. 6. Ceiling.

rected rotor speed only (Fig. 6-right). Once the dimensionless wing loading is known, the static pressure at the ceiling can be calculated; subsequently, the altitude can be determined from the tables of the standard
atmosphere (see Appendix). Incidentally, the drag ratio at the ceiling
is given by

$$R = \frac{2 + (C_{DO}/K_t)_M}{2 + (K_t/K)_M} \qquad (32)$$

and reduces to $R = 1$ if the logarithmic derivatives of the aerodynamic
and thrust coefficients with respect to the Mach number vanish; this
result is in agreement with the low-speed theory which was developed in
Chapter 9.

4.3 Range and endurance. If the first and the fifth of Eqs. (27) are
employed and the weight is selected as the new independent variable, the
differential relationships for the range and the endurance are given by

$$-\frac{dX}{dW} = \frac{V}{cT} = \frac{V}{cD}$$

$$-\frac{dt}{dW} = \frac{1}{cT} = \frac{1}{cD} \qquad (33)$$

and can be reduced to a dimensionless form if the variables

$$\xi = \frac{Xg}{a_*^2}, \qquad \theta = \frac{tga}{a_*^2} \qquad (34)$$

are introduced. In fact, after Eqs. (33) and (34) are combined with the

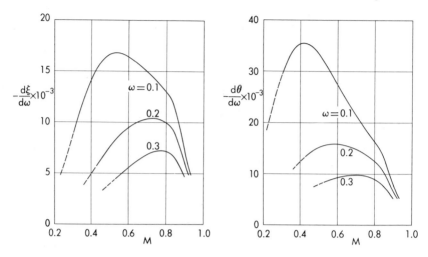

FIG. 7. Instantaneous range and endurance in level flight.

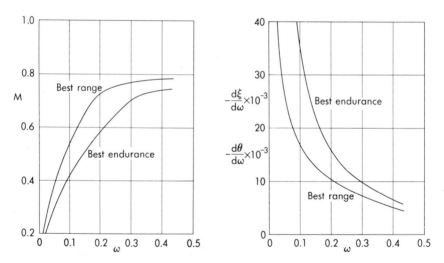

FIG. 8. Optimum range and endurance conditions in level flight.

drag function (10), the following relationships are obtained:

$$-\frac{d\xi}{d\omega} = \frac{M^3}{K_c(C_{DO}M^4 + K\omega^2)}$$

$$-\frac{d\theta}{d\omega} = \frac{M^2}{K_c(C_{DO}M^4 + K\omega^2)}$$

(35)

After these functions are plotted versus the Mach number for several values of the dimensionless wing loading (Fig. 7), the best range and endurance conditions can be found graphically by determining the highest points of the $\omega = $ Const curves.

An alternative procedure consists of differentiating the right-hand sides of Eqs. (35) with respect to the Mach number and setting the results equal to zero. Simple manipulations yield the expressions

$$\omega = M^2 \sqrt{\frac{C_{DO}}{K}} \sqrt{\frac{1 + (C_{DO}K_c)_M}{3 - (KK_c)_M}}$$

$$\omega = M^2 \sqrt{\frac{C_{DO}}{K}} \sqrt{\frac{2 + (C_{DO}K_c)_M}{2 - (KK_c)_M}} \tag{36}$$

the first of which determines the Mach number for maximum range and the second, that for maximum endurance (Fig. 8-left). Since these expressions have the form $M = M(\omega)$, the maximum instantaneous range and endurance can be expressed in terms of the dimensionless wing loading only (Fig. 8-right). In closing, the following remarks are noteworthy:

(a) If the instantaneous condition for best range or best endurance is maintained everywhere along the trajectory, the optimum Mach number continuously decreases, owing to the consumption of fuel and the associated decrease in the parameter ω. Consequently, the maximum range and endurance must be evaluated by integrating the functions represented in Fig. 8-right with respect to the independent variable ω. Generally speaking, approximate methods are needed, since analytical solutions are possible only for special cases (see Chapter 9 and exercises).

(b) The drag ratios for maximum range and for maximum endurance are given by

$$R = \frac{1 + (C_{DO}K_c)_M}{3 - (KK_c)_M}$$

$$R = \frac{2 + (C_{DO}K_c)_M}{2 - (KK_c)_M} \tag{37}$$

and depend strongly on the instantaneous Mach number. For the particular case where the logarithmic derivatives of the aerodynamic and engine coefficients with respect to the Mach number are zero, these drag ratios reduce to $R = 1/3$ and $R = 1$, respectively, in accordance with the low-speed theory which was developed in Chapter 9.

5. QUASI-LEVEL FLIGHT

In the previous section, level paths were investigated; in this section, quasi-level paths are considered. Hence, after hypotheses (8–20) are employed, the equations of motion are rewritten in the form

$$
\begin{aligned}
\dot{X} - V &= 0 \\
\dot{h} - V\gamma &= 0 \\
T - D &= 0 \\
L - W &= 0 \\
\dot{W} + cT &= 0
\end{aligned}
\tag{38}
$$

and are now investigated with the assumptions that flight takes place in the stratosphere* and that the corrected rotor speed is constant.

5.1 Point performance. If quantities evaluated at the tropopause are denoted by an asterisk and if the dimensionless variables

$$
\pi = \frac{p}{p_*}, \qquad \omega_* = \frac{2W}{kp_*S}
$$
$$
\xi = \frac{Xg}{a_*^2}, \qquad \theta = \frac{tg}{a_*}
\tag{39}
$$

are introduced, Eqs. (33) yield the expressions

$$
-\frac{d\xi}{d\omega_*} = \frac{M}{\pi K_c K_t}
$$
$$
-\frac{d\theta}{d\omega_*} = \frac{1}{\pi K_c K_t}
\tag{40}
$$

whose right-hand sides depend on the Mach number and the pressure ratio. However, these variables are not independent but must be consistent with the level flight equation (29). Hence, after it is observed that

$$
\pi = \frac{\omega_*}{\omega} = \frac{\omega_*}{M} \sqrt{\frac{K}{K_t - C_{DO}M^2}}
\tag{41}
$$

and after the pressure ratio is eliminated, the following relationships are obtained:

$$
-\frac{d\xi}{d\log \omega_*} = \frac{ME}{K_c} = \frac{M^2}{K_c K_t} \sqrt{\frac{K_t - C_{DO}M^2}{K}}
$$
$$
-\frac{d\theta}{d\log \omega_*} = \frac{E}{K_c} = \frac{M}{K_c K_t} \sqrt{\frac{K_t - C_{DO}M^2}{K}}
\tag{42}
$$

---

* In the following developments, this assumption has a relevant importance only as far as the endurance is concerned; the formulas relative to the range are also valid for tropospheric flight.

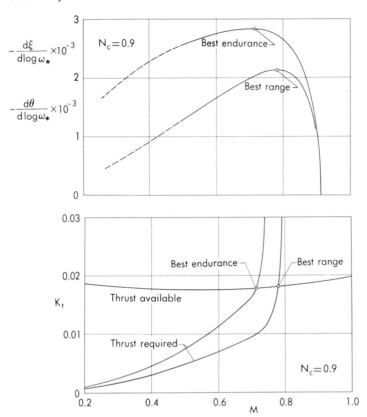

FIG. 9. Determination of the best range and endurance conditions for quasi-level flight with a constant corrected rotor speed.

The left-hand sides of these equations are called the *range factor* and the *endurance factor*, respectively, and are plotted in Fig. 9-top versus the Mach number for a constant corrected rotor speed. The conditions for best range and best endurance can be determined graphically by finding the highest points of the $N_c = $ Const curves indicated in the figure. They can also be obtained by differentiating the right-hand sides of Eqs. (42) with respect to the Mach number and setting the results equal to zero. Laborious manipulations yield the expressions

$$K_t = C_{DO}M^2 \frac{6 + (C_{DO}/KK_c^2K_t^2)_M}{4 - (KK_c^2K_t)_M}$$

$$K_t = C_{DO}M^2 \frac{4 + (C_{DO}/KK_c^2K_t^2)_M}{2 - (KK_c^2K_t)_M}$$

(43)

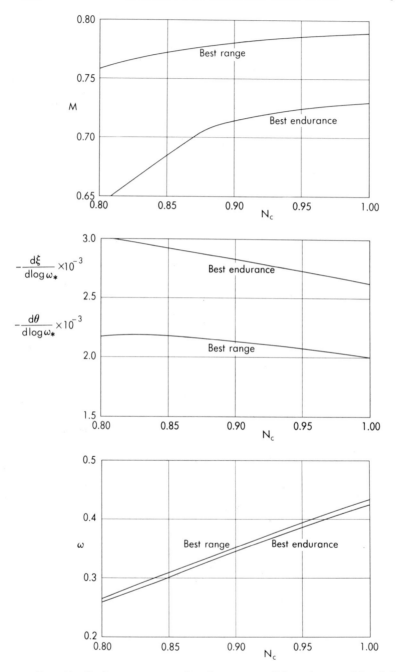

FIG. 10. Optimum range and endurance conditions for quasi-level flight with a constant corrected rotor speed.

the first of which determines the Mach number for best instantaneous range and the second, that for best instantaneous endurance. Since the left-hand sides of Eqs. (43) represent the thrust available and the right-hand sides, the thrust required, the optimum Mach numbers can be determined with the procedure described in Fig. 9-bottom. If this procedure is repeated for several corrected rotor speeds, the functions $M(N_c)$, which are the loci of the best range and endurance conditions for a given corrected rotor speed, can be determined and are plotted in Fig. 10-top; in consideration of Eqs. (43), the range and endurance factors become functions of the corrected rotor speed only and are plotted in Fig. 10-center. Also, the dimensionless wing loadings for best range and best endurance (which determine the local atmospheric pressure and, hence, the flight altitude) are given by the expressions

$$\omega = M^2 \sqrt{\frac{C_{DO}}{K}} \sqrt{\frac{2 + (C_{DO}/K_t)_M}{4 - (KK_c^2 K_t)_M}}$$

$$\omega = M^2 \sqrt{\frac{C_{DO}}{K}} \sqrt{\frac{2 + (C_{DO}/K_t)_M}{2 - (KK_c^2 K_t)_M}}$$

(44)

which are plotted in Fig. 10-bottom. In closing, the following remarks are of interest:

(a) The Mach number for best instantaneous range is higher than the Mach number at the ceiling, while the latter is higher than the Mach number for best endurance.

(b) If the corrected rotor speed is increased, the Mach numbers for best range and best endurance increase; an analogous remark applies to the corresponding optimum operating altitudes.

(c) While the endurance is favored by the use of relatively low corrected rotor speeds, the range of the swept-wing transport under consideration is a maximum when $N_c = 0.825$. Any increase in the corrected rotor speed with respect to this optimum value is accompanied by a decrease in the range and by a simultaneous increase in the Mach number. Thus, shifting the corrected rotor speed from 0.825 to 0.9 causes a 2.5% decrease in the range and a 1.8% increase in the Mach number.

(d) The optimum drag ratios are given by the expressions

$$R = \frac{2 + (C_{DO}/K_t)_M}{4 - (KK_c^2 K_t)_M}$$

$$R = \frac{2 + (C_{DO}/K_t)_M}{2 - (KK_c^2 K_t)_M}$$

(45)

the first of which applies to the range problem and the second, to the endurance problem. For the hypothetical case where the coefficients of zero-lift drag, induced drag, thrust, and specific fuel consumption are independent of the Mach number, these drag ratios reduce to $R = 1/2$ and $R = 1$, respectively, in accordance with the low-speed theory which was developed in Chapter 9.

5.2 Integral performance. Consider, now, a trajectory which is flown with constant corrected rotor speed, and assume that either the best instantaneous range condition or the best instantaneous endurance condition is maintained at all time instants. Since the weight is nowhere present in Eqs. (43), the optimum Mach number is independent of the amount of fuel consumed between the initial point and any arbitrary point of the trajectory. Since the Mach number is constant, the range and endurance factors are simultaneously constant. Consequently, after the end-conditions

$$\xi_i = 0, \qquad \theta_i = 0$$
$$\xi_f = \xi, \qquad \theta_f = \theta \tag{46}$$

are assumed and it is observed that

$$\frac{\omega_{*f}}{\omega_{*i}} = \frac{W_f}{W_i} = 1 - \zeta \tag{47}$$

where ζ is the fuel-to-weight ratio, the integration of Eqs. (42) yields the following expressions for the dimensionless range and endurance:

$$\xi = \frac{M^2}{K_c K_t} \sqrt{\frac{K_t - C_{DO}M^2}{K}} \log \frac{1}{1 - \zeta}$$
$$\theta = \frac{M}{K_c K_t} \sqrt{\frac{K_t - C_{DO}M^2}{K}} \log \frac{1}{1 - \zeta} \tag{48}$$

which can be rewritten in either of the equivalent forms

$$\xi = \frac{\omega M}{K_c K_t} \log \frac{1}{1 - \zeta} = \frac{ME}{K_c} \log \frac{1}{1 - \zeta}$$
$$\theta = \frac{\omega}{K_c K_t} \log \frac{1}{1 - \zeta} = \frac{E}{K_c} \log \frac{1}{1 - \zeta} \tag{49}$$

where E is the lift-to-drag ratio or aerodynamic efficiency.

An interesting consequence of the Mach number being constant is that the lift coefficient, the drag coefficient, the aerodynamic efficiency, and the dimensionless wing loading are constant everywhere. In particular, the fact that the dimensionless wing loading is constant implies that

$$\frac{W}{p} = \text{Const} \tag{50}$$

Hence, if a constant corrected rotor speed and a constant Mach number are maintained, fuel is consumed in such a way that the instantaneous weight is proportional to the local atmospheric pressure. The resulting flight technique is called the *cruise-climb* and has the following property: the difference between the instantaneous ceiling and the optimum operating altitude is constant along the flight path (see exercises). Since the static pressures at the endpoints of the trajectory are related by

$$\frac{p_f}{p_i} = \frac{W_f}{W_i} = 1 - \zeta \tag{51}$$

the equations of the standard atmosphere lead to the following expression for the increase in altitude:

$$h_f - h_i = \frac{a_*^2}{kg} \log \frac{1}{1 - \zeta} \tag{52}$$

6. CLIMBING FLIGHT

Climbing flight is now considered and, for didactic purposes, the discussion is divided into two parts. In the first part, the approximation $n = 1$ is employed in the evaluation of the drag function; in the second part, an exact analysis is presented.

6.1 Simplified analysis. If the approximation $n = 1$ is employed in Eq. (9), the drag function reduces to Eq. (10). Consequently, the dynamical equation on the tangent to the flight path yields the following solution for the sine of the path inclination:

$$\sin \gamma = \frac{T - D}{W} = \frac{K_t - C_{DO}M^2}{\omega} - K \frac{\omega}{M^2} \tag{53}$$

while the rate of climb becomes

$$\frac{C}{a} = M \sin \gamma = \frac{K_t - C_{DO}M^2}{\omega} M - K \frac{\omega}{M} \tag{54}$$

Hence, if $\eta = hg/a_*^2$ denotes the dimensionless altitude, the *climb economy factor* (derivative of the logarithm of the weight with respect to the dimensionless altitude) can be written in the form

$$- \frac{d \log W}{d\eta} = \frac{K_c K_t}{\omega C/a} = \frac{K_c K_t}{(K_t - C_{DO}M^2)M - K\omega^2/M} \tag{55}$$

After these functions are plotted versus the Mach number for several values of the dimensionless wing loading and for a constant corrected rotor speed (Fig. 11), the optimum climbing conditions can be determined graphically by finding the stationary points of the $\omega = $ Const curves.

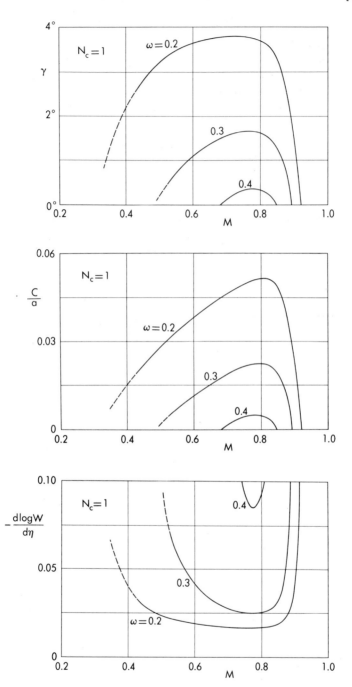

FIG. 11. Path inclination, rate of climb, and climb economy factor.

An alternative procedure consists of differentiating the right-hand sides of Eqs. (53) through (55) with respect to the Mach number and setting the results equal to zero. Laborious manipulations yield the expressions

$$\omega = M^2 \sqrt{\frac{C_{DO}}{K}} \sqrt{\frac{2 + C_{DOM} - K_{tM}K_t/C_{DO}M^2}{2 - K_M}}$$

$$\omega = M^2 \sqrt{\frac{C_{DO}}{K}} \sqrt{\frac{3 + C_{DOM} - (1 + K_{tM})K_t/C_{DO}M^2}{1 - K_M}} \qquad (56)$$

$$\omega = M^2 \sqrt{\frac{C_{DO}}{K}} \sqrt{\frac{3 + (C_{DO}/K_cK_t)_M - (1 - K_{cM})K_t/C_{DO}M^2}{1 + (K_cK_t/K)_M}}$$

which determine the Mach numbers for steepest climb, fastest climb, and most economic climb, respectively. These functions have the form $M = M(\omega, N_c)$ and are plotted in Figs. 12 through 14-left; the corresponding values for the path inclination, the rate of climb, and the fuel consumed per unit increase of altitude are indicated in Figs. 12 through 14-right. In connection with these results, the following comments are of particular importance:

(a) Since the atmospheric pressure decreases as the aircraft climbs toward higher altitudes, the parameter ω increases along the flight path.

(b) The Mach number for fastest climb is greater than the Mach number for most economic climb; in turn, the latter is greater than the Mach number for steepest climb. However, for a hypothetical engine whose product K_cK_t is independent of the Mach number, the most economic climb and the fastest climb would be identical.

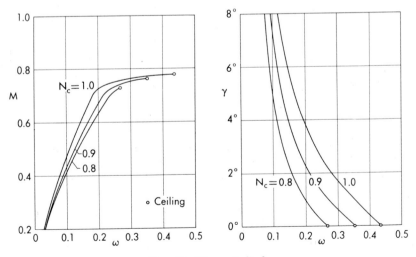

FIG. 12. Steepest climb.

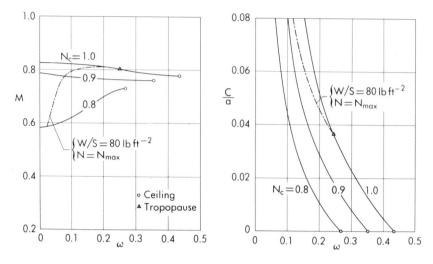

FIG. 13. Fastest climb.

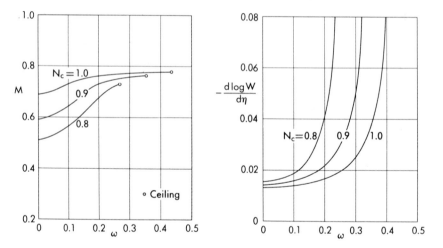

FIG. 14. Most economic climb.

(c) The climbing performance improves as the corrected rotor speed increases. Hence, the steepest climb, the fastest climb, and the most economic climb should be performed by maintaining $N = N_{max}$ everywhere.

(d) Each of the N_c = Const curves represents the climbing technique of the aircraft only if a constant corrected rotor speed is maintained. Should the aircraft employ a constant actual rotor speed N, the corrected rotor speed would increase with the altitude, and the optimum operating point would shift continuously from one $N_c =$ Const curve to another in the course of the climb (see Fig. 13 and Section 8).

(e) For some climbing paths, the variation in kinetic energy might not be negligible with respect to the variation in potential energy; under such conditions, the quasi-steady approach is no longer justified, and the results of this section must be corrected in order to account for the unsteadiness of the motion. More specifically, the actual values of the path inclination, the rate of climb, and the fuel consumed per unit increase of altitude are different from those predicted with the quasi-steady approach. The correction factor depends on the rate of variation of the kinetic energy with respect to the potential energy and can be calculated with the procedure which was developed in Chapter 8.

6.2 Exact analysis. Climbing flight is now investigated by considering the exact expression (9) for the drag function, where $n \neq 1$. By simple algebraic manipulations, the dynamical equations can be rewritten as

$$K_t - C_{DO}M^2 - \frac{K}{M^2}\omega^2 n^2 - \omega \sin \gamma = 0, \qquad n - \cos \gamma = 0 \qquad (57)$$

so that, after the load factor is eliminated, the following relationship is obtained:

$$K_t - C_{DO}M^2 - \frac{K}{M^2}\omega^2 \cos^2 \gamma - \omega \sin \gamma = 0 \qquad (58)$$

If this expression is rearranged in the form

$$\frac{K}{M^2}\omega^2 \sin^2 \gamma - \omega \sin \gamma + K_t - C_{DO}M^2 - \frac{K}{M^2}\omega^2 = 0 \qquad (59)$$

the following solution is obtained for the sine of the path inclination:

$$\sin \gamma = \frac{M^2}{2K\omega}\left[1 \overset{(+)}{-} \sqrt{1 - \frac{4K}{M^2}\left(K_t - C_{DO}M^2 - \frac{K}{M^2}\omega^2\right)}\right] \qquad (60)$$

where the lower sign is to be exclusively employed if the thrust-to-weight ratio is less than one, while both signs may yield physically possible solutions if the opposite is true. Furthermore, the rate of climb and the climb economy factor become

$$\frac{C}{a} = \frac{M^3}{2K\omega}\left[1 \overset{(+)}{-} \sqrt{1 - \frac{4K}{M^2}\left(K_t - C_{DO}M^2 - \frac{K}{M^2}\omega^2\right)}\right] \qquad (61)$$

$$-\frac{d \log W}{d\eta} = \frac{2KK_cK_t/M^3}{1 \overset{(+)}{-} \sqrt{1 - \frac{4K}{M^2}\left(K_t - C_{DO}M^2 - \frac{K}{M^2}\omega^2\right)}}$$

The discussion of the exact climbing problem is entirely analogous to the discussion of the simplified climbing problem, the only difference being that Eqs. (60) and (61) replace Eqs. (53) through (55); hence, no special comment is necessary. In closing, an interesting relationship between the present and the previous solutions can be pointed out. If x denotes the quantity

$$x = \frac{4K}{M^2}\left(K_t - C_{DO}M^2 - \frac{K\omega^2}{M^2}\right) \qquad (62)$$

and the approximation $x \ll 1$ is employed in combination with the Maclaurin approximation

$$\sqrt{1 - x} \cong 1 - \frac{x}{2} \qquad (63)$$

the present exact solutions reduce to the simplified solutions represented by Eqs. (53) through (55).

7. FLIGHT IN A HORIZONTAL PLANE

In this section, curvilinear flight in a horizontal plane is considered, and all the hypotheses of Section 8–8 are retained. Consequently, the equations of motion are written as

$$
\begin{aligned}
\dot{X} - V \cos \chi &= 0 \\
\dot{Y} - V \sin \chi &= 0 \\
T - D &= 0 \\
L \sin \mu - \frac{W}{g} V\dot{\chi} &= 0 \\
L \cos \mu - W &= 0 \\
\dot{W} + cT &= 0
\end{aligned}
\qquad (64)
$$

where X and Y denote Cartesian coordinates in the horizontal plane, while χ and μ indicate the velocity yaw and roll angles, respectively.

7.1 Solution of the dynamical equations. If the similarity parameters defined in Section 2 are employed, the dynamical equations on the tangent, the principal normal, and the binormal can be reduced to the dimensionless set

$$K_t - C_{DO}M^2 - \frac{K}{M^2}\omega^2 n^2 = 0$$

$$n \sin \mu - M\frac{\dot{\chi}a}{g} = 0 \qquad (65)$$

$$n \cos \mu - 1 = 0$$

which admits the solutions

$$n = \frac{M}{\omega} \sqrt{\frac{K_t - C_{DO}M^2}{K}}$$

$$\cos \mu = \frac{\omega}{M} \sqrt{\frac{K}{K_t - C_{DO}M^2}} \tag{66}$$

$$\frac{\dot{\chi}a}{g} = \sqrt{\frac{K_t - C_{DO}M^2}{K\omega^2} - \frac{1}{M^2}}$$

Hence, the dimensionless radius of curvature is given by

$$\frac{rg}{a^2} = \frac{M}{\dot{\chi}a/g} = \frac{M}{\sqrt{\dfrac{K_t - C_{DO}M^2}{K\omega^2} - \dfrac{1}{M^2}}} \tag{67}$$

In conclusion, the turning performance can be expressed in terms of a three-parameter family of solutions, the parameters being the Mach number, the dimensionless wing loading, and the corrected rotor speed.

7.2 Special maneuvers. Among the infinite number of properly banked horizontal turns which the aircraft can execute, there are some special turns which have particular significance. They are the turns with maximum load factor (or maximum angle of bank), maximum evolutory velocity, and minimum radius of curvature. If the right-hand side of the first of Eqs. (66) is differentiated with respect to the Mach number for constant values of the dimensionless wing loading and the corrected rotor speed and the result is equated to zero, the condition for maximum load factor is represented by

$$K_t = C_{DO}M^2 \frac{4 + (C_{DO}/K)_M}{2 + (K_t/K)_M} \tag{68}$$

Since this equation is identical with Eq. (30), the Mach number for maximum load factor is identical with the Mach number at the ceiling, regardless of the dimensionless wing loading. If a similar procedure is followed, the maximum evolutory velocity and the minimum radius of curvature can be shown to occur when the Mach number satisfies the following relationships, respectively:

$$\omega = M^2 \sqrt{\frac{C_{DO}}{2K}} \sqrt{2 + (C_{DO}/K)_M + (K/K_t)_M K_t/C_{DO}M^2}$$

$$\omega = \frac{M^2}{2} \sqrt{\frac{C_{DO}}{K}} \sqrt{(C_{DO}/K)_M + [2 + (K/K_t)_M]K_t/C_{DO}M^2} \tag{69}$$

In connection with these results, the following comments are pertinent:

(a) Since the atmospheric pressure decreases with the altitude, the parameter ω increases as the turn is executed at higher altitudes.

(b) While the Mach number for maximum load factor or maximum angle of bank is independent of the dimensionless wing loading (and, hence, independent of the altitude if the corrected rotor speed is constant), the Mach numbers for maximum evolutory velocity and minimum radius of curvature increase with ω and, hence, increase as the altitude increases.

(c) The Mach number for maximum load factor is greater than the Mach number for maximum evolutory velocity; in turn, the latter is greater than the Mach number for minimum radius of curvature.

(d) As the corrected rotor speed increases, the turning performance improves; hence, the maneuverability of the aircraft in the horizontal plane improves.

8. PERFORMANCE FOR A GIVEN ROTOR SPEED IN A SPECIFIED ATMOSPHERE

In the previous sections, the performance of a turbofan aircraft was investigated independently of the distribution of the atmospheric properties versus the altitude and represented in terms of several dimensionless groups, one of which is the corrected rotor speed of the engine. This quantity is a natural similarity parameter of the engine and, consequently, is instrumental in representing flight performance in terms of the lowest number of independent variables.

There are many problems, however, in which the behavior of the aircraft in a specified atmosphere must be determined under the assumption that the quantity which is prescribed and constant is the actual rotor speed N rather than the corrected rotor speed N_c. Consequently, before the coordinate transformation from the previous system to any new system is performed, the following question arises: What is the form of the analytical results for the case where N rather than N_c is given?

In order to answer this question, two situations must be discussed: stratospheric flight and tropospheric flight. Concerning stratospheric flight, the static temperature (and, hence, the speed of sound) is constant; since the actual rotor speed is proportional to the corrected rotor speed, both the nonoptimum and the optimum results derived in the previous sections are still valid. Regarding tropospheric flight, the static temperature (and, hence, the speed of sound) is not constant; since the actual rotor speed is not proportional to the corrected rotor speed, the conversion of the results obtained for a given N_c into those valid for a given N must be done according to the following precepts: (a) the nonoptimum performance formulas already established in terms of the corrected rotor speed are also valid for the case where the rotor speed is given; and (b) an analogous remark holds for the optimum performance, as long as the altitude is kept constant in the differentiation process; if the altitude is not constant in this process, new relationships are generally needed for the optimum performance, unless it is proved otherwise.

In connection with the previous discussion, a few particular problems are now illustrated. For example, consider the level flight equation (29), and rewrite it in the functional form

$$M = f_1(\omega, N_c) \tag{70}$$

which is equivalent to

$$\frac{V}{a} = f_1\left(\frac{2W}{kpS}, \frac{N}{N_{\max}} \frac{a_*}{a}\right) \tag{71}$$

Observe that, for a given atmospheric model (for instance, the 1959 ARDC Model Atmosphere), the pressure and the speed of sound are known functions of the altitude, that is,

$$p = p(h), \qquad a = a(h) \tag{72}$$

Consequently, if Eqs. (71) and (72) are combined, the following relationship is obtained:

$$V = f_2(h, W, N) \tag{73}$$

and, if the weight and the rotor speed are specified, reduces to the form

$$V = f_2(h) \tag{74}$$

which is represented in Fig. 15.

As a second example, consider the steepest climb, the fastest climb, and the most economic climb, and observe that the optimum solutions (56) can all be rewritten in the functional form (70). Consequently, if the weight and the rotor speed are prescribed, the optimum climbing techniques can be represented by relationships having the form (74), which are plotted in Fig. 15. Comparison of this figure and Fig. 8–14 shows that, for the particular aircraft under consideration, compressibility effects have a substantial influence on the optimum flight technique. Thus, while the velocity for fastest climb increases monotonically with the altitude in the low-speed case (Fig. 8–14), it has a maximum at the altitude of 15,000 ft if compressibility effects are considered. Also, while the velocity for most economic climb increases monotonically with the altitude in the low-speed case (Fig. 8–14), it has two stationary points if compressibility effects are considered: a maximum at the altitude of 30,000 ft and a minimum at the tropopause.

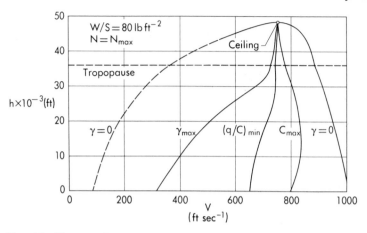

FIG. 15. Characteristic velocities for powered flight in a vertical plane.

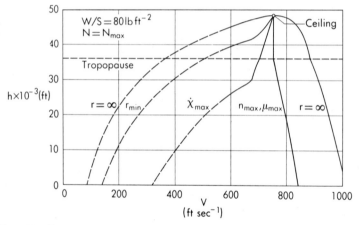

FIG. 16. Characteristic velocities for powered flight in a horizontal plane.

As a third example, consider curvilinear flight in a horizontal plane, and focus attention on the turning maneuvers with maximum load factor, maximum evolutory velocity, and minimum radius of curvature. Observe that the optimum solutions (68) and (69) can all be rewritten in the functional form (70). Consequently, if the weight and the rotor speed are specified, the optimum turning conditions can be represented by relationships having the form (74), which are plotted in Fig. 16. Comparison of this figure and Fig. 8–18 shows that compressibility effects have a considerable influence on the optimum flight conditions. In particular, while the velocity for maximum load factor increases with the altitude in the low-speed case (Fig. 8–18), the same is not true if compressibility effects are included.

9. PERFORMANCE OF AN AIRCRAFT WITH AN ARBITRARY POLAR

In the previous sections, the performance of an aircraft was calculated under the assumption of a parabolic polar. A more general case occurs when the polar is arbitrary, that is, obeys the relationship

$$C_D = C_D(C_L, M) \tag{75}$$

in which C_D is the drag coefficient, C_L the lift coefficient, and M the Mach number. The treatment of this case is conceptually analogous to that developed for the parabolic case and, hence, is not systematically repeated. The main difference is that analytical solutions are no longer possible, so that graphical methods must be employed. In this connection, the main results relative to gliding flight, level flight, quasi-level flight, climbing flight, and turning flight are summarized in Table 1 and are now illustrated by means of a few examples.

Consider gliding flight, and multiply the dynamical equations by the factor $2/kpS$. Simple manipulations yield the results

$$\omega\gamma + C_D M^2 = 0, \qquad \omega - C_L M^2 = 0 \tag{76}$$

so that the glide angle and the sinking speed become

$$-\gamma = \frac{C_D M^2}{\omega}, \qquad -\frac{C}{a} = \frac{C_D M^3}{\omega} \tag{77}$$

Consequently, the following procedure is suggested for each given combination of dimensionless wing loading and Mach number: (a) determine the equilibrium lift coefficient from the second of Eqs. (76); (b) determine the drag coefficient from the polar of the vehicle; and (c) calculate the glide angle and the sinking speed with Eqs. (77). If this procedure is repeated several times, the functions $\gamma(M, \omega)$ and $(C/a)(M, \omega)$ which solve the glide problem can be determined. After these functions are plotted as in Fig. 3, the optimum conditions (flattest glide and glide with minimum sinking speed) can be determined graphically.

As a second example, consider level flight, and multiply the dynamical equations by the factor $2/kpS$. Simple manipulations yield the relationships

$$K_t - C_D M^2 = 0, \qquad \omega - C_L M^2 = 0 \tag{78}$$

which must be solved with the following procedure for each given combination of corrected rotor speed and Mach number: (a) determine the modified thrust coefficient from the engine performance diagrams; (b) calculate the drag coefficient from the first of Eqs. (78); (c) determine the lift coefficient from the polar of the vehicle; and (d) calculate the

TABLE 1

PERFORMANCE OF AN AIRCRAFT WITH AN ARBITRARY POLAR

Flight condition	Physical magnitude	Dynamical equations
Gliding flight	$-\gamma = \dfrac{C_D M^2}{\omega}$ $-\dfrac{C}{a} = \dfrac{C_D M^3}{\omega}$	$\omega\gamma + C_D M^2 = 0$ $\omega - C_L M^2 = 0$
Level flight	$-\dfrac{d\xi}{d\log\omega} = \dfrac{EM}{K_c}$ $-\dfrac{d\theta}{d\log\omega} = \dfrac{E}{K_c}$	$K_t - C_D M^2 = 0$ $\omega - C_L M^2 = 0$
Quasi-level flight (stratosphere)	$-\dfrac{d\xi}{d\log\omega_*} = \dfrac{EM}{K_c}$ $-\dfrac{d\theta}{d\log\omega_*} = \dfrac{E}{K_c}$	$K_t - C_D M^2 = 0$ $\omega - C_L M^2 = 0$
Climbing flight	$\sin\gamma = \dfrac{K_t - C_D M^2}{\omega}$ $\dfrac{C}{a} = \dfrac{K_t - C_D M^2}{\omega} M$ $-\dfrac{d\log W}{d\eta} = \dfrac{K_c K_t}{(K_t - C_D M^2)M}$	$K_t - \omega\sin\gamma - C_D M^2 = 0$ $\omega\cos\gamma - C_L M^2 = 0$
Turning flight	$n = \dfrac{C_L M^2}{\omega}$ $\cos\mu = \dfrac{\omega}{C_L M^2}$ $\left(\dfrac{\dot\chi a}{g}\right)^2 = \left(\dfrac{C_L M}{\omega}\right)^2 - \dfrac{1}{M^2}$ $\left(\dfrac{a^2}{rg}\right)^2 = \left(\dfrac{C_L}{\omega}\right)^2 - \dfrac{1}{M^4}$	$K_t - C_D M^2 = 0$ $n\sin\mu - M\dfrac{\dot\chi a}{g} = 0$ $n\cos\mu - 1 = 0$

dimensionless wing loading from the second of Eqs. (78). If this procedure is repeated several times, the function $\omega(M, N_c)$ which solves the level flight problem can be determined. After this function is plotted as in Fig. 5, the level flight Mach number corresponding to given values of the dimensionless wing loading and the corrected rotor speed can be determined graphically.

10. SUPERSONIC AIRCRAFT PERFORMANCE

In the previous sections, a general method for analyzing the performance of high-speed aircraft was developed, and its application to a high subsonic–low transonic aircraft was demonstrated. In this section, the case of an aircraft designed for supersonic speeds is considered. Even though the analytic method is identical with that employed for the subsonic aircraft, the engineering results can be considerably different, depending on the characteristics of the aircraft and the engine. Some of the essential differences between supersonic aircraft performance and subsonic aircraft performance are now illustrated with reference, for the sake of discussion, to a Mach 3, delta-wing transport powered by turbojet engines. No systematic analysis is presented in that only a few important topics are discussed.

10.1 Aerodynamic drag. The aerodynamic drag of a supersonic aircraft in flight with load factor $n = 1$ is expressed by Eq. (10) and is plotted in Fig. 17 versus the Mach number for several values of the dimensionless wing loading. While the drag has only one stationary point for a subsonic aircraft, it may have one or three stationary points for a supersonic aircraft, depending on the dimensionless wing loading. When three stationary points exist, the first is generally subsonic and yields a relative minimum for the drag, the second is generally transonic and yields a relative maximum, and the third is generally supersonic and yields a relative minimum. In conclusion, the behavior of the supersonic

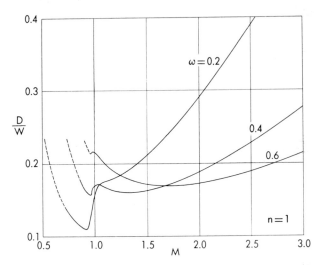

FIG. 17. Drag per unit weight versus Mach number and dimensionless wing loading.

aircraft is considerably different from that of the subsonic aircraft from the drag standpoint, a circumstance which has a considerable influence on the entire performance problem.

10.2 Level flight. For a supersonic aircraft, the totality of level flight solutions is still represented by Eq. (29) and is plotted in Fig. 18 in the Mach number–dimensionless wing loading domain for several values of the corrected rotor speed. For given values of the dimensionless wing loading and the corrected rotor speed, there are only two solutions for a subsonic aircraft (Fig. 5), while there may be two or four solutions for a supersonic aircraft. In addition, while the ceiling associated with a given corrected rotor speed is unique for a subsonic aircraft, it may not be unique for a supersonic aircraft. More specifically, there exists a small interval of the corrected rotor speed for which two ceilings occur, one subsonic and one supersonic.

10.3 Quasi-level flight. The range factor of a supersonic aircraft in quasi-level flight with a constant corrected rotor speed is represented by the first of Eqs. (42) and is plotted in Fig. 19 versus the Mach number for several values of the corrected rotor speed. While the range factor of a subsonic aircraft exhibits only one stationary point (Fig. 9), the range factor of a supersonic aircraft exhibits three stationary points: one subsonic, one transonic, and one supersonic. The first point yields a relative maximum, the second yields a relative minimum, and the third a relative maximum. For the particular example under consideration, the

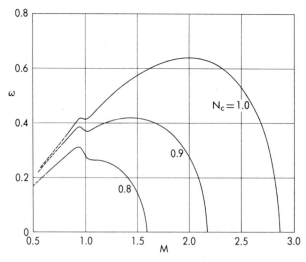

FIG. 18. Level flight solutions.

supersonic maximum is also an absolute maximum; hence, the supersonic solution must be preferred to the subsonic solution not only from the time standpoint but also from the range standpoint.

10.4 Climbing Flight.* There exist two important differences between the climb of subsonic aircraft and the climb of supersonic aircraft. In the first place, the solutions for the optimum climbing performance are single-valued in the subsonic case but may be multivalued for the supersonic case (this point has been already emphasized in connection with level and quasi-level flight and, hence, is not reiterated here). In the second place, while it is logical to calculate the climbing performance of a subsonic aircraft using the quasi-steady approach in combination with the kinetic energy correction developed in Chapter 8, the same might not be true for a supersonic aircraft. This point can be readily clarified, if the following two examples are considered:

(a) For a subsonic aircraft which is transferred from take-off speed and sea level to $M = 0.9$ and $h = 35,000$ ft, the variation in kinetic energy is about one-third the variation in potential energy. On the other hand, for a supersonic aircraft which is transferred from take-off speed and sea level to $M = 3$ and $h = 60,000$ ft, the variation in kinetic energy is more than twice the variation in potential energy.

(b) For a climb with constant dynamic pressure, the acceleration factor, that is, the ratio of the accelerated rate of climb C_a to the quasi-steady rate of climb C_s is given by Eq. (9–122) and is plotted in Fig. 20

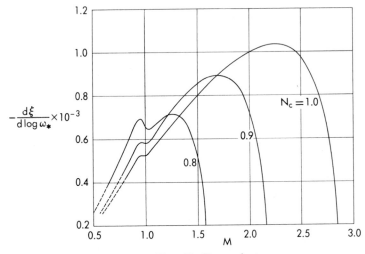

FIG. 19. Range factor.

---

* The conclusions of this section are also valid for descending flight.

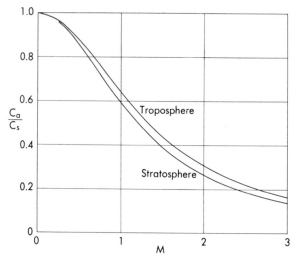

FIG. 20. Kinetic energy correction for flight with constant dynamic pressure.

versus the Mach number for both tropospheric and stratospheric flight. Thus, for the particular case of stratospheric flight, the accelerated rate of climb is 85% of its quasi-steady value at $M = 0.5$ but 26% at $M = 2$.

From these examples, it is concluded that the quasi-steady approach in combination with the kinetic energy correction yields a reasonably accurate prediction of the optimum climbing performance for subsonic aircraft but perhaps not for supersonic aircraft. This is due to the fact that the term neglected in the first approximation (the kinetic energy term) is small with respect to that accounted for (the potential energy term) for a subsonic aircraft but not for a supersonic aircraft. Thus, a radically different approach to the optimum climb performance of supersonic aircraft is in order and must be carried out with due regard to the inertia terms in the formulation of the problem. More specifically, the flight path can no longer be examined from a local point of view but must be investigated from an integral point of view, that is, with the methods of the Calculus of Variations developed in Volume 2.

EXERCISES

1. Assuming constant altitude flight, prove that the condition for a stationary zero-lift drag is that

$$C_{DOM} = -2 \tag{79}$$

Generally speaking, this equation has no real solutions, as can be shown by numerical analyses; hence, the zero-lift drag is a monotonically increasing function of the Mach number.

2. Assuming constant altitude flight, prove that the induced drag is stationary when the Mach number satisfies the relationship

$$K_M = 2 \tag{80}$$

Numerical analyses show that this equation may have imaginary or real solutions, depending on the aircraft configuration. In the former case, the induced drag is a monotonically decreasing function of the Mach number; in the latter case, the induced drag generally has a minimum in the low transonic region and a maximum in the high transonic region.

3. Consider an aircraft in level flight. Assuming that the Mach number is given, show that the drag is a minimum at the altitude where

$$R = 1 \tag{81}$$

which implies that

$$\frac{E}{E_{\max}} = 1 \tag{82}$$

On the other hand, if the altitude is prescribed, show that the drag is a minimum when the drag ratio satisfies the relationship

$$R = \frac{2 + C_{DOM}}{2 - K_M} \tag{83}$$

which implies that

$$\frac{E}{E_{\max}} = \frac{2\sqrt{(2 + C_{DOM})(2 - K_M)}}{4 + (C_{DO}/K)_M} \tag{84}$$

For the particular case of low subsonic flight, the logarithmic derivatives of the aerodynamic coefficients with respect to the Mach number vanish; hence, Eqs. (83) and (84) become identical with Eqs. (81) and (82).

4. Consider gliding flight in an isothermal atmosphere, and denote by λ a constant and by

$$\frac{p}{p_o} = \exp\left(-\frac{h}{\lambda}\right) \tag{85}$$

the pressure-altitude relationship. Show that the range X and the endurance t can be expressed in the form

$$\frac{X}{\lambda} = \int_{\omega_i}^{\omega_f} \frac{d\omega}{\gamma(M, \omega)\omega}, \qquad \frac{ta}{\lambda} = \int_{\omega_i}^{\omega_f} \frac{d\omega}{\dfrac{C}{a}(M, \omega)\omega} \tag{86}$$

Hence, by specifying the relationship between the Mach number and the dimensionless wing loading (for instance, flattest glide, glide with minimum sinking speed, constant Mach number glide), the range and the endurance can be determined. For the particular case of a constant Mach number glide, prove that the following expressions hold:

$$\frac{X}{\lambda} = \frac{tV}{\lambda} = 2E_{\max} \arctan \frac{\sqrt{R_i} - \sqrt{R_f}}{1 + \sqrt{R_i R_f}} \tag{87}$$

where R is the drag ratio.

5. Consider level flight with a constant Mach number. Denoting by ξ the dimensionless range, θ the dimensionless endurance, and R the drag ratio, show that the following expressions hold:

$$\frac{\xi}{M} = \theta = \frac{2E_{\max}}{K_c} \arctan \frac{\sqrt{R_i} - \sqrt{R_f}}{1 + \sqrt{R_i R_f}} \tag{88}$$

6. Consider the stratospheric quasi-level flight of a turbofan aircraft, and assume that the corrected rotor speed is constant. Show that the difference between the instantaneous ceiling and the operational altitude for the best range or the best endurance is a constant at all the points of the flight path.

7. Consider the simplified climbing flight with constant corrected rotor speed and constant Mach number. Assume that the atmosphere is isothermal (see Exercise 4), and neglect the effect of the fuel consumption on the path inclination and the rate of climb. Show that the distance traveled X, the time to climb t, and the fuel-to-weight ratio ζ are given by the approximate relationships

$$\frac{X}{\lambda M} = \frac{ta}{\lambda} = x \log \left(\frac{1 + \alpha_f}{1 - \alpha_f} \frac{1 - \alpha_i}{1 + \alpha_i} \right)$$

$$\zeta = 1 - \left(\frac{\alpha_i^2}{1 - \alpha_i^2} \frac{1 - \alpha_f^2}{\alpha_f^2} \right)^y \tag{89}$$

where

$$x = \frac{1}{2\sqrt{K(K_t - C_{DO}M^2)}}$$

$$y = \frac{K_c K_t}{2k(K_t - C_{DO}M^2)M} \tag{90}$$

$$\alpha = \frac{\omega}{M} \sqrt{\frac{K}{K_t - C_{DO}M^2}}$$

8. Consider the exact climbing flight of a turbofan aircraft whose polar is parabolic. Show that the equilibrium lift coefficient associated with given values of the corrected rotor speed, the dimensionless wing loading, and the Mach number is defined by the biquadratic equation

$$AC_L^4 + BC_L^2 + C = 0 \tag{91}$$

where

$$A = K^2$$

$$B = 1 + 2K\left(C_{DO} - \frac{K_t}{M^2}\right) \tag{92}$$

$$C = \left(C_{DO} - \frac{K_t}{M^2}\right)^2 - \frac{\omega^2}{M^4}$$

9. Consider the exact climbing flight of a turbofan aircraft whose polar is arbitrary, that is, obeys the relationship

$$C_D = C_D(C_L, M) \tag{93}$$

Show that the equilibrium lift coefficient associated with given values of the corrected rotor speed, the dimensionless wing loading, and the Mach number is defined by the relationship

$$\left(C_D - \frac{K_t}{M^2}\right)^2 + C_L^2 = \frac{\omega^2}{M^4} \tag{94}$$

With reference to the drag coefficient-lift coefficient domain, this relationship is a circle of radius ω/M^2 and center at $K_t/M^2, 0$. Consequently, the equilibrium lift coefficient can be determined graphically by intersecting the circle (94) with the drag polar (93).

References

1. HAYES, W. D., *Performance Methods for High-Speed Aircraft*, Journal of the Aerospace Sciences, Vol. 12, No. 3, 1945.
2. EDELBAUM, T., *Maximum Range Flight Paths*, United Aircraft Corporation, Report No. R-22465-24, 1955.
3. LEBEDEV, V. B., *Calculation of the Flight Characteristics of a Supersonic Airplane with Turbojet Engines*, The Rand Corporation, Translation No. T-120, 1959.
4. ANONYMOUS, *Jet Transport Performance Methods*, The Boeing Company, Document No. D6-1420, 1959.
5. STAFF OF THE LANGLEY RESEARCH CENTER, *The Supersonic Transport. A Technical Summary*, NASA TN No. D-423, 1960.

6. MIELE, A. and LUSTY, A. H., *Performance Analysis of High-Speed Aircraft*, Boeing Scientific Research Laboratories, Flight Sciences Laboratory, TR No. 44, 1961.

7. MIELE, A., *Lagrange Multipliers and Quasi-Steady Flight Mechanics*, Journal of the Aerospace Sciences, Vol. 26, No. 9, 1959.

8. MIELE, A., *Variational Approach to the Stratospheric Cruise of a Turbojet-Powered Aircraft*, ZFW, Vol. 6, No. 9, 1958.

Part III

NONSTEADY FLIGHT OVER
A FLAT EARTH

INTRODUCTION TO PART III

The analysis of the flight paths of rocket-powered aircraft, ballistic missiles, satellite vehicles, skip vehicles, and hypervelocity gliders as well as the study of the transient behavior of aircraft propelled by air-breathing jet engines require that the nonsteady point of view be adopted, that is, that the acceleration terms be included in the equations of motion. When this approach is used, the flight path can no longer be treated from a local point of view but must be considered in its entirety. Consequently, any information on the behavior of an aircraft or a missile in flight can only be deduced by integrating the equations of motion subject to the appropriate command programs for the angle of attack, the thrust modulus, and the thrust direction as well as to the appropriate initial and/or final conditions.

Because of the complicated distribution of the physical properties of the atmosphere versus the altitude as well as the complicated behavior of the drag function at high subsonic, transonic, and supersonic speeds, closed form solutions are not usually attainable in nonsteady flight. Consequently, numerical solutions by means of digital computing equipment are necessary (*precision approach*). However, closed form solutions are possible if particular hypotheses are accepted for the distribution of the atmospheric properties versus the altitude, the flow regime, and the characteristics of the flight path (*feasibility approach*). Since feasibility studies have led to the greatest conceptual advances in the engineering applications of Flight Mechanics in the past, they must also be expected to do so in the future; therefore, analytical solutions are emphasized throughout Part III.

With these ideas in mind, the succeeding chapters consider the nonsteady flight of a vehicle over a flat Earth in conjunction with the following topics. First, the unpowered flight and the powered flight of an aircraft operating at low subsonic speeds are analyzed in Chapter 12. Next, the other extreme of the velocity spectrum, the hypervelocity regime, is investigated in Chapter 13 in connection with sounding rockets, ballistic missiles, glide vehicles, and skip vehicles. Since problems of a thermal nature are of paramount importance for hypervelocity vehicles, they are considered in Chapter 14. Then, Chapters 15 and 16 analyze the performance of a single-stage rocket and a multi-stage rocket in a vacuum. Finally, Chapter 17 presents the effects of the aerodynamic forces on the performance of sounding rockets, air-to-air missiles, and rocket-powered aircraft.

CHAPTER 12

NONSTEADY AIRCRAFT PERFORMANCE

1. INTRODUCTION

In the previous four chapters, the performance of an aircraft was analyzed from a quasi-steady point of view, that is, the inertia terms appearing in the equations of motion were neglected. In this chapter, the more difficult case where the inertia terms are significant is considered in connection with flight in a vertical plane over a flat Earth with the thrust tangent to the flight path. In the light of these hypotheses and of Eq. (7–6), Eqs. (4–42) are rewritten in the form

$$\dot{X} - V \cos \gamma = 0$$

$$\dot{h} - V \sin \gamma = 0$$

$$T - D - W \left(\sin \gamma + \frac{\dot{V}}{g} \right) = 0 \qquad (1)$$

$$L - W \left(\cos \gamma + \frac{V \dot{\gamma}}{g} \right) = 0$$

$$\dot{W} + cT = 0$$

where X denotes the horizontal distance, h the altitude, V the velocity, γ the path inclination, W the weight, D the drag, L the lift, T the thrust, c the specific fuel consumption, g the acceleration of gravity, and the dot sign a derivative with respect to time.

1.1 General integration problem. If the drag is assumed to have the form $D = D(h, V, L)$ and if the thrust and the specific fuel consumption are expressed as $T = T(h, V, \pi)$ and $c = c(h, V, \pi)$, where π is the control parameter of the engine, the previous differential system has one independent variable, the time, and seven dependent variables (X, h, V, γ, W, L, π). Therefore, there are two degrees of freedom, which is logical since the flight path can be changed by varying the elevator position and the power setting. Thus, for a given set of initial conditions for X, h, V, γ, W, infinite trajectories exist, more specifically, one trajectory for each arbitrarily prescribed pair of functions $L(t)$, $\pi(t)$ or equivalent conditions. Because of the dissipative nature of the aerodynamic forces, no first integral can be written for the general case; consequently, the study of particular flight conditions is of great interest from an engineering point of view.

1.2 Numerical versus analytical solutions. Because of the complicated distribution of the physical characteristics of the atmosphere versus the altitude as well as the complicated behavior of the drag function at high subsonic, transonic, and supersonic speeds, closed form solutions are not usually attainable. Consequently, numerical solutions by means of digital computing equipment are necessary. However, closed form solutions are possible if particular hypotheses are accepted for the distribution of the atmospheric properties versus the altitude, the flow regime (e.g., subsonic), and the characteristics of the flight path. With this point of view in mind, the following special problems are now considered: glide paths flown at constant altitude, glide paths flown with constant angle of attack, level paths flown with constant thrust, conservative paths flown with constant load factor, and conservative paths flown with constant lift coefficient. From the same point of view, take-off and landing performance is also investigated in this chapter, even though the third and the fourth of Eqs. (1) must be modified by the inclusion of additional terms which are due to the physical contact of the aircraft with the ground.

1.3 Simplified problem. Except for the class of glide paths, the fifth of Eqs. (1) always interacts with the remaining four equations. Consequently, the equations composing the previous differential system must be integrated simultaneously; however, there are many problems in which the variation of the weight due to the fuel consumed is small with respect to the initial weight. For these problems, Eqs. (1) become uncoupled, in the sense that the first four equations can be integrated independently of the fifth by regarding the weight as a constant. In turn, the fifth equation is employed a posteriori to determine the fuel consumed during the maneuver under consideration.

2. GLIDE AT CONSTANT ALTITUDE

The problem of decelerating a glider from one velocity to another in level flight is now considered. If the conditions $\gamma = 0$ and $T = 0$ are imposed, the second and the fifth of Eqs. (1) can be integrated to give $h = \text{Const}$ and $W = \text{Const}$, respectively. The remaining equations simplify to

$$\dot{X} - V = 0$$

$$\dot{V} + g\frac{D}{W} = 0 \tag{2}$$

$$L - W = 0$$

Because of the third of these equations, the expression $C_L V^2$ is constant everywhere; therefore, owing to the progressive decrease in the speed, the angle of attack must be continuously increased in order to satisfy the condition of dynamic equilibrium on the normal to the flight path.

A mathematical consequence of the kinematic relationship in the horizontal direction and the dynamic relationship on the tangent to the flight path is the set of differential equations

$$\frac{dX}{dV} = -\frac{WV}{gD}$$

$$\frac{dt}{dV} = -\frac{W}{gD} \tag{3}$$

whose integration must generally be accomplished by means of approximate procedures. However, an analytical solution is possible if the drag polar is assumed to be parabolic with constant coefficients (Ref. 10).

For such a case, it is convenient to introduce the dimensionless coordinates (see Chapter 9)

$$u = \frac{V}{V_R}, \qquad \xi = \frac{Xg}{V_R^2 E_{\max}}, \qquad \theta = \frac{tg}{V_R E_{\max}} \tag{4}$$

where

$$E_{\max} = \frac{1}{2\sqrt{KC_{DO}}} \tag{5}$$

is the maximum aerodynamic efficiency of an aircraft with zero-lift drag coefficient C_{DO} and induced drag factor K and where the reference velocity

$$V_R = \sqrt{\frac{2W}{\rho S}} \sqrt[4]{\frac{K}{C_{DO}}} \tag{6}$$

is the speed at which minimum drag occurs in level flight. Because of the equation of motion on the normal to the flight path, the drag per unit

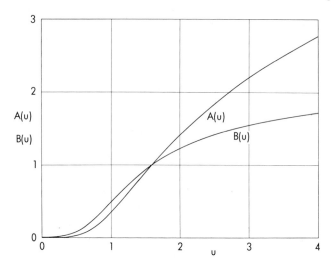

FIG. 1. The functions $A(u)$ and $B(u)$.

weight can be written in the form

$$\frac{D}{W} = \frac{1}{2E_{\text{max}}}\left(u^2 + \frac{1}{u^2}\right) \tag{7}$$

Consequently, Eqs. (3) yield the differential set

$$\frac{d\xi}{du} = -\frac{2u^3}{1+u^4}$$

$$\frac{d\theta}{du} = -\frac{2u^2}{1+u^4} \tag{8}$$

whose general integral is given by

$$\xi = -A(u) + \text{Const}$$

$$\theta = -B(u) + \text{Const} \tag{9}$$

where the functions A and B are defined as

$$A(u) = \frac{1}{2}\log(1+u^4)$$

$$B(u) = \frac{1}{\sqrt{2}}\left[\arctan\frac{u\sqrt{2}}{1-u^2} - \frac{1}{2}\log\frac{1+u^2+u\sqrt{2}}{1+u^2-u\sqrt{2}}\right] \tag{10}$$

and are plotted in Fig. 1 versus the dimensionless speed.

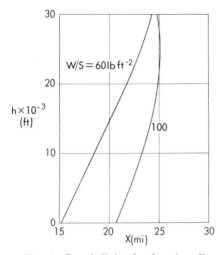

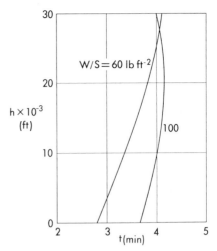

FIG. 2. Level flight deceleration distance of a typical jet transport.

FIG. 3. Level flight deceleration time of a typical jet transport.

In conclusion, if a glider is decelerated at constant altitude between prescribed initial and final velocities and if the following end-conditions are considered:

$$\xi_i = \theta_i = 0, \qquad \xi_f = \xi, \qquad \theta_f = \theta \qquad (11)$$

the distance and the time are given by

$$X = \frac{V_R^2 E_{\max}}{g} [A(u_i) - A(u_f)]$$

$$t = \frac{V_R E_{\max}}{g} [B(u_i) - B(u_f)] \qquad (12)$$

Since the reference velocity depends on the altitude, the deceleration distance and time also depend on the altitude. In this connection, a typical example is plotted in Figs. 2 and 3 for the end-conditions

$$V_i = 750 \text{ ft sec}^{-1}, \qquad V_f = 300 \text{ ft sec}^{-1}$$

and for a jet transport aircraft whose aerodynamic characteristics are

$$C_{DO} = 0.015, \qquad K = 0.042$$

Two values of the wing loading are considered, that is, 60 and 100 lb ft^{-2}. The graphs indicate that the low wing loading aircraft decelerates in a shorter distance and time near sea level than the high wing loading aircraft, while the opposite occurs in the neighborhood of the tropopause.

The physical justification for this result lies in the fact that, of the two vehicles compared here, the low wing loading aircraft has a greater zero-lift drag and a smaller induced drag. Since, for the particular example under consideration, the zero-lift drag is the predominant component of the drag at low altitudes, the low wing loading aircraft has a greater total drag and, hence, better deceleration performance at low altitudes. Conversely, since the induced drag is the predominant component of the drag at high altitudes, the high wing loading aircraft has a greater over-all drag and, hence, better deceleration performance at high altitudes.

3. GLIDE AT CONSTANT ANGLE OF ATTACK

This section considers the class of gliding paths which are smooth and shallow, that is, glide trajectories which are characterized by a negligible curvature and a small inclination with respect to the horizon. Because of the weight being constant and because of the hypotheses

$$\cos \gamma \cong 1, \quad \sin \gamma \cong \gamma, \quad \frac{V\dot{\gamma}}{g} \ll 1 \tag{13}$$

Eqs. (1) simplify to

$$\dot{X} - V = 0$$
$$\dot{h} - V\gamma = 0$$
$$\dot{V} + g\left(\gamma + \frac{D}{W}\right) = 0 \tag{14}$$
$$L - W = 0$$

If the relative density $\sigma = \rho/\rho_o$ and the reference velocity

$$V_R = \sqrt{\frac{2W}{\rho_o S}} \tag{15}$$

are introduced, the equation of motion on the normal to the flight path becomes

$$V = \frac{V_R}{\sqrt{C_L \sigma}} \tag{16}$$

Furthermore, if the aerodynamic efficiency is denoted by $E = C_L/C_D$ and it is observed that $D = W/E$ and $\gamma = \dot{h}/V$, the equation of motion on the tangent to the flight path and the kinematic relationship in the horizontal direction yield the differential set

$$\frac{dX}{E} + dh + \frac{V \, dV}{g} = 0$$
$$\frac{dt}{E} + \frac{dh}{V} + \frac{dV}{g} = 0 \tag{17}$$

which is now integrated with the assumptions that the drag polar has the form $C_D = C_D(C_L)$ and that the lift coefficient is constant (Ref. 10). Hence, the distance is given by

$$\frac{X}{E} + h + \frac{V^2}{2g} = \text{Const} \tag{18}$$

while the time is expressed in the form

$$\frac{t}{E} + \sqrt{C_L} \frac{I(h)}{V_R} + \frac{V}{g} = \text{Const} \tag{19}$$

where the function $I(h)$ is defined as (Fig. 9-2)

$$I(h) = \int_0^h \sqrt{\sigma} \, dh \tag{20}$$

In conclusion, Eqs. (16), (18), and (19) supply the solution of the proposed problem in parametric form, the parameter being the instantaneous altitude. More specifically, Eq. (16) determines the velocity distribution at all points of the flight path. Once the velocity is known, Eq. (18) determines the distance, and Eq. (19), the time. Since the instantaneous inclination of the flight path is given by

$$\gamma = -\frac{1}{E} \frac{1}{1 - \frac{V^2}{2g} \frac{d \log \rho}{dh}} \tag{21}$$

both the altitude and the velocity continuously decrease along the trajectory.

Consider, now, a trajectory flown between given initial and final conditions, and assume that

$$X_i = 0, \quad t_i = 0, \quad X_f = X, \quad t_f = t \tag{22}$$

After the distance and time integrals are written in the form

$$X = E\left(h_i - h_f + \frac{V_i^2 - V_f^2}{2g}\right)$$

$$t = \frac{E\sqrt{C_L}}{V_R}[I(h_i) - I(h_f)] + E\frac{V_i - V_f}{g} \tag{23}$$

it becomes clear that the glider is capable of converting both potential and kinetic energies into the work necessary to achieve range in a resisting medium. Since the transformation factor is the aerodynamic efficiency, it is concluded that, if the total energy or energy height

$$h_e = h + \frac{V^2}{2g} \tag{24}$$

is prescribed at both the initial and final points, the maximum range is achieved by flying at the angle of attack which maximizes the aerodynamic efficiency. On the other hand, the maximum endurance is achieved by flying at a higher angle of attack, more specifically, one between that which maximizes the function E and that which maximizes the function $E\sqrt{C_L}$.

3.1 **Quasi-steady solution.** If the variation in kinetic energy is small with respect to the variation in potential energy,* the previous equations simplify to

$$X = E(h_i - h_f)$$
$$t = \frac{E\sqrt{C_L}}{V_R} [I(h_i) - I(h_f)] \tag{25}$$

Consequently, under the assumption that the initial and final altitudes are given, the range is proportional to the aerodynamic efficiency, while the endurance is proportional to $E\sqrt{C_L}$, a result already known from Chapter 10.

4. ACCELERATION AT CONSTANT ALTITUDE

The problem of accelerating an aircraft from one velocity to another at constant altitude is now considered. If the condition $\gamma = 0$ is imposed, the kinematic relationship on the vertical direction can be integrated to give $h = $ Const. Furthermore, if the variation in the weight due to the fuel consumption is neglected in the dynamical equations, that is, if the present problem is treated within the framework of the simplified approach outlined in Section 1.3, the motion of the vehicle is described by the differential set

$$\dot{X} - V = 0$$
$$\dot{V} - \frac{g}{W}(T - D) = 0 \tag{26}$$
$$L - W = 0$$

Because of the third of these equations, the product $C_L V^2$ is constant along the trajectory; since the velocity is increasing, the angle of attack

---

* This approximation is equivalent to neglecting the inertia term in the equation of motion on the tangent to the flight path.

must be continuously decreased in order to satisfy the condition of dynamic equilibrium on the normal to the flight path.

A mathematical consequence of the kinematic relationship in the horizontal direction and the dynamic relationship on the tangent to the flight path are the differential equations

$$\frac{dX}{dV} = \frac{W}{g} \frac{V}{T - D}$$

$$\frac{dt}{dV} = \frac{W}{g} \frac{1}{T - D} \tag{27}$$

whose integration must usually be carried out by means of approximate procedures. However, an analytical solution is possible if it is assumed that the thrust is independent of the velocity and that the drag polar is parabolic with constant coefficients. After the dimensionless coordinates defined by Eqs. (4) are introduced, the following differential relationships are obtained:

$$\frac{d\xi}{du} = -\frac{2u^3}{u^4 - 2zu^2 + 1}$$

$$\frac{d\theta}{du} = -\frac{2u^2}{u^4 - 2zu^2 + 1} \tag{28}$$

where $z = TE_{\max}/W$ is the thrust-to-minimum drag ratio. Consequently, the integration process leads to

$$\xi = -A(z, u) + \text{Const}$$

$$\theta = -B(z, u) + \text{Const} \tag{29}$$

where the functions A and B are defined as (Figs. 4 and 5)

$$A(z, u) = \frac{1}{u_1^2 - u_2^2} [u_1^2 \log(u_1^2 - u^2) - u_2^2 \log(u^2 - u_2^2)]$$

$$B(z, u) = \frac{1}{u_1^2 - u_2^2} \left[-u_1 \log \frac{u_1 + u}{u_1 - u} + u_2 \log \frac{u + u_2}{u - u_2} \right] \tag{30}$$

and where

$$u_1 = \sqrt{z + \sqrt{z^2 - 1}}, \qquad u_2 = \sqrt{z - \sqrt{z^2 - 1}} \tag{31}$$

denote the solutions of the biquadratic equation which results by setting the denominator of the expressions on the right-hand side of Eqs. (28) equal to zero; hence, u_1 and u_2 are the two velocities which are physically possible in unaccelerated level flight with the given thrust.

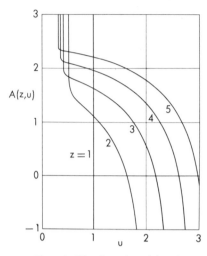

FIG. 4. The function $A(z, u)$.   FIG. 5. The function $B(z, u)$.

In conclusion, if an aircraft operating with a constant thrust is accelerated at constant altitude between prescribed initial and final velocities and if the following end-conditions are assumed:

$$\xi_i = \theta_i = 0, \qquad \xi_f = \xi, \qquad \theta_f = \theta \tag{32}$$

the distance and the time are given by

$$X = \frac{V_R^2 E_{\max}}{g} [A(z, u_i) - A(z, u_f)]$$

$$t = \frac{V_R E_{\max}}{g} [B(z, u_i) - B(z, u_f)] \tag{33}$$

Notice that the reference velocity depends on the altitude and that, if the power setting is given, the thrust depends on the altitude; hence, the time and the distance necessary to obtain a given increase in velocity with a given power setting are functions of the altitude. In this connection, a typical example is plotted in Figs. 6 and 7 for the end-conditions

$$V_i = 300 \text{ ft sec}^{-1}, \qquad V_f = 750 \text{ ft sec}^{-1}$$

and for a jet transport aircraft whose aerodynamic characteristics are

$$C_{DO} = 0.015, \qquad K = 0.042$$

Two values of the wing loading are considered, that is, 60 and 100 lb ft^{-2}; furthermore, the thrust-to-weight ratio is 0.4 at sea level and varies with

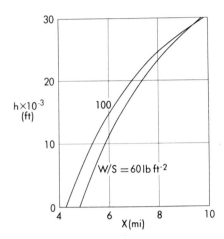

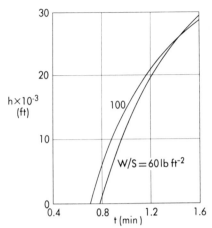

Fig. 6. Acceleration distance of a typical jet transport.   Fig. 7. Acceleration time of a typical jet transport.

the altitude according to the 0.7-power of the density. The graphs indicate that the high wing loading aircraft accelerates in a shorter distance and time than the low wing loading aircraft near sea level, while the opposite occurs in the neighborhood of the tropopause. The physical justification for this result lies in the fact that, of the two aircraft being compared, the one with the high wing loading has a smaller zero-lift drag and a greater induced drag. Since, for the particular example under consideration, the zero-lift drag is the predominant component of the drag at low altitudes, the high wing loading aircraft has a smaller total drag and, hence, better acceleration performance at low altitudes. Conversely, since the induced drag is the predominant component of the drag at high altitudes, the low wing loading aircraft has a smaller over-all drag and, hence better acceleration performance at high altitudes.

If the limiting process $z \rightarrow 0$ is carried out, the equations of this section reduce to those of Section 2 relative to the deceleration distance and time of a glider. The rather laborious manipulations, omitted for the sake of brevity, are based on the circumstance that the unaccelerated level flight solutions (31) become imaginary for a glider. They are given by

$$u_1 = \sqrt{i}, \qquad u_2 = \sqrt{-i} \qquad (34)$$

where i is the imaginary unit and can be rewritten in the form

$$u_1 = \frac{1+i}{\sqrt{2}}, \qquad u_2 = \frac{1-i}{\sqrt{2}} \qquad (35)$$

5. CONSERVATIVE PATHS

The class of flight paths flown with the thrust equal to the drag at all time instants is now considered within the framework of Section 1.3; hence, the equations of motion are written as (Ref. 1)

$$\dot{X} - V \cos \gamma = 0$$
$$\dot{h} - V \sin \gamma = 0$$
$$\dot{V} + g \sin \gamma = 0 \tag{36}$$
$$\dot{\gamma} - \frac{g}{V}(n - \cos \gamma) = 0$$

where $n = L/W$ is the load factor. A mathematical consequence of the kinematic relationship in the vertical direction and the dynamic relationship on the tangent to the flight path is the energy integral

$$h + \frac{V^2}{2g} = \text{Const} \tag{37}$$

which holds regardless of the load factor distribution and is indicative of the conservative nature of the flight path. This result is logical, since the power delivered by the propulsion system is entirely expended in generating and maintaining the aerodynamic field around the aircraft.

In the following sections, two particular types of conservative paths are investigated, one in which the load factor is constant and one in which the lift coefficient is constant. The analysis can be simplified substantially if the time is eliminated, the path inclination is selected as the new independent variable, and the dimensionless coordinates

$$\xi = \frac{Xg}{V_i^2}, \qquad \eta = \frac{hg}{V_i^2}, \qquad u = \frac{V}{V_i} \tag{38}$$

are introduced, where V_i is the initial velocity. In this way, the following differential system is obtained:

$$\frac{d\xi}{d\gamma} = \frac{u^2 \cos \gamma}{n - \cos \gamma}$$
$$\frac{d\eta}{d\gamma} = \frac{u^2 \sin \gamma}{n - \cos \gamma} \tag{39}$$
$$\frac{du}{d\gamma} = -\frac{u \sin \gamma}{n - \cos \gamma}$$

while the energy integral is rewritten in the form

$$\eta + \frac{u^2}{2} = \text{Const} \tag{40}$$

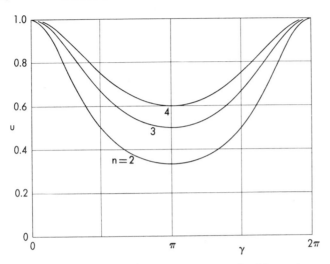

FIG. 8. Velocity distribution for a constant load factor loop.

5.1 Constant load factor. The case where the load factor is constant is now discussed in connection with the initial conditions

$$\gamma_i = \xi_i = \eta_i = 0, \qquad u_i = 1 \tag{41}$$

the last of which is due to the way the reference velocity has been selected. After the variables are separated, the integration of the third of Eqs. (39) leads to

$$u(n - \cos \gamma) = \text{Const} \tag{42}$$

which, in consideration of the initial conditions (41), implies that

$$u = \frac{n - 1}{n - \cos \gamma} \tag{43}$$

This function, which supplies the velocity distribution along the flight path, is plotted in Fig. 8 for several values of the load factor. Notice that the trajectory is a loop as long as the load factor is larger than one; in particular, the velocity at the highest point of the loop ($\gamma = \pi$) is given by

$$u = \frac{n - 1}{n + 1} \tag{44}$$

and, therefore, is one-third the velocity at the lowest point if the load factor is two.

Once the velocity distribution is known, the geometry of the trajectory can be obtained by employing the first of Eqs. (39) and the energy

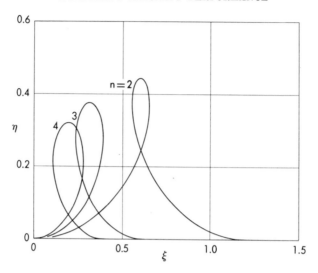

FIG. 9. Geometry of a constant load factor loop.

integral (40). In fact, the differential equation for the distance becomes

$$\frac{d\xi}{d\gamma} = (n - 1)^2 \frac{\cos \gamma}{(n - \cos \gamma)^3} \tag{45}$$

and, because of the initial conditions (41), leads to the particular solution

$$\xi = \frac{1}{2} \frac{n - 1}{n + 1} \frac{\sin \gamma}{n - \cos \gamma} \left(\frac{n}{n - \cos \gamma} + \frac{n^2 + 2}{n^2 - 1} \right)$$

$$+ \frac{3n}{(n + 1)^2 \sqrt{n^2 - 1}} \arctan \left(\sqrt{\frac{n + 1}{n - 1}} \tan \frac{\gamma}{2} \right) \tag{46}$$

Furthermore, the distribution of altitudes is given by

$$\eta = \frac{1}{2} \left[1 - \left(\frac{n - 1}{n - \cos \gamma} \right)^2 \right] \tag{47}$$

The last two equations supply the geometry of the trajectory in para-metric form, the parameter being the path inclination. Elimination of γ from these equations leads to a functional relationship of the form

$$F(\xi, \eta, n) = 0 \tag{48}$$

which is plotted in Fig. 9 for several values of the load factor. Incidentally, the coordinates of the highest point of the loop are given by

$$\xi = \frac{3\pi}{2} \frac{n}{(n+1)^2\sqrt{n^2-1}}, \qquad \eta = \frac{2n}{(n+1)^2} \tag{49}$$

In closing, it is important to note that the lift coefficient required along a constant load factor loop flown in a homogeneous atmosphere is given by

$$C_L = \frac{C_{Li}}{u^2} \tag{50}$$

which implies that

$$\frac{C_L}{C_{Li}} = \left(\frac{n+1}{n-1}\right)^2 \tag{51}$$

at the highest point. Since the required lift coefficient cannot exceed the stalling lift coefficient C_{LS}, a constant load factor loop is physically possible only if the following inequality is satisfied:

$$n > \frac{\sqrt{C_{LS}} + \sqrt{C_{Li}}}{\sqrt{C_{LS}} - \sqrt{C_{Li}}} \tag{52}$$

5.2 Constant lift coefficient. In the year 1908, Lanchester attempted to supply one of the first analytical theories of the flight paths of an aircraft and considered the class of *phugoid trajectories*, that is, conservative trajectories flown with constant lift coefficient in a homogeneous medium. In order to investigate these trajectories, the initial conditions (41) are retained, and Eqs. (39) are employed with this provision: since the lift coefficient is constant, the load factor is no longer constant but varies according to the law

$$n = n_i u^2 \tag{53}$$

where n_i is the load factor at the initial point.

After the third of Eqs. (39) is combined with Eq. (53), the following differential relationship is obtained:

$$n_i u^2\, du - \cos \gamma\, du + u \sin \gamma\, d\gamma = 0 \tag{54}$$

and leads to the general integral

$$n_i \frac{u^3}{3} - u \cos \gamma = \text{Const} \tag{55}$$

Consequently, in consideration of the initial conditions (41), the velocity-path inclination relationship is represented by

$$\cos \gamma = \frac{1}{3}\left(n_i u^2 + \frac{3 - n_i}{u}\right) \tag{56}$$

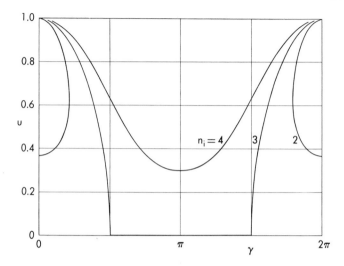

FIG. 10. Velocity distribution for phugoid trajectories.

and is plotted in Fig. 10 for several values of the initial load factor. In this connection, the following remarks are in order:

(a) For $n_i = 1$, Eq. (56) becomes

$$\cos \gamma = \frac{1}{3}\left(u^2 + \frac{2}{u}\right) \tag{57}$$

and its only real solution is represented by $u = 1$ and $\gamma = 0$; hence, the resulting phugoid is a constant velocity-constant altitude rectilinear path.

(b) For $1 < n_i < 3$, the right-hand side of Eq. (56) is always positive. Hence, a closed loop is not possible, and the resultant phugoid trajectory has a wavelike, undulatory form.

(c) For $n_i = 3$, Eq. (56) reduces to

$$\cos \gamma = u^2 \tag{58}$$

which, for $u = 0$, is solved by $\gamma = \pm \pi/2$; hence, a cusp exists in the geometry of the flight path.

(d) Finally, for $n_i > 3$, the cosine of the path inclination may become negative. Consequently, the resulting phugoid is a looped path.

Once the velocity distribution is known, the distribution of abscissas can be obtained by integrating the differential equation

$$\frac{d\xi}{d\gamma} = \frac{u^2 \cos \gamma}{n_i u^2 - \cos \gamma} \tag{59}$$

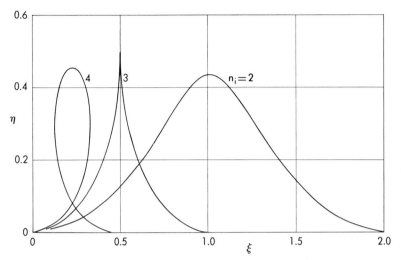

FIG. 11. Geometry of phugoid trajectories.

which results from the first of Eqs. (39) in combination with Eq. (53). Furthermore, because of the energy integral, the distribution of altitudes is given by

$$\eta = \frac{1 - u^2}{2} \tag{60}$$

Consequently, after the initial conditions (41) are accounted for, the integration process leads to the parametric equations

$$\xi = \xi(\gamma, n_i), \qquad \eta = \eta(\gamma, n_i) \tag{61}$$

which, after γ is eliminated, yield the functional relationship

$$F(\xi, \eta, n_i) = 0 \tag{62}$$

which is plotted in Fig. 11 for several values of the initial load factor.

Since, generally speaking, the integration of Eq. (59) must be accomplished by approximate methods, an analytical expression for the geometry of the trajectory is not possible. However, an exception is the case where $n_i = 3$, in which one obtains

$$\xi^2 + \eta(\eta - 1) = 0 \tag{63}$$

for the ascending branch and

$$(1 - \xi)^2 + \eta(\eta - 1) = 0 \tag{64}$$

for the descending branch.

6. TAKE–OFF AND LANDING

Take-off and landing are accelerated maneuvers which include two phases: a ground phase (considered here) and an airborne phase (see exercises). Owing to the fundamental role played by the human element in these maneuvers, it is not convenient to introduce too many mathematical complications in the analysis. Rather, it is appropriate to consider those simplifying assumptions which, without violating the essence of the phenomena, yield closed form solutions (Refs. 3 through 9).

6.1 Definitions. The following velocities are particularly significant in take-off and landing analyses: the *stalling velocity* (minimum velocity at which the aircraft can be maintained in level flight), the *lift-off velocity* (velocity at which the aircraft becomes airborne in take-off), and the *touchdown velocity* (velocity at which the aircraft makes contact with the runway in landing). The stalling velocity is defined by

$$V_S = \sqrt{\frac{2W}{C_{LS}\rho S}} \tag{65}$$

where C_{LS} is the *stalling lift coefficient.** On the other hand, the lift-off and touchdown velocities can be identified with the same symbol

$$V_o = \sqrt{\frac{2W}{C_{LO}\rho S}} \tag{66}$$

provided C_{LO} is regarded as the *lift-off lift coefficient* in take-off and the *touchdown lift coefficient* in landing.

Existing regulations prescribe that the lift-off and touchdown velocities be somewhat greater than the stalling velocity, that is,

$$V_o = K_o V_S \tag{67}$$

where the coefficient $K_o > 1$ depends on the aircraft and has slightly different values for take-off and landing. Consequently, the lift-off and touchdown lift coefficients satisfy the relationship

$$C_{LO} = \frac{C_{LS}}{K_o^2} \tag{68}$$

---

* The stalling lift coefficient of an aircraft is primarily a function of the geometry of the wing, increasing with the camber ratio and decreasing with the angle of sweep. The most common way of augmenting C_{LS} during take-off or landing consists of using flaps and/or slots. Typical values of the maximum lift coefficient for subsonic wings without flaps are in the neighborhood of 1.0–1.4; these values can be augmented as much as 0.4–0.8 (and, sometimes, even more) depending on the flap design.

where C_{LS} is the stalling lift coefficient. For example, if $K_o = 1.2$ for take-off, the lift-off lift coefficient is about 70% of the stalling lift coefficient.

6.2 Equations of motion. While in the airborne phase the forces acting on the aircraft are the thrust, the drag, the lift, and the weight, two additional forces are present in the ground phase: the normal reaction of the runway on the aircraft and the tangential force due to the rolling friction plus the possible application of brakes. Therefore, if it is assumed that the runway is horizontal ($\gamma = 0$) and if the weight variation due to the fuel consumption is neglected, the equations governing the take-off and landing runs are written as

$$\dot{X} - V = 0$$

$$T - D - \mu R - \frac{W}{g}\dot{V} = 0 \tag{69}$$

$$R + L - W = 0$$

where R is the reaction exerted by the runway on the aircraft, μ the friction coefficient,* and μR the friction force. If the reaction of the runway on the aircraft is eliminated from Eqs. (69) and the velocity is selected as the new independent variable, the differential equations for the distance and the time become

$$\frac{dX}{dV} = \frac{W}{g}\frac{V}{T - D - \mu(W - L)}$$

$$\frac{dt}{dV} = \frac{W}{g}\frac{1}{T - D - \mu(W - L)} \tag{70}$$

and must generally be integrated by means of approximate procedures. However, an analytical solution is possible if it is assumed that the take-off and landing runs are divided into parts, in each of which the thrust, the friction coefficient, and the angle of attack are constant. In such a case, it is convenient to introduce the nondimensional coordinates

$$u = \frac{V}{V_o}, \qquad \xi = \frac{Xg}{V_o^2}(\tau - \mu), \qquad \theta = \frac{tg}{V_o}(\tau - \mu) \tag{71}$$

where $\tau = T/W$ is the thrust-to-weight ratio and where V_o is the lift-off velocity in take-off and the touchdown velocity in landing. After the dimensionless ratio

$$y = \frac{\mu C_L - C_D}{C_{LO}(\tau - \mu)} \tag{72}$$

---

* The coefficient of friction depends on the nature of the surface on which the aircraft is rolling. If brakes are not applied, a typical value is $\mu = 0.02$ for a dry concrete surface. If brakes are applied, the coefficient of friction can be as high as 0.3–0.4.

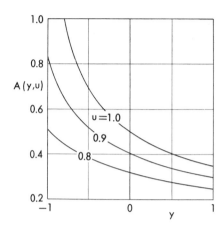

FIG. 12. The function $A(y, u)$.   FIG. 13. The function $B(y, u)$.

is defined, Eqs. (70) yield the differential equations

$$\frac{d\xi}{du} = \frac{u}{1 + yu^2}, \qquad \frac{d\theta}{du} = \frac{1}{1 + yu^2} \tag{73}$$

Consequently, the integration process leads to

$$\xi = A(y, u) + \text{Const}, \qquad \theta = B(y, u) + \text{Const} \tag{74}$$

where the functions A and B are expressed by

$$(y > 0), \qquad A(y, u) = \frac{1}{2y} \log (1 + yu^2),$$

$$B(y, u) = \frac{1}{\sqrt{y}} \arctan (\sqrt{y}\, u)$$

$$(y = 0), \qquad A(y, u) = \frac{u^2}{2}$$

$$B(y, u) = u \tag{75}$$

$$(y < 0), \qquad A(y, u) = \frac{1}{2y} \log (1 + yu^2),$$

$$B(y, u) = \frac{1}{2\sqrt{-y}} \log \frac{1 + \sqrt{-y}\, u}{1 - \sqrt{-y}\, u}$$

and are plotted in Figs. 12 and 13 versus the parameter y for several values of the dimensionless speed.

6.3 Take-off run. While the previous solutions are simultaneously valid for both take-off and landing, they are now applied to the specific case of the take-off run in connection with the end-conditions

$$u_i = \xi_i = \theta_i = 0$$

$$u_f = 1, \qquad \xi_f = \xi, \qquad \theta_f = \theta$$

(76)

It is assumed that the thrust is independent of the speed, that the entire take-off run takes place at a constant lift coefficient $C_L < C_{LO}$, and that, when the lift-off velocity is reached, the aircraft is rotated instantaneously to the angle of attack which corresponds to the lift-off condition. Consequently, the following expressions are obtained for the nondimensional distance and time:

$$\xi = A(y, 1)$$

$$\theta = B(y, 1)$$

(77)

and imply that

$$X = \frac{K_o^2 V_S^2}{g} \frac{A(y, 1)}{\tau - \mu}$$

$$t = \frac{K_o V_S}{g} \frac{B(y, 1)}{\tau - \mu}$$

(78)

These relationships indicate that the take-off performance improves as the thrust-to-weight ratio increases, the wing loading decreases, and the stalling lift coefficient increases. Therefore, it becomes clear why high lift devices (e.g., flaps, slots) have been introduced in aeronautics and why so much attention is being devoted to their improvement.

It is worth noting that, for given values of the thrust-to-weight ratio, the wing loading, and the stalling lift coefficient, the ground run is a monotonically decreasing function of the parameter y. Since this parameter depends on the angle of attack employed, the lift coefficient which minimizes the ground run is identical with that which maximizes the parameter y. For an arbitrary drag polar, this occurs when the following condition is satisfied:

$$\frac{dC_D}{dC_L} = \mu$$

(79)

which reduces to

$$C_L = \frac{\mu}{2K}$$

(80)

for the particular case of a parabolic polar.* The associated optimum

---

* Because of ground interference effects, the induced drag factor K in take-off is somewhat smaller than in free flight.

value for the parameter y is given by

$$y = \frac{C_{DO}}{C_{LO}} \frac{(\mu E_{\max})^2 - 1}{\tau - \mu} \tag{81}$$

where C_{DO} is the zero-lift drag coefficient and C_{LO} the lift-off lift coefficient.

6.4 Landing run. The landing performance is now calculated in connection with the end-conditions

$$\begin{aligned} u_i &= 1, & \xi_i &= \theta_i = 0 \\ u_f &= 0, & \xi_f &= \xi, & \theta_f &= \theta \end{aligned} \tag{82}$$

It is assumed that the aircraft is rotated instantaneously from the touchdown lift coefficient to the landing run lift coefficient and that the latter is subsequently kept constant; that mechanical brakes are applied at the instant of touchdown and that the friction coefficient is subsequently kept constant; and that the engines are idling during the entire landing run $(T = 0)$. Consequently, the nondimensional distance and time are written in the form

$$\begin{aligned} \xi &= -A(y, 1) \\ \theta &= -B(y, 1) \end{aligned} \tag{83}$$

and imply that

$$\begin{aligned} X &= \frac{K_o^2 V_S^2}{g} \frac{A(y, 1)}{\mu} \\ t &= \frac{K_o V_S}{g} \frac{B(y, 1)}{\mu} \end{aligned} \tag{84}$$

where the parameter y is given by

$$y = \frac{C_D - \mu C_L}{\mu C_{LO}} \tag{85}$$

6.5 Effect of thrust reversal on the landing performance. A modification of the previous problem occurs in the case where reverse thrust is applied over a portion of the landing run. In order to analyze this problem, denote by V_r the velocity at which the thrust is reversed, and assume that the engines are idling in the velocity interval V_o, V_r and producing a constant negative thrust in the velocity interval V_r, 0. If all the other

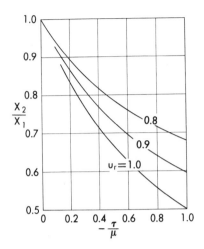

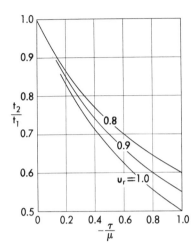

FIG. 14. Effect of the thrust reversal on the landing distance.

FIG. 15. Effect of the thrust reversal on the landing time.

conditions of the previous paragraph are retained, the landing distance and time are given by

$$X = \frac{K_o^2 V_S^2}{g}\left[\frac{A(y_o, 1) - A(y_o, u_r)}{\mu} + \frac{A(y_r, u_r)}{\mu - \tau}\right]$$

$$t = \frac{K_o V_S}{g}\left[\frac{B(y_o, 1) - B(y_o, u_r)}{\mu} + \frac{B(y_r, u_r)}{\mu - \tau}\right]$$

(86)

where y_o is the value of the parameter y when the engines are idling and y_r the value obtained when the reverse thrust is applied.

To understand the significance of the previous formulas, consider the particular case in which the angle of attack is such that $y_o = y_r = 0$. By simple manipulations, the previous equations lead to

$$X_1 = \frac{K_o^2 V_S^2}{2g\mu}$$

$$t_1 = \frac{K_o V_S}{g\mu}$$

(87)

if no reverse thrust is applied and to

$$X_2 = \frac{K_o^2 V_S^2}{2g\mu}\left(1 - u_r^2 \frac{\tau}{\tau - \mu}\right)$$

$$t_2 = \frac{K_o V_S}{g\mu}\left(1 - u_r \frac{\tau}{\tau - \mu}\right)$$

(88)

if the reverse thrust τ is applied at the velocity u_r. Consequently, the effect of thrust reversal on the landing performance is represented by the ratios

$$\frac{X_2}{X_1} = 1 - u_r^2 \frac{\tau}{\tau - \mu}$$

$$\frac{t_2}{t_1} = 1 - u_r \frac{\tau}{\tau - \mu} \tag{89}$$

which are plotted in Figs. 14 and 15 for several values of the dimensionless speed at which the reverse thrust is applied. For example, under the assumption that $\tau = -0.4 \ \mu$ and $u_r = 0.9$, thrust reversal yields a 23% decrease in the landing run and a 26% decrease in the landing time.

EXERCISES

1. Consider a smooth, shallow glide path flown with constant angle of attack, and denote by $\lambda = d \log C_L/d \log C_D$ the logarithmic derivative of the lift coefficient with respect to the drag coefficient. Assuming that the end-altitudes are fixed, show that the maximum range is obtained when the following condition is satisfied:

$$\lambda = 1 + \frac{W}{gSC_L} \frac{1/\rho_i - 1/\rho_f}{h_i - h_f} \tag{90}$$

On the other hand, if the total energies are fixed at the endpoints or if the end-velocities are fixed and the atmosphere is exponential, show that the maximum range occurs for $\lambda = 1$.

2. Consider a smooth, shallow glide path flown in an exponential atmosphere whose scale-height factor is λ. Introducing the dimensionless coordinates

$$u = \frac{V}{\sqrt{\lambda g}}, \qquad \xi = \frac{X}{\lambda}, \qquad \eta = \frac{h}{\lambda}, \qquad \theta = t \sqrt{\frac{g}{\lambda}} \tag{91}$$

solve the glide problem in terms of the instantaneous dimensionless speed. More specifically, assuming that the angle of attack is constant, show that the distributions of path inclination, abscissa, altitude, and time are represented by

$$\gamma = -\frac{1}{E} \frac{2}{2 + u^2}$$

$$\frac{\xi}{E} = -2 \log u - \frac{u^2}{2} + \text{Const}$$

$$\eta = \log K_L + 2 \log u \tag{92}$$

$$\frac{\theta}{E} = \frac{2}{u} - u + \text{Const}$$

where

$$K_L = C_L \rho_o S \lambda g / 2W$$

Furthermore, assuming the end-conditions

$$\xi_i = \theta_i = 0, \qquad \xi_f = \xi, \qquad \theta_f = \theta \tag{93}$$

prove that

$$\xi = E\left(\eta_i - \eta_f + \frac{u_i^2 - u_f^2}{2}\right)$$

$$\theta = 2E\sqrt{K_L}\,(\sqrt{\sigma_f} - \sqrt{\sigma_i}) + E(u_i - u_f) \tag{94}$$

3. Consider a smooth, shallow glide path flown with constant angle of attack. Show that the rate of change of the kinetic energy with respect to the potential energy is given by

$$\frac{d(V^2/2)}{d(gh)} = -\frac{V^2}{2g}\frac{d\log\rho}{dh} \tag{95}$$

which reduces to

$$\frac{d(V^2/2)}{d(gh)} = \frac{V^2}{2g\lambda} = \frac{u^2}{2} \tag{96}$$

for flight in an exponential atmosphere whose scale-height factor is λ. Hence, the quasi-steady solution holds provided that $u^2 \ll 2$.

4. Consider a glide trajectory characterized by a relatively small curvature, and write the equations of motion in the form

$$\dot{X} - V\cos\gamma = 0$$

$$\dot{h} - V\sin\gamma = 0$$

$$D + W\left(\sin\gamma + \frac{\dot{V}}{g}\right) = 0 \tag{97}$$

$$L - W\cos\gamma = 0$$

Assuming that the angle of attack is constant, show that Eq. (18) is still valid.

5. Consider an aircraft accelerating along an arbitrarily inclined rectilinear path in a homogeneous atmosphere, and assume a parabolic polar with constant coefficients. Define the dimensionless coordinates

$$\theta = \frac{tg\cos\gamma}{V_R E_{\max}}, \qquad \xi = \frac{Xg}{V_R^2 E_{\max}}, \qquad u = \frac{V}{V_R} \tag{98}$$

where the reference velocity

$$V_R = \sqrt{\frac{2W\cos\gamma}{\rho S}}\,\sqrt[4]{\frac{K}{C_{DO}}} \tag{99}$$

is the velocity for minimum drag along the prescribed path. After introducing the dimensionless parameter

$$z = \frac{T - W \sin \gamma}{W \cos \gamma} E_{max} \qquad (100)$$

show that the differential equations governing the distance and the time can be reduced to Eqs. (28). Hence, Eqs. (29), which were established for level flight, are also formally valid for inclined trajectories provided that the new definitions for θ, ξ, u, z are used.

6. Study a conservative circular trajectory employing the dimensionless coordinates (38). Retaining the initial conditions (41), show that the distributions of abscissa, ordinate, and velocity are given by

$$\xi = \frac{\sin \gamma}{n_i - 1}, \qquad \eta = \frac{1 - \cos \gamma}{n_i - 1}, \qquad u = \sqrt{\frac{n_i - 3 + 2 \cos \gamma}{n_i - 1}} \qquad (101)$$

where n_i is the load factor at the initial point. Prove that the dimensionless radius of curvature is given by

$$r = \frac{1}{n_i - 1} \qquad (102)$$

Finally, show that a loop is physically possible if, and only if, $n_i > 5$.

7. Consider a trajectory flown with constant lift coefficient and constant thrust in a homogeneous atmosphere. Define the dimensionless coordinates

$$u = \frac{V}{V_R}, \qquad \xi = \frac{Xg}{V_R^2}, \qquad \eta = \frac{hg}{V_R^2} \qquad (103)$$

and select the quantity $V_R = \sqrt{2W/C_L \rho S}$ as the reference velocity. After eliminating the time, show that the equations of motion lead to the differential set

$$\frac{du^2}{d\gamma} = \frac{2u^2}{E} \frac{E(\tau - \sin \gamma) - u^2}{u^2 - \cos \gamma}$$

$$\frac{d\xi}{d\gamma} = \frac{u^2 \cos \gamma}{u^2 - \cos \gamma} \qquad (104)$$

$$\frac{d\eta}{d\gamma} = \frac{u^2 \sin \gamma}{u^2 - \cos \gamma}$$

where E is the aerodynamic efficiency and τ is the thrust-to-weight ratio. The integration of these equations, which are of interest for the transition arc connecting the take-off point and the beginning of the climbing phase, must generally be performed by approximate procedures. However, an analytical solution is possible if the path inclination is small and the velocity variation is negligible; more specifically, assuming that $\gamma_i = \xi_i = \eta_i = 0$, show that the geometry of the trajectory is given by

$$\eta = \frac{n-1}{2n} \xi^2 \qquad (105)$$

where n is the load factor.

REFERENCES

1. CROCCO, G. A., *Equazione Generale della Gran Volta*, L'Aerotecnica, Vol. 22, Nos. 1, 2, 9, 10, 1942.
2. EHLERS, F. E. and BRIGHAM, G., *On Aircraft Maneuvers in the Vertical Plane under Assumptions Leading to Easy Integrability of the Flight Path Equations*, Journal of the Aerospace Sciences, Vol. 28, No. 7, 1961.
3. DOUWES DEKKER, F. E. and LEAN, D., *Take-Off and Landing Performance*, AGARD Flight Test Manual, Vol. 1, Chapter 8, Pergamon Press, Inc., New York, 1959.
4. GARBELL, M. A. and YOUNG, W. M., *The Ground Run of Aircraft in Landing and Take-Off*, Garbell Aeronautical Series, No. 3, 1951.
5. MEYERHOFF, L. and MEYERHOFF, S., *Reverse Thrust, Vertical Lift, and Jet Side Force by Means of Controlled Jet Deflection*, AFOSR TN No. 56–168, 1956.
6. KELBER, C. C., *The Effects of Reversed Thrust on Landing Distance*, The Rand Corporation, RM No. 1334, 1954.
7. KETTLE, D. J., *Ground Performance at Take-off and Landing*, Aircraft Engineering, Vol. 30, No. 347, 1958.
8. BUCKINGHAM, W. R., *A Theoretical Analysis of the Airborne Path During Take-off*, Aircraft Engineering, Vol. 30, No. 347, 1958.
9. ROGERSON, G. E., *Estimation of Take-off and Landing Airborne Paths*, Aircraft Engineering, Vol. 32, No. 381, 1960.
10. MIELE, A., *Analytical Theory of the Flight Paths of a Glider Over a Flat Earth*, Boeing Scientific Research Laboratories, Flight Sciences Laboratory, TR No. 23, 1960.

CHAPTER 13

PERFORMANCE OF
HYPERVELOCITY VEHICLES

1. INTRODUCTION

In the previous chapter, the nonsteady flight of an aircraft was analyzed with particular regard to the low subsonic regime. Here, the other extreme of the velocity spectrum, the hypervelocity regime, is explored in connection with vehicles flying with engine shut off at all points of the flight path. Because of the assumption that $T = 0$, the weight is constant. Consequently, Eqs. (12–1) are rewritten as

$$\dot{X} - V \cos \gamma = 0$$

$$\dot{h} - V \sin \gamma = 0$$

$$D + W \left(\sin \gamma + \frac{\dot{V}}{g} \right) = 0 \tag{1}$$

$$L - W \left(\cos \gamma + \frac{V\dot{\gamma}}{g} \right) = 0$$

where X denotes the horizontal distance, h the altitude, V the velocity, γ the path inclination, D the drag, L the lift, W the weight, g the acceleration of gravity, and the dot sign a derivative with respect to time.

1.1 General integration problem. If a drag function of the form $D = D(h, V, L)$ is assumed, the previous differential system has one independent variable, the time, and five dependent variables (X, h, V, γ, L). Consequently, there is one degree of freedom, which is logical since the flight path can be changed by operating the elevator control. Thus, for a given set of initial conditions for X, h, V, γ, infinite trajectories exist which are physically and mathematically possible, more specifically, one trajectory for each arbitrarily prescribed lift program $L(t)$ or equivalent condition. In view of the dissipative nature of the aerodynamic forces, no first integral can be written for the general case and, as a consequence, the study of particular flight conditions is of great interest from an engineering standpoint. In this connection, the following sections discuss the integration of Eqs. (1) under various approximations relative to the atmosphere (e.g., exponential), the flow regime

284

(e.g., hypervelocity), and the relative magnitude of the forces involved. Attention is focused on the ascent of a sounding rocket and on the reentry of ballistic missiles, glide vehicles, and skip vehicles.

2. ASCENT OF A SOUNDING ROCKET

The ascent of a sounding rocket includes in general two phases: one in which power is applied (see Chapter 17) and one in which the engine is shut off. In this section, the unpowered portion of the trajectory is analyzed under the assumption that $\gamma = \pi/2$. For vertical flight, the kinematic relationship on the horizontal direction can be integrated to give $X = \text{Const}$. Furthermore, since the equation of motion on the normal to the flight path implies that $L = 0$, the drag function is reduced to the form

$$D = D(h, V) \tag{2}$$

The remaining equations (1) are written as

$$\dot{h} - V = 0$$
$$\dot{V} + g\left(\frac{D}{W} + 1\right) = 0 \tag{3}$$

and involve only two unknown functions, that is, the functions $h(t)$ and $V(t)$; furthermore, after the time is eliminated, they imply that

$$\frac{dV}{dh} + \frac{g}{V}\left(\frac{D}{W} + 1\right) = 0 \tag{4}$$

Generally speaking, this differential equation must be integrated by approximate methods. However, an analytical solution is possible if the drag coefficient is assumed to be constant and if the following exponential law is assumed for the relative density-altitude relationship

$$\sigma = \exp\left(-\frac{h}{\lambda}\right) \tag{5}$$

where λ is a constant (see Appendix). If the dimensionless variables

$$\eta = \frac{h}{\lambda}, \qquad u = \frac{V}{\sqrt{\lambda g}} \tag{6}$$

are introduced and it is observed that the drag per unit weight is given by

$$\frac{D}{W} = K_D u^2 \exp(-\eta), \qquad K_D = \frac{C_D \rho_o S \lambda g}{2W} \tag{7}$$

Eq. (4) is transformed into

$$\frac{du}{d\eta} + K_D u \exp(-\eta) + \frac{1}{u} = 0 \tag{8}$$

This nonlinear differential equation can be converted into a relatively simple linear form if a further coordinate transformation is performed. If the expressions

$$\pi = 2K_D \exp(-\eta), \qquad \epsilon = \frac{u^2}{2} \tag{9}$$

denote the drag per unit weight at $u = \sqrt{2}$ and the dimensionless kinetic energy per unit mass, respectively, the following differential equation is obtained:

$$\frac{d\epsilon}{d\pi} - \epsilon - \frac{1}{\pi} = 0 \tag{10}$$

and its general solution is given by

$$\epsilon = [C + Ei(-\pi)] \exp(\pi) \tag{11}$$

where C is a constant. The *exponential-integral function* appearing in this equation is defined as

$$Ei(-\pi) = \int_{\infty}^{\pi} \frac{e^{-\pi}}{\pi} d\pi \tag{12}$$

and is tabulated in Ref. 4; furthermore, it can be expanded in the following manner:

$$Ei(-\pi) = \gamma_E + \log \pi + \sum_{n=1}^{\infty} \frac{(-\pi)^n}{n!\,n} \tag{13}$$

where $\gamma_E \cong 0.5772$ is the *Euler constant*.

Assume, now, that the initial values of the velocity and the altitude are prescribed, and consider the problem of determining the peak altitude reached by a sounding rocket, that is, the altitude achieved when the final velocity is zero. After the integration constant is determined in terms of both the initial and final conditions, the following result is obtained (Ref. 13):

$$Ei(-\pi_f) - Ei(-\pi_i) + \frac{u_i^2}{2} \exp(-\pi_i) = 0 \tag{14}$$

and contains the solution to the proposed problem implicitly. In particular, if the final conditions are such that $\pi_f \ll 1$ (peak altitudes in the order of 200,000 ft or higher), the final altitude can be approximated by

$$\eta_f = \gamma_E + \log(2K_D) - Ei(-\pi_i) + \frac{u_i^2}{2} \exp(-\pi_i) \tag{15}$$

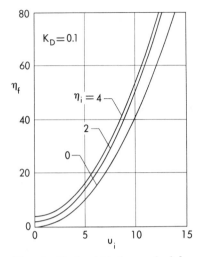

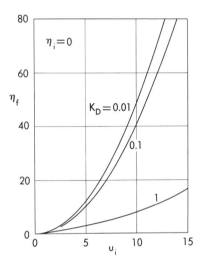

FIG. 1. Peak altitude reached by a sounding rocket versus the initial velocity and the initial altitude.

FIG. 2. Peak altitude reached by a sounding rocket versus the initial velocity and the drag factor.

which reduces to

$$\eta_f = \eta_i + \frac{u_i^2}{2} \tag{16}$$

for flight in a vacuum; this is logical, since the sum of the potential and kinetic energies must be constant if no dissipative effects are present.

In connection with these results, Fig. 1 shows the peak altitude reached by a sounding rocket versus the initial velocity and the initial altitude for $K_D = 0.1$; furthermore, Fig. 2 shows the peak altitude versus the initial velocity and the drag factor for $\eta_i = 0$. Now, consider a family of geometrically similar sounding rockets, and observe that the cross-sectional area varies as the square of a characteristic dimension l, while the weight varies as the cube. Consequently, the parameter K_D (and, therefore, the drag per unit weight) is inversely proportional to the characteristic dimension l, increasing as the size of the rocket decreases. It appears that, for $u_i = 10$ and $K_D = 0.1$, the peak altitude shown in Fig. 2 is about 82% of that which would be obtained in a vacuum; on the other hand, if the size of the rocket is decreased to one-tenth of the original ($K_D = 1$), the peak altitude is only 16% of that corresponding to flight in a vacuum. In closing, it is emphasized that, while the results of this section are qualitatively correct, they must be considered with caution from a quantitative point of view, since the dependence of the acceleration of gravity on the altitude and that of the drag factor on the Mach number have been disregarded. For these reasons, this problem will be analyzed again in Volume 3.

3. REENTRY OF A BALLISTIC MISSILE

The trajectory of a ballistic missile can be divided into three parts: launch, ballistic flight, and reentry. Because of the great ranges associated with the ballistic portion of the flight path, the consideration of the sphericity of the Earth is indispensable. On the other hand, launch and reentry involve relatively short ranges and, hence, can be investigated within the framework of the flat Earth model. Here, the reentry portion is analyzed under the assumption that $L = 0$, so that the drag function has the form $D = D(h, V)$. For didactic purposes, the discussion is divided into two parts: in the first part, the effect of gravity in the equation of motion on the tangent to the flight path is neglected; in the second part, the effect of gravity is considered (Refs. 1 and 9).

3.1 **Analysis neglecting gravity.** In this section, a constant-geometry configuration is considered, and an approximate analysis of the reentry problem is developed under the assumption that

$$W \sin \gamma \ll D \tag{17}$$

which means that the weight component on the tangent to the flight path is negligible with respect to the drag. Consequently, the motion of the missile is governed by the set of differential equations

$$\dot{X} - V \cos \gamma = 0$$

$$\dot{h} - V \sin \gamma = 0$$

$$\dot{V} + g \frac{D}{W} = 0 \tag{18}$$

$$\dot{\gamma} + g \frac{\cos \gamma}{V} = 0$$

which, after the time is eliminated and the altitude is selected as the new independent variable, become

$$\frac{dX}{dh} = \cot \gamma$$

$$\frac{dV}{dh} = - \frac{g}{V} \frac{D}{W \sin \gamma} \tag{19}$$

$$\frac{d\gamma}{dh} = - \frac{g}{V^2} \cot \gamma$$

From the third equation, it is seen that the over-all variation in the slope of the flight path during reentry is proportional to the average value of $\cot \gamma / V^2$. Hence, for the velocities which are characteristic of intermediate range and long range ballistic missiles and for relatively steep trajectories, the over-all variation in the path inclination is small, a circumstance which simplifies the integration problem considerably. In fact, after the sine of the path inclination is approximated by its value at the initial point, the second of Eqs. (19) yields the velocity-altitude distribution; in turn, the third equation can be employed a posteriori in order to determine the distribution of path inclinations; finally, once the function $\gamma(h)$ is known, the first equation yields the geometry of the flight path.

Assume, now, that the drag coefficient is constant and that the density is an exponential function of the altitude; also, retain definitions (6) and (7). After the *modified drag factor* or *ballistic factor* is defined as

$$K_B = - \frac{K_D}{\sin \gamma_i} = - \frac{C_D \rho_o S \lambda g}{2W \sin \gamma_i} \tag{20}$$

and the dimensionless variables

$$\pi = 2K_B \exp(-\eta), \quad \epsilon = \frac{u^2}{2} \tag{21}$$

are introduced, the second of Eqs. (19) can be rewritten in the form

$$\frac{d\epsilon}{d\pi} + \epsilon = 0 \tag{22}$$

The general solution of this equation is given by

$$\epsilon = C \exp(-\pi) \tag{23}$$

where the integration constant C can be approximated by

$$C \cong \frac{u_i^2}{2} \tag{24}$$

for initial altitudes in the order of 200,000 ft or higher. Typical values of such a constant are $C = 100\text{–}200$ for intermediate range missiles and $C = 300\text{–}400$ for long range missiles.

Because of Eqs. (21), (23), and (24), the velocity along a reentry path is given by

$$\frac{u}{u_i} = \exp\left(-\frac{\pi}{2}\right) \tag{25}$$

and is plotted in Fig. 3 versus the altitude for several values of the ballistic factor. As the diagram indicates, for small values of the ballistic factor the over-all velocity variation during reentry is small. On the other hand, for $K_B > 0.5$ a considerable decrease in velocity occurs; this means that a large fraction of the kinetic energy of the missile is expended in generating and maintaining the aerodynamic field around the body. Incidentally, although current designs are characterized by ballistic

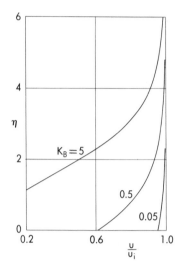 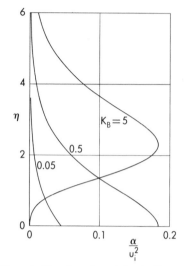

FIG. 3. Velocity-altitude diagram for several values of the ballistic factor.   FIG. 4. Deceleration-altitude diagram for several values of the ballistic factor.

factors between 1 and 10, the engineering trend is toward smaller values in order to decrease the reentry time and, hence, the probability of interception as well as the drift due to wind.

In order to study the deceleration of a ballistic missile, it is convenient to define the parameter

$$\alpha = \frac{\dot{V}}{g \sin \gamma_i} \tag{26}$$

and observe that, because of the equation of motion on the tangent to the flight path, it can be rewritten in the form

$$\alpha = \epsilon \pi \tag{27}$$

Consequently, if Eqs. (23), (24), and (27) are combined, the following expression is obtained:

$$\frac{\alpha}{u_i^2} = \frac{\pi \exp(-\pi)}{2} \tag{28}$$

and is plotted in Fig. 4 versus the altitude for several values of the ballistic factor. The deceleration history has two possible behaviors depending on whether the ballistic factor is larger or smaller than 1/2.

If the missile configuration is such that $K_B > 0.5$, the deceleration has the following analytical maximum:

$$\frac{\alpha}{u_i^2} = \frac{1}{2e} \tag{29}$$

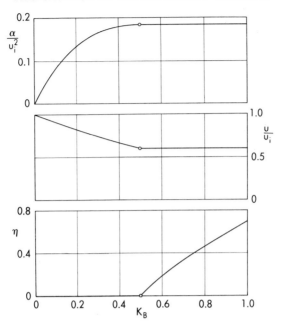

FIG. 5. Largest reentry decelerations and corresponding values of the velocity and the altitude.

which occurs for $\pi = 1$, that is, for

$$\eta = \log (2K_B) \tag{30}$$

Since the corresponding velocity ratio is given by

$$\frac{u}{u_i} = \frac{1}{\sqrt{e}} \tag{31}$$

one concludes that the maximum deceleration occurs at that point of the reentry path where the instantaneous velocity is approximately 61% of the entrance velocity.

On the other hand, if the missile configuration is such that $K_B < 0.5$, the largest deceleration, not an analytical maximum, occurs at sea level and is given by

$$\frac{\alpha}{u_i^2} = K_B \exp (-2K_B) \tag{32}$$

The corresponding velocity ratio is

$$\frac{u}{u_i} = \exp (-K_B) \tag{33}$$

These results are summarized in Fig. 5, which supplies the envelope of the largest decelerations occurring in the reentry of a constant geometry missile as well as the corresponding velocities and altitudes. It should be noted that, if the ballistic factor is larger than 1/2, *the largest reentry deceleration $\dot{V}$ varies linearly with the sine of the entrance angle and quadratically with the entrance velocity.* For example, if a missile with a ballistic factor $K_B = 1$ reenters the atmosphere with a path inclination $\gamma_i = -30°$ and a dimensionless velocity $u_i = 12$, the maximum deceleration is approximately 13.25 times the acceleration of gravity; if the entrance velocity is doubled, the maximum deceleration becomes four times as large, that is, 53 times the acceleration of gravity (Ref. 1).

3.1.1 *Variable-Geometry Missile.* A considerable reduction in the maximum reentry deceleration is possible if a variable-geometry configuration is employed. For example, consider a missile equipped with spoilers which are controllable in flight. In the hypervelocity regime, each spoiler position corresponds to a different drag coefficient and, therefore, to a different ballistic factor. Of particular interest is the case where the spoilers are continuously retracted according to the exponential law

$$K_B = K_{BO} \exp (x\eta) \qquad (34)$$

where K_{BO} is the ballistic factor at sea level and x is a constant such that $0 < x < 1$ (Ref. 12).

The mathematical model pertinent to this case can be reduced to that used in the investigation of the constant-geometry missile if the coordinate transformation

$$\pi = \frac{2K_{BO}}{1 - x} \exp [- (1 - x)\eta], \qquad \epsilon = (1 - x) \frac{u^2}{2} \qquad (35)$$

is introduced. In fact, it can be verified that the second of Eqs. (19) reduces once more to Eq. (22); hence, the kinetic energy distribution (23) is still valid for the variable-geometry missile provided that the integration constant C is no longer defined by Eq. (24) but by the expression

$$C = (1 - x) \frac{u_i^2}{2} \qquad (36)$$

After it is observed that Eq. (27) is still valid and after the instantaneous deceleration is written as

$$\frac{\alpha}{u_i^2} = \frac{(1 - x)}{2} \pi \exp (- \pi) \qquad (37)$$

comparison of Eqs. (28) and (37) leads to the following conclusion: If the ballistic factor at sea level satisfies the inequality $K_{BO} > (1 - x)/2$, the ratio r of the maximum deceleration of a variable-geometry missile to the maximum deceleration of a constant-geometry missile is given by (Ref. 13)

$$r = 1 - x \qquad (38)$$

Thus, by increasing the value of x, the maximum reentry deceleration can be decreased. However, since increasing the value of x corresponds to increasing the size of the spoilers, there exists a practical upper limit to x. If this upper limit is assumed to be 0.4, it is seen that the maximum deceleration of the variable-geometry missile is 60% of that of the basic configuration.

3.2 Analysis including gravity. The limitation of the previous section is now removed, and the motion of the ballistic missile is analyzed including the effect of the weight component on the tangent to the flight path. Consequently, after the time is eliminated and the altitude is selected as the new independent variable, Eqs. (1) yield the set of differential equations

$$\frac{dX}{dh} = \cot \gamma$$

$$\frac{dV}{dh} = - \frac{g}{V}\left(\frac{D}{W \sin \gamma} + 1\right) \qquad (39)$$

$$\frac{d\gamma}{dh} = - \frac{g}{V^2} \cot \gamma$$

The second of these equations is now integrated under the assumptions that the sine of the path inclination can be approximated by its value at the initial point, that the drag coefficient is constant, and that the density is an exponential function of the altitude. After the dimensionless variables (21) are introduced, the distribution of kinetic energy is governed by the linear differential equation

$$\frac{d\epsilon}{d\pi} + \epsilon - \frac{1}{\pi} = 0 \qquad (40)$$

which admits the general solution

$$\epsilon = [C + Ei(\pi)] \exp(-\pi) \qquad (41)$$

where C is a constant. The *exponential-integral function* is defined as

$$Ei(\pi) = \int_{-\infty}^{\pi} \frac{e^{\pi}}{\pi} \, d\pi \qquad (42)$$

and is tabulated in Ref. 4; furthermore, it can be expanded in the following manner:

$$Ei(\pi) = \gamma_E + \log \pi + \sum_{n=1}^{\infty} \frac{\pi^n}{n!\,n} \tag{43}$$

The integration constant appearing in Eq. (41) must be determined from the known initial conditions. In particular, if initial altitudes in the order of 200,000 ft or higher are considered, the following approximate result is obtained:

$$C = \frac{u_i^2}{2} + \eta_i - \gamma_E - \log\,(2K_B) \tag{44}$$

Because of Eqs. (21) and (41), the velocity along a reentry path is given by

$$u = \sqrt{2[C + Ei(\pi)]\exp\,(-\pi)} \tag{45}$$

and has a maximum at the altitude where

$$C = \frac{\exp\,(\pi)}{\pi} - Ei(\pi) \tag{46}$$

Such a maximum can be calculated by substituting the value of π which satisfies Eq. (46) into either Eq. (45) or

$$u = \sqrt{\frac{2}{\pi}} \tag{47}$$

Physically speaking, the existence of a maximum velocity is due to the fact that, during the initial part of a reentry trajectory, the weight of the missile is generally predominant with respect to the aerodynamic drag, whereas this condition is usually reversed at lower altitudes.

If definition (26) is employed, the dimensionless deceleration can be written in the form

$$\alpha = \epsilon\pi - 1 \tag{48}$$

which implies that

$$\alpha = \pi[C + Ei(\pi)]\exp\,(-\pi) - 1 \tag{49}$$

Notice that the deceleration has a maximum at the altitude where

$$C = \frac{\exp\,(\pi)}{\pi - 1} - Ei(\pi) \tag{50}$$

Such a maximum can be calculated by substituting the value of π which

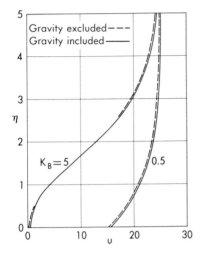

FIG 6. Velocity distribution calculated including gravitational forces (solid lines) and excluding them (dashed lines).

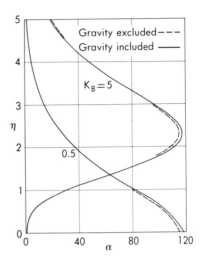

FIG. 7. Acceleration distribution calculated including gravitational forces (solid lines) and excluding them (dashed lines).

satisfies Eq. (50) into either Eq. (49) or

$$\alpha = \frac{1}{\pi - 1} \tag{51}$$

Furthermore, this maximum occurs above sea level if, and only if, the following inequality is satisfied:

$$C - \frac{\exp(2K_B)}{2K_B - 1} + Ei(2K_B) > 0 \tag{52}$$

If the missile configuration and the initial conditions are not consistent with this inequality, then the highest deceleration, not an analytical maximum, occurs at sea level and is given by

$$\alpha = 2K_B[C + Ei(2K_B)] \exp(-2K_B) - 1 \tag{53}$$

3.2.1 *Comparison of Results.* In the previous sections, the reentry problem has been analyzed in two ways, first by neglecting the gravitational forces and then by including them. A comparison of these approaches is shown in Figs. 6 and 7, where the velocity-altitude relationship and the acceleration-altitude relationship are plotted for the initial conditions $\eta_i = 10$, $u_i = 25$ and for two values of the ballistic factor: $K_B = 0.5$ and $K_B = 5$. As the diagrams show, the reentry performance calculated by neglecting the gravitational forces (dashed lines) agrees quite well with that calculated by including them (solid lines). Thus, the use of approximation (17) yields a good engineering estimate of the reentry performance, even though the approximation in question may become locally invalid at either very high altitudes or very low altitudes. More specifically, at high altitudes the density of the air is so small that the aerodynamic drag may be smaller than the weight. Furthermore, at low altitudes the velocity of a missile with a large ballistic factor may become so small that the drag may have the same order of magnitude as the weight.

4. REENTRY OF A GLIDE VEHICLE

In this section, the problem of a glide vehicle travelling on a smooth, shallow path is investigated for the case where the weight component on the tangent to the flight path is negligible with respect to the drag. Because of the hypotheses

$$\cos \gamma \cong 1, \qquad \sin \gamma \cong \gamma$$
$$\frac{V\dot{\gamma}}{g} \ll 1, \qquad W\gamma \ll D \tag{54}$$

the equations of motion simplify to

$$\dot{X} - V = 0$$
$$\dot{h} - V\gamma = 0$$
$$\dot{V} + g\frac{D}{W} = 0 \tag{55}$$
$$L - W = 0$$

After it is observed that, because of the dynamical equation on the normal to the flight path, the aerodynamic drag is given by $D = W/E$ and after the velocity is selected as the new independent variable, the previous equations imply that

$$\frac{dX}{dV} = -\frac{EV}{g}$$
$$\frac{dt}{dV} = -\frac{E}{g} \tag{56}$$

Consequently, if the angle of attack is constant and the end-conditions

(12–22) are specified, the following definite integrals are obtained:

$$X = E \, \frac{V_i^2 - V_f^2}{2g}$$

$$t = E \, \frac{V_i - V_f}{g} \tag{57}$$

from which it is clear that the range and the endurance are simultaneously maximized when the lift-to-drag ratio is a maximum. These results are a particular case of those derived in the previous chapter for the nonsteady flight of a glider over a flat Earth; in fact, they can be obtained from Eqs. (12–23) by assuming that the variation in potential energy is negligible with respect to the variation in kinetic energy. The same results can also be viewed as a special case of those obtained in Refs. 7 and 8 for flight over a spherical Earth; in fact, they can be obtained from those of Refs. 7 and 8 by means of the limiting process $r_o \to \infty$, where r_o denotes the radius of the Earth.

In closing, a word of caution is in order. A verification of the assumptions employed shows that they are satisfied only for velocities between 1/6 and 1/3 of the satellite velocity at sea level. There are two reasons for these limitations: (a) if the final velocity is too low, hypotheses (54) may become invalid; and (b) if the initial velocity is too high, the range may become such that the flat Earth model is no longer justified (in particular, the equation of motion on the normal to the flight path is to be modified, in the sense that the weight is to be replaced by the so-called *apparent weight*, that is, the difference between the actual weight and the centrifugal force which is due to the curvature of the Earth). Because of these reasons, the motion of a hypervelocity glider operating over a spherical Earth will be considered in Volume 3.

5. REENTRY OF A SKIP VEHICLE

A trajectory of interest for long-range hypervelocity vehicles is the skip trajectory, which is composed of an alternate succession of ballistic phases and skipping phases. In the ballistic phase, the vehicle operates in a quasi-vacuum environment beyond the outer reach of the atmosphere. In the skipping phase, which is analyzed here, the vehicle enters the atmosphere, negotiates a turn, and is ejected from the atmosphere.

Because of the relatively short distance covered in the skipping phase (order of magnitude: 10^2 miles), the flat Earth hypothesis is justified. Furthermore, since the gravitational forces are, on the average, much smaller than the aerodynamic forces, a simple, though approximate, analysis can be carried out by disregarding the former with respect to the latter, that is, by assuming that

$$W \sin \gamma \ll D, \qquad W \cos \gamma \ll L \tag{58}$$

Consequently, the equations of motion simplify to

$$\dot{X} - V \cos \gamma = 0$$
$$\dot{h} - V \sin \gamma = 0$$
$$\dot{V} + g \frac{D}{W} = 0 \tag{59}$$
$$\dot{\gamma} - \frac{gL}{VW} = 0$$

and, after the time is eliminated and the path inclination is selected as the new independent variable, imply that

$$\frac{dX}{d\gamma} = \frac{V^2}{g} \frac{\cos \gamma}{L/W}$$
$$\frac{dh}{d\gamma} = \frac{V^2}{g} \frac{\sin \gamma}{L/W} \tag{60}$$
$$\frac{dV}{d\gamma} = -\frac{V}{E}$$

where E is the aerodynamic efficiency.

For the particular case of an exponential atmosphere, it is appropriate to introduce the dimensionless coordinates

$$\xi = \frac{X}{\lambda}, \qquad \eta = \frac{h}{\lambda}, \qquad u = \frac{V}{\sqrt{\lambda g}} \tag{61}$$

and observe that the aerodynamic forces per unit weight are expressed by

$$\frac{D}{W} = K_D u^2 \exp(-\eta)$$
$$\frac{L}{W} = K_L u^2 \exp(-\eta) \tag{62}$$

where the dimensionless parameters

$$K_D = \frac{C_D \rho_o S \lambda g}{2W}$$
$$K_L = \frac{C_L \rho_o S \lambda g}{2W} \tag{63}$$

are called the *drag factor* and the *lift factor*, respectively. Consequently, Eqs. (60) become

$$\frac{d\xi}{d\gamma} = \frac{\cos\gamma}{K_L}\exp(\eta)$$

$$\frac{d\eta}{d\gamma} = \frac{\sin\gamma}{K_L}\exp(\eta) \tag{64}$$

$$\frac{du}{d\gamma} = -\frac{u}{E}$$

and are now integrated under the assumptions that $K_D = K_D(K_L)$ and that the angle of attack is constant. Hence, the drag factor, the lift factor, and the aerodynamic efficiency are simultaneously constant.

5.1 Altitude distribution. After the variables are separated, the integration of the second of Eqs. (64) yields the result

$$\eta = \log\frac{K_L}{C + \cos\gamma} \tag{65}$$

where the constant C is given by

$$C = K_L\exp(-\eta_i) - \cos\gamma_i \tag{66}$$

Notice that the instantaneous altitude is a single-valued function of the cosine of the path inclination. Thus, if the initial and final conditions are assumed to be such that

$$\eta_i = \eta_f \tag{67}$$

the following result is obtained (Ref. 7):

$$\gamma_f = -\gamma_i \tag{68}$$

This means that, in a skipping path performed with constant angle of attack, the ejection angle is equal to the modulus of the entrance angle. Incidentally, the lowest point of a skipping path occurs when $\gamma = 0$; hence, in order to avoid hitting the ground during the skipping phase, it is necessary that the lift factor be consistent with the inequality

$$K_L > 1 - \cos\gamma_i \tag{69}$$

which is valid subject to the approximation

$$\frac{K_L\exp(-\eta_i)}{\cos\gamma_i} \ll 1 \tag{70}$$

5.2 Velocity distribution. After the variables are separated, the integration of the third of Eqs. (64) yields the general solution

$$u = C_1 \exp\left(-\frac{\gamma}{E}\right) \tag{71}$$

where C_1 is a constant. Since the ratio of the final velocity to the initial velocity is given by

$$\frac{u_f}{u_i} = \exp\left(2\frac{\gamma_i}{E}\right) \tag{72}$$

and since γ_i is negative, the final velocity is smaller than the initial velocity. Hence, the skipping phase occurs with a loss in kinetic energy, which increases as the modulus of the entrance angle increases and the aerodynamic efficiency decreases. Therefore, for a given entrance angle, relatively high values of the aerodynamic efficiency are necessary in order to reduce the loss in kinetic energy during the skipping phase.

5.3 Distribution of abscissas. If the first of Eqs. (64) is combined with Eq. (65), the following differential equation is obtained for the distance traveled:

$$\frac{d\xi}{d\gamma} = \frac{\cos\gamma}{\cos\gamma + C} \tag{73}$$

and its general solution is represented by

$$\xi = \gamma - A \log\left[\frac{B + \tan\frac{\gamma}{2}}{B - \tan\frac{\gamma}{2}}\right] + C_2 \tag{74}$$

where

$$A = \frac{C}{\sqrt{1 - C^2}}, \qquad B = \sqrt{\frac{1 + C}{1 - C}} \tag{75}$$

and where C_2 is a constant. If this constant is evaluated in terms of the initial conditions and it is assumed that $\xi_i = 0$, the expression for the distance becomes (see exercises)

$$\xi = \gamma - \gamma_i - A \log\left[\frac{B + \tan\frac{\gamma}{2}}{B - \tan\frac{\gamma}{2}} \frac{B - \tan\frac{\gamma_i}{2}}{B + \tan\frac{\gamma_i}{2}}\right] \tag{76}$$

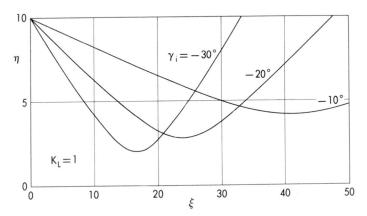

FIG. 8. Effect of the entrance angle on the geometry of a skipping path.

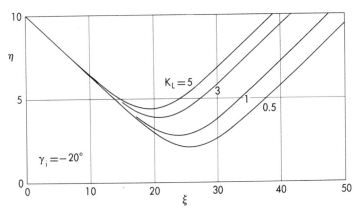

FIG. 9. Effect of the lift factor on the geometry of a skipping path.

5.4 Geometry of the trajectory. Relationships (65) and (76) are the parametric equations of the skipping trajectory, the parameter being the path inclination. Elimination of γ from these equations leads to the functional relationship

$$f(\xi,\, \eta,\, \eta_i,\, \gamma_i,\, K_L) = 0 \qquad (77)$$

which represents the geometry of the trajectory and is plotted in Figs. 8 and 9. More specifically, Fig. 8 illustrates the effect of the entrance angle on flight trajectories where $\eta_i = 10$ and $K_L = 1$; on the other hand, Fig. 9 illustrates the effect of the lift factor for $\eta_i = 10$ and $\gamma_i = -20°$. Both diagrams indicate that the range flown during the skipping phase decreases as the lift factor and the modulus of the entrance angle increase.

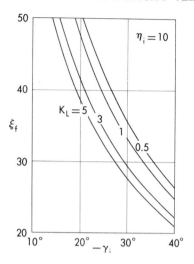

FIG. 10. Effect of the entrance angle and the lift factor on the over-all range.

This effect is clearly shown in Fig. 10 where the over-all range

$$\xi_f = -2\gamma_i - 2A \log \left[\frac{B - \tan \dfrac{\gamma_i}{2}}{B + \tan \dfrac{\gamma_i}{2}} \right] \tag{78}$$

is plotted versus the entrance angle for $\eta_i = 10$ and for several values of the lift factor (see exercises).

5.5 Acceleration distribution. The functional relationship (77) indicates that the geometry of the skipping trajectory depends on the initial altitude, the entrance angle, and the lift factor but is independent of the entrance velocity. Thus, as the entrance velocity increases, higher accelerations must be expected at all points of the flight path.

In order to compute the acceleration, it is convenient to define the dimensionless parameters

$$\alpha_n = \frac{V\dot{\gamma}}{g}$$

$$\alpha_t = -\frac{\dot{V}}{g} \tag{79}$$

$$\alpha = \frac{1}{g} \sqrt{(V\dot{\gamma})^2 + \dot{V}^2}$$

which are proportional to the normal, tangential, and total accelerations, respectively. Because of the equations of motion, the following relationships hold:

$$\alpha_n = K_L u^2 \exp(-\eta)$$
$$\alpha_t = K_D u^2 \exp(-\eta) \qquad (80)$$
$$\alpha = \sqrt{K_L^2 + K_D^2}\ u^2 \exp(-\eta)$$

and imply that

$$\alpha_t = \frac{\alpha_n}{E}$$
$$\alpha = \frac{\alpha_n}{E} \sqrt{E^2 + 1} \qquad (81)$$

Hence, if the skipping phase is performed at constant angle of attack, the tangential and total accelerations are proportional to the normal acceleration.

After considering the velocity distribution (71), calculating the integration constants in terms of the initial conditions, and using the approximation (70), one can derive the following expression for the normal acceleration:

$$\frac{\alpha_n}{u_i^2} \cong (\cos\gamma - \cos\gamma_i) \exp\left[\frac{2(\gamma_i - \gamma)}{E}\right] \qquad (82)$$

which attains a stationary value at that point of the descending branch where

$$\sin\gamma + \frac{2}{E}(\cos\gamma - \cos\gamma_i) = 0 \qquad (83)$$

The solution of this equation is represented by (Ref. 13)

$$\sin\gamma = \frac{2}{E^2 + 4}(E\cos\gamma_i - \sqrt{E^2 + 4\sin^2\gamma_i}) \qquad (84)$$

and is plotted in Fig. 11 versus the aerodynamic efficiency for several values of the entrance angle. The corresponding maximum values of the normal, tangential, and total accelerations are indicated in Figs. 12 through 14 versus the aerodynamic efficiency and the entrance angle.

The main conclusion to be derived from these diagrams is that the maximum acceleration increases very rapidly with the entrance velocity and the modulus of the entrance angle. Thus, accelerations in the order of 20–30 times the acceleration of gravity are possible during the skipping phase, a rather negative circumstance from a structural standpoint

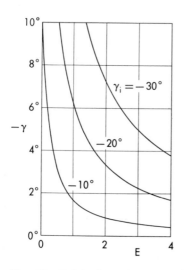

Fig. 11. Point of maximum acceleration.

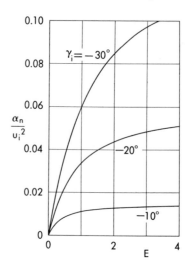

Fig. 12. Maximum normal acceleration.

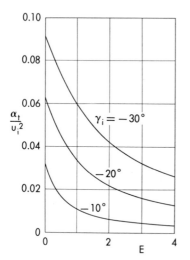

Fig. 13. Maximum tangential deceleration.

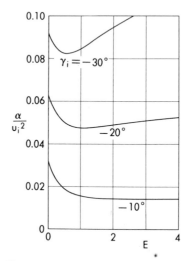

Fig. 14. Maximum total acceleration.

and, for manned vehicles, from a physiological viewpoint. Notice that, while the normal acceleration increases monotonically with the aerodynamic efficiency, the tangential acceleration decreases. Hence, the total acceleration has a minimum with respect to the aerodynamic efficiency; this minimum occurs for $E = 1$ if the entrance angle is $-20°$.

EXERCISES

1. Consider the reentry of a ballistic missile. Neglect the effects of gravity in the equation of motion on the tangent to the flight path, and assume that the drag coefficient is constant. With reference to an exponential atmosphere, determine the distributions of the nondimensional time $\theta = t\sqrt{g/\lambda}$ and the path inclination, assuming that $\sin \gamma$ and $\cot \gamma$ can be approximated by their values at the initial point. Show that

$$\theta = -\frac{Ei(\pi/2)}{u_i \sin \gamma_i} + \text{Const}, \qquad \gamma = \frac{\cot \gamma_i}{u_i^2} Ei(\pi) + \text{Const} \qquad (85)$$

2. Consider the reentry of a ballistic missile. Include the effects of gravity in the equation of motion on the tangent to the flight path, and assume that the drag coefficient is constant and that the density is an arbitrary function of the altitude. Define the dimensionless quantities

$$\epsilon = \frac{1}{2}\left(\frac{V}{a_o}\right)^2, \qquad \eta = \frac{hg}{a_o^2}, \qquad \alpha = -\frac{C_D S k p_o}{W \sin \gamma_i}, \qquad I(\eta) = \int_0^\eta \sigma \, d\eta \qquad (86)$$

where a_o is the speed of sound at sea level, p_o the atmospheric pressure at sea level, and k the ratio of the specific heats. Show that the distribution of dimensionless kinetic energy is given by

$$\epsilon = \left\{ C - \int_0^\eta \exp\left[-\alpha I(\eta)\right] d\eta \right\} \exp\left[\alpha I(\eta)\right] \qquad (87)$$

3. Consider the reentry of a variable-geometry ballistic missile in an exponential atmosphere. Include the effects of gravity in the equation of motion on the tangent to the flight path, and assume that the ballistic factor varies with the altitude according to Eq. (34). Prove that the coordinate transformation defined by Eqs. (35) reduces the second of Eqs. (39) to Eq. (40), that is, to the same differential equation which governs the reentry of a constant-geometry missile. Also, prove that the kinetic energy distribution (41) and the acceleration distribution (49) are still valid provided that the integration constant C is given by

$$C = (1 - x)\left(\frac{u_i^2}{2} + \eta_i\right) - \gamma_E - \log\frac{2K_{BO}}{1 - x} \qquad (88)$$

4. In connection with hypotheses (54), show that the instantaneous value of the path inclination associated with a glide trajectory is given by

$$\gamma = \frac{2g}{EV^2}\frac{dh}{d\log\rho} \qquad (89)$$

which reduces to

$$\gamma = -\frac{2}{Eu^2} \tag{90}$$

for flight in an exponential atmosphere.

5. In connection with hypotheses (54), prove that the geometry of a glide trajectory flown in an exponential atmosphere is given by

$$2K_D\xi + \exp(\eta) = \text{Const} \tag{91}$$

6. Consider a skipping path flown with constant angle of attack in an exponential atmosphere. After defining the quantity

$$\omega = \frac{K_L}{\sin^2 \gamma_i} \exp(-\eta_i) \tag{92}$$

and neglecting first-order terms in ω in the constant A but including them in the constant B (this is necessary in order to prevent the logarithmic expression appearing on the right-hand side of Eq. (76) from becoming infinitely large), show that

$$A = \cot \gamma_i, \qquad B = -(1 + \omega) \tan \frac{\gamma_i}{2} \tag{93}$$

Since the distribution of abscissas simplifies to

$$\xi = \gamma - \gamma_i - \cot \gamma_i \log \left[\frac{2 + \omega}{\omega} \frac{(1 + \omega) \tan \frac{\gamma_i}{2} - \tan \frac{\gamma}{2}}{(1 + \omega) \tan \frac{\gamma_i}{2} + \tan \frac{\gamma}{2}} \right] \tag{94}$$

prove that, under the further approximation $\omega \ll 1$, the over-all range flown during the skipping phase is given by

$$\xi_f = -2\gamma_i - 2 \cot \gamma_i \left[\eta_i + \log \frac{2 \sin^2 \gamma_i}{K_L} \right] \tag{95}$$

7. Consider a skipping path flown with constant angle of attack in an arbitrary atmosphere. Show that the following expressions hold:

$$V \exp\left(\frac{\gamma}{E}\right) = C_1, \qquad p - \frac{2W}{C_L S} \cos \gamma = C_2 \tag{96}$$

where p is the local atmospheric pressure. Furthermore, assuming that $X_i = 0$, prove that the geometry of the flight path is given by

$$X = \int_{h_i}^{h} \frac{dh}{\sqrt{\left(\frac{2W/C_L S}{p - C_2}\right)^2 - 1}} \tag{97}$$

REFERENCES

1. ALLEN, H. J. and EGGERS, A. J., *A Study of the Motion and Aerodynamic Heating of Missiles Entering the Earth's Atmosphere at High Supersonic Speeds*, NACA TN No. 4047, 1957.
2. LINNELL, R. D., *Vertical Reentry into the Earth's Atmosphere for Both Light and Heavy Bodies*, ARS Journal, Vol. 28, No. 5, 1958.
3. MALINA, F. J. and SMITH, A. M. O., *Flight Analysis of the Sounding Rocket*, Journal of the Aerospace Sciences, Vol. 5, No. 5, 1938.
4. NATIONAL BUREAU OF STANDARDS, *Tables of Sine, Cosine, and Exponential Integrals*, Vols. 1 and 2, 1940.
5. TURNACLIFF, R. D. and HARTNETT, J. P., *Generalized Trajectories for Free-Falling Bodies of High Drag*, ARS Journal, Vol. 28, No. 4, 1958.
6. KATZEN, E. D., *Terminal Phase of Satellite Entry into the Earth's Atmosphere*, ARS Journal, Vol. 29, No. 2, 1959.
7. EGGERS, A. J., ALLEN, H. J., and NEICE, S. E., *A Comparative Analysis of the Performance of Long-Range Hypervelocity Vehicles*, NACA TN No. 4046, 1957.
8. SÄNGER, E. and BREDT, J., *A Rocket Drive for Long Range Bombers*, Bureau of Aeronautics, Navy Department, Translation No. CGD-32, 1944.
9. GAZLEY, C., *Heat Transfer Aspects of the Atmospheric Reentry of Long-Range Ballistic Missiles*, The Rand Corporation, Report No. R-273, 1954.
10. ENKENHUS, K. R., *The Flight Environment of Long-Range Ballistic Missiles and Glide Vehicles*, US Naval Ordnance Laboratory, NAVORD Report No. 6745, 1959.
11. WARDEN, R. V., *Ballistic Reentries with a Varying $W/C_D A$*, ARS Journal, Vol. 31, No. 2, 1961.
12. BLUM, R., *Reentry Trajectories: Flat Earth Approximation*, ARS Journal, Vol. 32, No. 4, 1962.
13. MOE, M. M., *An Approximation to the Reentry Trajectory*, ARS Journal, Vol. 30, No. 1, 1960.
14. MIELE, A. and CAPPELLARI, J. O., *Effect of Drag Modulation on the Maximum Deceleration Encountered by a Reentering Ballistic Missile*, Purdue University, School of Aeronautical Engineering, Report No. A-59-6, 1959.
15. MIELE, A., *Analytical Theory of the Flight Paths of a Glider Over a Flat Earth*, Boeing Scientific Research Laboratories, Flight Sciences Laboratory, TR No. 23, 1960.

CHAPTER 14

AERODYNAMIC HEATING OF HYPERVELOCITY VEHICLES

by

Martin H. Bloom* and Angelo Miele

1. INTRODUCTION

The study of the thermal problems encountered by high-speed aircraft, missiles, and space vehicles is of fundamental interest to the engineer involved in planning flight operations and in designing a vehicle for a given mission. Owing to the many possible combinations of speed regimes and vehicle components, the literature on the subject is immense. However, since a complete discussion of heat transfer phenomena is beyond the scope of this textbook, only those elements which are necessary for the analytical development of the theory of hypervelocity flight paths and for the qualitative understanding of the relationships between Flight Mechanics, Heat Transfer, and Aerodynamic Design are presented.

In the following sections, the physical mechanisms of heat flow are discussed, and representative formulas for estimating heat transfer rates in the hypervelocity regime are presented. Then, attention is focused on the methods employed in order to protect and cool the surfaces of an aircraft or a missile. Finally, the aerodynamic heating of ballistic missiles, glide vehicles, and skip vehicles is analyzed, and an engineering comparison of these vehicles is carried out. To prevent confusion, units of the British Engineering System are used throughout the chapter; hence, forces, lengths, times, and temperatures are measured in pounds, feet, seconds, and degrees Rankine, respectively. Derived quantities are expressed in consistent units; in particular, heat energy, heat energy per unit time, and heat energy per unit time and unit area are measured in foot-pounds, foot-pounds per second, and pounds per foot and second, respectively.

2. MECHANISMS OF HEAT FLOW INTO THE VEHICLE

When an aircraft or a missile travels in the atmosphere, several phenomena occur which cause heat to be transferred from the surrounding medium to the vehicle. If, for the sake of discussion, supersonic flight

---

* Professor of Aerospace Sciences, Polytechnic Institute of Brooklyn.

is considered, it is clear that a system of shock waves is formed and that the resulting deceleration of the flow causes the formation of high temperature regions in the inviscid flow between the shock system and the body. In addition, since the velocity of the stream relative to the aircraft must vanish at the surface (zero-slip condition), an additional deceleration occurs in the boundary layer, resulting in a further increase in the static enthalpy of the air. Thus, if the temperature at a small distance from the body is higher than the surface temperature, thermal energy flows into the body. As the flight velocity increases, the temperatures in the inviscid flow and in the boundary layer increase and may reach levels where the following phenomena occur in succession: (a) *molecular vibration*; and (b) *dissociation, ionization,* and *recombination.* Furthermore, since these processes do not occur instantaneously, the flow may not be in thermodynamic equilibrium.

It can be surmised from the above discussion that the array of phenomena occurring in the immediate neighborhood of a body is extremely complex. The end result of all this is that heat is transferred in two ways: (a) *convective heating* associated with the transport processes in the boundary layer and (b) *radiant heating* associated with the electromagnetic properties of high-temperature gases. In particular, if convective heating is examined in detail, two coexisting mechanisms can be determined: heat conduction and mass diffusion. While *heat conduction* is the fraction of the convective heating which is due to the temperature gradients in the boundary layer, *mass diffusion* is the fraction due to the concentration gradients of chemical components. In turn, the latter are caused by the chemical reactions previously mentioned as well as by additional factors such as the injection of foreign matter into the boundary layer (for instance, a coolant or the particles leaving the surface because of ablative processes).

2.1 Convective heating. The analytical and functional representation of the convective heating rates can be reduced to its simplest form if the significant dimensionless groups are expressed in terms of the local flow conditions at the outer edge of the boundary layer. While this point of view is useful in heat transfer theory, it is necessary for Flight Mechanics analyses that the heating rates be expressed in terms of the free-stream conditions. Consequently, one must correlate the outer-edge conditions and the free-stream conditions; this operation does not offer any conceptual difficulties and can be achieved by analyzing the inviscid flow around the body. As a result, the convective heating rates can be functionally (and sometimes analytically) represented in terms of a new set of dimensionless parameters involving only free-stream conditions. In accordance with the philosophy of this chapter, the detailed transformations necessary to pass from one representation to the other are omitted; thus, the pertinent heat transfer relations are expressed directly in terms of flight conditions.

Now, for a family of geometrically similar, symmetric configurations operating at zero sideslip, dimensional analysis indicates that the following parameters are fundamental in representing the heat transfer rates:

(a) The angle of attack α.

(b) The *Mach number* $M = V/a$, where V is the velocity and a the speed of sound.

(c) The *Reynolds number* $R_e = \rho V l / \mu$, where ρ is the density, μ the dynamic viscosity, and l a characteristic length of the vehicle.

(d) The ratio of the specific heats k.

(e) The *Prandtl number* $P_r = \mu c_p / K$, where c_p is the specific heat at constant pressure and K the thermal conductivity. This number characterizes the interaction between viscous dissipation effects, heat capacity effects, and thermal conductivity effects. For air, its order of magnitude is one.

(f) The *Lewis number* $L_e = \rho D c_p / K$, where D is the diffusion coefficient. This number characterizes the interaction between mass diffusion effects, heat capacity effects, and thermal conductivity effects. For air, its order of magnitude is one.

(g) The temperature ratio $\tau = \theta_w / \theta$, where θ_w is the wall temperature and θ the free-stream temperature.

(h) The particular station P at which heat transfer is being calculated.

(i) The *Stanton number* $S_t = \dot{q} / \rho V E$, where $\dot{q}$ is the heat transferred per unit area and unit time and E a reference energy per unit mass. In particular, if this energy is chosen to be the kinetic energy per unit mass (that is, if $E = V^2/2$), the Stanton number takes the form

$$S_t = \frac{2\dot{q}}{\rho V^3} \tag{1}$$

which is used henceforth in this chapter.

When these definitions are employed, the convective heat transfer from the boundary layer to the surface can be represented by the functional relationship*

$$S_t = F(\alpha, M, R_e, k, P_r, L_e, \tau, P) \tag{2}$$

---

* Other dimensionless groups may arise by a more detailed consideration of chemical reactions, mass transfer, and ablation. Furthermore, the groups appearing in Eq. (2) can be replaced by any other set formed by combination of those cited. Thus, the widely used Nusselt number is defined as the product of the Stanton, Prandtl, and Reynolds numbers and may replace the Stanton number as a measure of the heat transfer rates.

TABLE 1

	C	x	y	z
Stagnation point (laminar flow)	1.55×10^{-5}	0.5	3	0.5
Sonic point (turbulent flow)	7.45×10^{-4}	0.8	3	0.2

in which the function F depends on the geometry of the body. Once this function is known, one can determine the distribution of heating rates over the surface and, thus, investigate the possible existence of regions which are critical from a thermal point of view; furthermore, upon integration of the heating rate over the wetted area, one can calculate the over-all heating rate to the vehicle.

The leading edge of the wing and the nose of the fuselage are among the regions where the heating rate achieves its highest values and, for this reason, deserve special attention. In particular, for a relatively cool* hemispheric nose in hypersonic flow with the Prandtl and Lewis numbers equal to one, two typical behaviors are possible. For relatively low Reynolds numbers, the boundary layer is entirely laminar, and the distribution of heating rates over the nose exhibits a maximum at the stagnation point. On the other hand, for relatively high Reynolds numbers, the boundary layer becomes turbulent at some distance from the stagnation point, and a second maximum occurs at approximately the sonic point, that is, the point where the flow at the outer edge has a Mach number of one. For these special points, Eq. (2) can be written in the simplified form

$$S_t = \frac{f(M)}{R_e^z} \tag{3}$$

where z is a contant. In particular, if the function $f(M)$ is approximated by a power law and if convenient average values are assumed for the speed of sound and the dynamic viscosity, Eq. (3) becomes

$$\dot{q} = C \, \frac{\rho^x V^y}{r^z} \tag{4}$$

The dimensional constant C and the dimensionless exponents x, y, z have the representative values indicated in Table 1 (Refs. 3 and 14). Inci-

---

* By definition, a surface is relatively cool if the difference between the static enthalpy at the wall and the free-stream static enthalpy is negligible with respect to the free-stream kinetic energy per unit mass.

dentally, the heat transfer rates calculated with Eq. (4) neglect non-equilibrium thermodynamic effects (Ref. 8) and, for that reason, are overestimated for most engineering applications.

In order to determine the over-all heating rate $\dot{Q}$, it is necessary to integrate the local heating rate over the entire wetted area of the vehicle. Thus, if $d\sigma$ denotes the element of exposed area and S_w the wetted area, the relationship

$$\dot{Q} = \int_{S_w} \dot{q}\, d\sigma = \frac{\rho V^3}{2} \int_{S_w} S_t\, d\sigma \tag{5}$$

holds. Owing to the common origin of heat flux phenomena and skin friction phenomena, the Stanton number is related to the skin friction coefficient. The relationship in question is called *Reynolds' analogy* and, for a relatively cool, curved surface in hypersonic flow, can be expressed in the form (Ref. 1)

$$S_t = \frac{C_f}{2} \frac{\rho_e V_e}{\rho V} \tag{6}$$

where the subscript e denotes quantities evaluated at the outer edge of the boundary layer. Consequently, the over-all heating rate becomes

$$\dot{Q} = \tfrac{1}{4} C_F \rho S_w V^3 \tag{7}$$

where

$$C_F = \frac{1}{S_w} \int_{S_w} C_f \frac{\rho_e V_e}{\rho V}\, d\sigma \tag{8}$$

is a weighted mean friction coefficient called the *equivalent skin-friction coefficient*. The evaluation of the integral on the right-hand side of Eq. (8) requires that the properties of the inviscid flow and the skin-friction coefficient be known at all points of the wetted area. Since these elements depend mainly on the angle of attack, the Reynolds number, and the Mach number, the equivalent skin friction coefficient of a body of given geometry also depends on the angle of attack, the Reynolds number, and the Mach number. However, for ballistic missiles and skip vehicles reentering the atmosphere at zero or constant angle of attack, the variation in the equivalent skin-friction coefficient along the flight trajectory can be neglected as far as preliminary design estimates are concerned (Refs. 1 and 2). Since this point of view yields considerable simplifications in the analysis of flight paths, it is retained throughout the remainder of this chapter.

2.2 Radiant heating. There are two forms of radiant heating from the outside environment to the vehicle: the radiation due to the gaseous cap surrounding the vehicle and the solar radiation. Both are governed by the Stefan-Boltzmann law and, therefore, depend on the emissivity and the temperature of the source.

To evaluate the radiation from the gaseous cap to the vehicle, the distribution of emissivities and temperatures in the flow field must be known. Since these quantities can be related to the free-stream condition, the radiant heating rate at a given point of a body of given geometry can be expressed in terms of the free-stream conditions only. As an example, for a hemispheric nose in hypersonic flow at velocities below 30,000 ft sec^{-1}, the radiant heating rate from the gaseous cap (assumed to be in thermodynamic equilibrium) to the body in the neighborhood of the stagnation point can be approximated by (Ref. 15)

$$\dot{q} = Cr\rho^{1.6}V^{8.5} \qquad (9)$$

where $C = 1.23 \times 10^{-25}$. Generally speaking, radiant heating is negligible with respect to convective heating in the velocity-altitude domain of interest for ballistic missiles, glide vehicles, and skip vehicles (see exercises). On the other hand, the radiant heat transfer is important for the reentry of satellite vehicles and space vehicles. For these vehicles, deviations from thermodynamic equilibrium may increase the radiant heating rate somewhat.

- The term *solar radiation* is employed to designate the combined effect of the direct solar radiation and that due to terrestrial and interstellar sources; it varies with time and depends on the position and the orientation of the vehicle in space. Its absolute value is usually negligible with respect to the other forms of heat transfer encountered by vehicles operating within the atmosphere.

3. VEHICLE PROTECTION AND COOLING

The next step is to examine the devices by which a surface can be protected and cooled. Customarily, these devices are separated into the following main classes: heat exchangers, heat sinks, radiant shields, mass transfer systems, and ablative systems.

In the usual *heat exchanger,* a coolant is circulated in the interior of a structure and withdraws heat from the structure by convection.

In the *heat-sink system,* a mass of material is employed to conduct away and store the heat entering the surfaces of the body. Two particular properties determine the merit of such a system: (a) the thermal diffusivity and, hence, the ability to conduct heat energy away before local melting occurs and (b) the heat-retention capacity per unit weight. Rarely do these properties go together. Thus, copper has an extremely high thermal diffusivity but a poor heat-retention capacity, while the opposite is true of beryllium.

Even though every system radiates thermal energy to some degree, it is appropriate to define a *radiant shield* as any system in which radiation to the surrounding environment is a major factor in the protection from thermal effects. The heat radiated per unit time and unit area is given by the well-known formula

$$\dot{q} = \epsilon \sigma \theta_w^4 \qquad (10)$$

where $\sigma = 3.70 \times 10^{-10}$ is the Stefan-Boltzmann radiation constant, ϵ the emissivity (it varies between 0 and 1), and θ_w the absolute temperature of the surface. For ballistic missiles, skip vehicles, satellite vehicles, and reentering spacecraft, the radiant cooling is generally small with respect to the convective heating; consequently, these vehicles require protection by means of heat sink or ablation systems. On the other hand, for hypervelocity gliders and supersonic aircraft, the radiant cooling rate may have the same order of magnitude as the convective heating rate; thus, effective use can be made of radiant shields if the surface temperature is allowed to be 2000°R or higher.

In the *mass transfer system*, a coolant is injected into the flow through either a porous surface or slots and holes in the wall. Because of this, a thin film of gas or liquid forms over the surface and modifies the flow field within the boundary layer. Consequently, the passage of heat to the body is reduced or blocked by a combined effect of heat absorption, vaporization, and thickening of the boundary layer. While this scheme has considerable scientific interest, it has practical disadvantages because of the difficulty of building porous surfaces, the necessity of using additional equipment, and the associated decrease in reliability.

In the *ablative system*, a solid surface is permitted to be destroyed systematically while maintaining the integrity of the structure (Refs. 12 and 13). When subjected to a heat flux, this system behaves initially as a heat sink. As the temperature increases, heat is radiated to the surrounding medium, while mass may be lost due to degassing phenomena. Finally, ablation starts and may involve processes such as melting, vaporization, sublimation, and pyrolysis. Hence, heat is absorbed or blocked from the surface by phase changes, mass transfer, and radiation. Two particular properties determine the merit of an ablative system: (a) the ability to insulate the back-up surface and (b) the capacity to absorb thermal energy. Hence, the combination of poor thermal diffusivity with high effective heats of ablation is desirable. Owing to the fact that, with materials such as teflon, effective heats of ablation equal to several times that required to vaporize water are possible, ablative systems have become of primary interest for reentering ballistic missiles, satellites, and spacecraft.

4. REENTRY OF A BALLISTIC MISSILE

In the previous chapter, the reentry of a ballistic missile was analyzed under the assumptions that the lift is zero, that the drag coefficient is constant, and that the air density is an exponential function of the altitude. Solutions for the velocity and the deceleration in terms of the altitude were derived disregarding the changes in the path inclination caused by the force of gravity.

In this section, the aerodynamic heating of the missile is considered, and the following topics are analyzed: (a) the over-all heat transfer to the wetted area; (b) the rate of heat transfer to the wetted area; and (c) the rate of heat transfer at either the laminar stagnation point or the turbulent sonic point of the nose. The solution of the first problem is of paramount importance in determining the amount and the type of thermal protection (e.g., heat sink system or ablation system) which is required by the missile. In turn, the solution of the second and third problems determines the engineering precautions to be used in order to prevent excessive thermal stresses and/or deterioration of the surface.

Since the results of the previous chapter indicated that only a small error is introduced in the velocity distribution by neglecting the effect of gravity in the equation of motion on the tangent to the flight path, this point of view is retained here. Furthermore, since the radiant heating is generally negligible with respect to the convective heating, only the latter is considered.

4.1 Over-all heat transfer. If the hypotheses of Section 2.1 are employed, the rate of heat transfer to the wetted area is governed by the differential relationship

$$\dot{Q} = \tfrac{1}{4} C_F \rho S_w V^3 \tag{11}$$

in which C_F is the equivalent skin-friction coefficient, ρ the density, S_w the wetted area, and V the velocity. If gravitational effects are neglected, the third of Eqs. (13–18) in combination with the definition of the aerodynamic drag yields the following expression for the instantaneous deceleration:

$$\dot{V} = -\frac{g C_D \rho S V^2}{2W} \tag{12}$$

where W is the weight, g the acceleration of gravity, C_D the drag coefficient, and S a reference area. Consequently, the heat transfer per unit velocity variation becomes

$$\frac{dQ}{dV} = -\frac{W}{2g} \frac{C_F S_w}{C_D S} V \tag{13}$$

After the end-conditions

$$Q_i = 0, \qquad Q_f = Q \tag{14}$$

are employed and constant values are assumed for the equivalent skin-friction coefficient and the drag coefficient, the above differential equation can be integrated to give

$$Q = \frac{W}{4g} \frac{C_F S_w}{C_D S} (V_i^2 - V_f^2) \tag{15}$$

The meaning of this equation becomes clear if the law of conservation of energy is applied to the endpoints of the path under the assumption that the variation of potential energy is negligible with respect to the variation of kinetic energy. Clearly, the initial kinetic energy must be equal to the sum of the final kinetic energy and the energy dissipated because of the aerodynamic drag. While part of the latter is contained in the wake of the missile, the remainder Q enters the body in the form of heat.

Now, consider an exponential atmosphere whose scale-height factor is λ, and assume that the final point is located at sea level. After the ballistic factor and the frictional ballistic factor (that part of the ballistic factor which is due to the friction drag) are defined as

$$K_B = -\frac{C_D \rho_o S \lambda g}{2W \sin \gamma_i}, \qquad K_{BF} = -\frac{C_F \rho_o S_w \lambda g}{2W \sin \gamma_i} \tag{16}$$

the following relationship holds:

$$\frac{C_F S_w}{C_D S} = \frac{K_{BF}}{K_B} \tag{17}$$

Furthermore, after the reference energy $Q_R = WV_i^2/2g$ is introduced and it is observed that the ratio of the final velocity to the initial velocity is given by [see Eq. (13–33)]

$$\frac{V_f}{V_i} = \exp(-K_B) \tag{18}$$

the fraction of the initial kinetic energy which is transferred to the missile in the form of heat can be rewritten as

$$\frac{Q}{Q_R} = \frac{1}{2} \frac{K_{BF}}{K_B} [1 - \exp(-2K_B)] \tag{19}$$

This relationship can be employed to study the effect of the geometry of the configuration on the over-all heat transfer. However, since detailed design considerations are beyond the scope of this section, attention is focused on two limiting cases only: that of a relatively light ballistic missile $(K_B \gg 1)$ and that of a relatively heavy ballistic missile $(K_B \ll 1)$.

For a relatively light ballistic missile (one strongly retarded by aerodynamic forces), the final velocity is negligible with respect to the initial velocity. Consequently, the previous equation simplifies to

$$\frac{Q}{Q_R} = \frac{1}{2} \frac{K_{BF}}{K_B} \tag{20}$$

from which it is clear that the fraction of the initial kinetic energy transferred to the body by convective heating is equal to one-half the ratio of the friction drag to the total drag. Hence, in order to minimize the heat convected to the missile, the *bluntness ratio* K_{BF}/K_B must be made as small as possible, that is, the ratio of the pressure drag to the friction drag must be made as large as possible.* This can be achieved by employing a shape of high pressure drag, that is, a blunt shape (Ref. 1).

For a relatively heavy ballistic missile (one slightly retarded by aerodynamic forces), the final velocity is almost equal to the initial velocity. Consequently, the Maclaurin approximation

$$\exp\,(-2K_B) \cong 1 - 2K_B \tag{21}$$

is justifiable, and Eq. (19) becomes

$$\frac{Q}{Q_R} = K_{BF} \tag{22}$$

Since the fraction of the initial kinetic energy transferred to the missile in the form of heat is equal to the frictional ballistic factor, the latter must be made as small as possible. Consequently, a shape of low friction drag must be employed. Incidentally, in several of the cases investigated in Ref. 1, this shape is a slender body.

4.2 Over-all heating rate. In this section, the distribution of heating rates along a reentry path is investigated. Since the density increases and the velocity decreases along the path, the heating rate exhibits a stationary point. To determine this point, the velocity distribution is written in the form [see Eq. (13–25)]

$$\frac{V}{V_i} = \exp\left(-\frac{\pi}{2}\right) \tag{23}$$

---

* In several actual designs, the bluntness factor is on the order of 1/10. Hence, about 1/20 of the initial kinetic energy is transferred to the body in the form of heat. This reduction is significant, in that the initial kinetic energy has the same order of magnitude as the thermal energy required to vaporize the missile regardless of its construction.

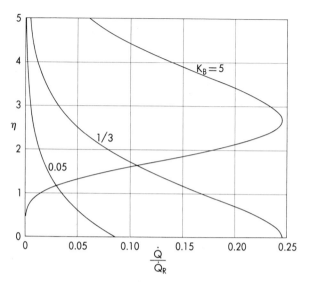

Fig. 1. Over-all heating rate–altitude diagram for several values of the ballistic factor.

where $\pi = 2K_B\rho/\rho_o$. Consequently, after the reference heating rate

$$\dot{Q}_R = -\frac{W}{4\lambda g}\frac{K_{BF}}{K_B}V_i^3 \sin \gamma_i \tag{24}$$

is introduced, the heating rate to the wetted area becomes

$$\frac{\dot{Q}}{\dot{Q}_R} = \pi \exp\left(-\frac{3\pi}{2}\right) \tag{25}$$

and is plotted in Fig. 1 versus the dimensionless altitude for several values of the ballistic factor. It appears that the heating rate has two possible behaviors depending on whether the ballistic factor is larger or smaller than 1/3.

If the configuration is such that $K_B > 1/3$, the heating rate has the following analytical maximum:

$$\frac{\dot{Q}}{\dot{Q}_R} = \frac{2}{3e} \tag{26}$$

which occurs when $\pi = 2/3$, that is, when the dimensionless altitude $\eta = h/\lambda$ has the value

$$\eta = \log\ (3K_B) \tag{27}$$

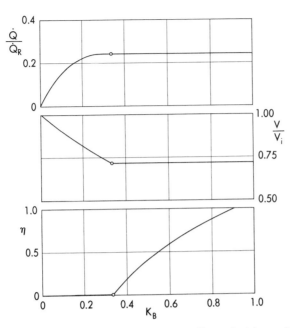

FIG. 2. Peak over-all heating rates and corresponding velocities and altitudes.

Since the corresponding velocity ratio is given by

$$\frac{V}{V_i} = \frac{1}{\sqrt[3]{e}} \tag{28}$$

the maximum heating rate occurs at the point where the instantaneous velocity is 72% of the entrance velocity. On the other hand, if the configuration is such that $K_B < 1/3$, the peak heating rate, not an analytical maximum, occurs at sea level and is given by

$$\frac{\dot{Q}}{\dot{Q}_R} = 2K_B \exp{(-3K_B)} \tag{29}$$

These results are summarized in Fig. 2, which supplies the envelope of the peak heating rates to the wetted area as well as the corresponding velocities and altitudes.

The main conclusion of this analysis is that, if the weight, the initial velocity, and the initial path inclination are given and if the ballistic factor is larger than 1/3 (in particular, if the missile is relatively light), the peak heating rate satisfies the proportionality relationship

$$\dot{Q} \sim \frac{K_{BF}}{K_B} \tag{30}$$

and, hence, is minimized if a blunt shape is employed. On the other hand, if the missile is relatively heavy, the previous equation must be replaced by

$$\dot{Q} \sim K_{BF} \tag{31}$$

so that the peak heating rate is minimized if a shape with a low friction drag is employed.

4.3 Heating rate to the nose. If the hypotheses of Section 2.1 are retained, the rate of heat transfer at either of the two critical points of the nose region can be represented in the form

$$\dot{q} = C \frac{\rho^x V^y}{r^z} \tag{32}$$

Since the density increases and the velocity decreases along the path, the heating rate has a stationary point. Prior to evaluating this point, it is convenient to introduce the reference heating rate

$$\dot{q}_R = C \left(\frac{\rho_o}{2K_B} \right)^x \frac{V_i^y}{r^z} \tag{33}$$

and rewrite the previous equation in the form

$$\frac{\dot{q}}{\dot{q}_R} = \pi^x \exp\left(-\frac{y\pi}{2} \right) \tag{34}$$

It appears that the rate of heat transfer has two possible behaviors depending on whether the ballistic factor is larger or smaller than x/y (that is, 1/6 for the laminar stagnation point and 4/15 for the turbulent sonic point).

If the configuration is such that $K_B > x/y$, the heating rate has the following analytical maximum:

$$\frac{\dot{q}}{\dot{q}_R} = \left(\frac{2x}{ey} \right)^x \tag{35}$$

which occurs for $\pi = 2x/y$, that is, for

$$\eta = \log\left(\frac{yK_B}{x} \right) \tag{36}$$

Since the corresponding velocity ratio is given by

$$\frac{V}{V_i} = \exp\left(-\frac{x}{y} \right) \tag{37}$$

the maximum heating rate at the laminar stagnation point occurs when the velocity is 85% of the entrance velocity, while the maximum heating rate at the turbulent sonic point occurs when the velocity is 77% of the entrance velocity. On the other hand, if the configuration is such that $K_B < x/y$, the peak heating rate, not an analytical maximum, occurs at sea level and is given by

$$\frac{\dot{q}}{\dot{q}_R} = (2K_B)^x \exp(-yK_B) \tag{38}$$

The main conclusion of this analysis is that, if the weight, the initial velocity, and the initial path inclination are given and if the ballistic factor is larger than x/y (in particular, if the missile is relatively light), the peak heating rate satisfies the proportionality relationship

$$\dot{q} \sim \frac{1}{K_B^x \, r^z} \tag{39}$$

and, therefore, is minimized if a large ballistic factor is employed in combination with a large radius of curvature at the nose. On the other hand, if the missile is relatively heavy, the previous equation must be replaced by

$$\dot{q} \sim \frac{1}{r^z} \tag{40}$$

so that the maximum heating rate becomes a function of the nose radius of curvature only; the higher the radius is, the lower the peak heating rate is.

In closing, the following remarks are pertinent:

(a) For a missile whose ballistic factor is larger than 4/15, the ratio of the peak heating rate at the turbulent sonic point (subscript T) to the peak heating rate at the laminar stagnation point (subscript L) is given by

$$\frac{\dot{q}_T}{\dot{q}_L} = C \left(\frac{r}{K_B}\right)^{0.3} \tag{41}$$

where $C \cong 4.9$ and is plotted in Fig. 3 versus the ballistic factor for several values of the radius at the nose. Thus, the peak turbulent heating rate is several times larger than the peak laminar heating rate.

(b) From the present discussion and from that of the previous chapter, it appears that several *critical points* exist along a reentry path. They are the points where the peak values of the heating rates and the deceleration occur. Although the altitudes associated with these points depend on the ballistic factor, their relative positions are independent of it (Fig. 4). More specifically, the peak heating rate at the stagnation point occurs first; the peak heating rate at the turbulent sonic point, the peak heating

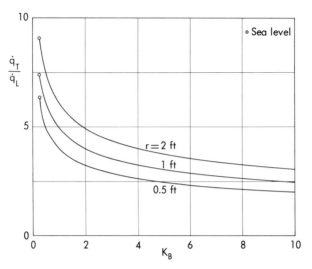

FIG. 3. Ratio of the peak heating rate at the turbulent sonic point to the peak heating rate at the laminar stagnation point.

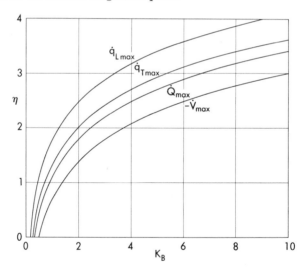

FIG. 4. Critical points in the reentry of a ballistic missile.

rate to the wetted area, and the peak deceleration follow in sequence; their corresponding altitudes are located 11,200 ft lower, 16,500 ft lower, and 26,100 ft lower, respectively, than the altitude corresponding to the peak heating rate at the stagnation point. In this connection, a particular example is shown in Fig. 5, where $\xi = X/\lambda$ denotes the dimensionless abscissa; this example refers to a missile whose ballistic factor is 5 and whose initial conditions are $\xi_i = 0$, $\eta_i = 10$, $\gamma_i = -30°$, $V_i/\sqrt{\lambda g} = 25$.

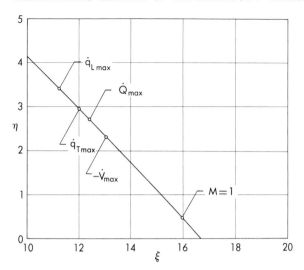

FIG. 5. Critical points in the reentry of a ballistic missile.

4.4 Remark. With reference to the *relatively heavy ballistic missile,* these comments are pertinent: (a) Although the engineering trend is toward lower values of the ballistic factor, the limiting case where $K_B \ll 1$ is difficult to achieve at present; (b) the heat transfer results of the previous sections can also be obtained by introducing into the pertinent relations the assumption that the velocity is constant, as is logical owing to the simultaneous neglect of the aerodynamic and gravitational forces; and (c) for intermediate range and long range ballistic missiles, the errors due to neglecting gravity are small, since the heating rates depend on the over-all velocity rather than on the velocity change and since the velocity change due to gravity is small with respect to the initial velocity.

5. REENTRY OF A GLIDE VEHICLE

In the previous chapter, the motion of a glide vehicle was analyzed under the assumptions that the path is smooth and shallow, that the weight component on the tangent to the flight path is negligible with respect to the aerodynamic drag, and that the angle of attack is constant. Here, the thermal problem is investigated in a manner similar to that of the ballistic missile. In particular, the following topics are investigated: (a) the over-all heat transfer to the wetted area and (b) the heating rates to the wetted area, the laminar stagnation point, and the turbulent sonic point.

5.1 Over-all heat transfer. For the glide vehicle, the expressions for the heating rate to the wetted area (11) and the instantaneous acceleration

(12) are identical with those of the ballistic missile. For this reason, the differential equation (13) and its integral (15) are still valid. Thus, after the *drag factor* and the *frictional drag factor* (that part of the drag factor which is due to the friction drag) are defined as

$$K_D = \frac{C_D \rho_o S \lambda g}{2W}, \qquad K_{DF} = \frac{C_F \rho_o S_w \lambda g}{2W} \tag{42}$$

Eq. (15) can be rewritten as

$$Q = \frac{W}{4g} \frac{K_{DF}}{K_D} (V_i^2 - V_f^2) \tag{43}$$

and simplifies to

$$\frac{Q}{Q_R} = \frac{1}{2} \frac{K_{DF}}{K_D} \tag{44}$$

if the final kinetic energy is small with respect to the initial kinetic energy (this is necessary in order to achieve range). Comparison of this equation with Eq. (20) shows that the over-all heat input for the glide vehicle is formally identical with the over-all heat input for the relatively light ballistic missile. Now, for the relatively light ballistic missile, the total heating is minimized by using a shape of high pressure drag, that is, a blunt shape. Unfortunately, this course of action is not possible for the glide vehicle, since a blunt shape is unavoidably characterized by a low lift-to-drag ratio and, hence, its ability to convert kinetic energy into range is poor. From the range viewpoint, it is essential that a glide configuration be relatively slender, even though some blunting can be tolerated in such regions as the leading edge of the wing and the nose of the fuselage. Now, if the *bluntness ratio* K_{DF}/K_D is dictated by range considerations, its value is higher than that of the ballistic missile; hence, for the same initial velocity, the glide vehicle absorbs more convective heating than the ballistic missile. In spite of this, the glide vehicle requires less coolant than the ballistic missile. The reason is that, while the order of magnitude of the over-all heat input is essentially the same for the two vehicles, the flight time of a glider is in the order of 100 times larger than that of a reentering ballistic missile; hence, the heating rates are reduced by a factor of 100. Thus, the glider is capable of radiating heat back to the atmosphere at a rate comparable to the convective heating rate,* while the ballistic missile is not.

---

* Computations presented in Ref. 2 indicate that a large fraction of the convective heating can be radiated back to the atmosphere if the surface temperature is allowed to rise to 2000°R and if a relatively low wing loading is employed.

Considerations of a local nature indicate that, while the thermal problem is especially severe for the nose of the fuselage and the leading edge of the wing, it can be alleviated by blunting the nose and rounding the leading edge. The negative aspects of blunting (namely, the increase in the drag and the decrease in the lift-to-drag ratio) can be offset by sweeping the wing, with the simultaneous advantage of reducing the drag and the heat transfer at the leading edge. Thus, the delta-wing configuration appears to be a logical engineering solution for the hypervelocity glider.

5.2 Heating rates. If the equation of motion on the normal to the flight path is combined with Eq. (11) and the density is eliminated, the over-all heating rate can be shown to be proportional to V. By a similar procedure, the heating rate at the nose becomes proportional to V^2 for the laminar stagnation point and to $V^{1.4}$ for the turbulent sonic point. Since the velocity decreases as the glider descends toward the lower layers of the atmosphere, the heating rates decrease along the flight path.

In closing, a word of caution is in order. A verification of the assumptions employed shows that they are satisfied only for velocities between 1/6 and 1/3 of the satellite velocity at sea level. For lower velocities, the relatively cool wall hypothesis as well as the assumption of a smooth, shallow path characterized by a negligible weight component on the tangent to the flight path become invalid. For higher velocities, the range may become such that the flat Earth model is no longer justified; in particular, the equation of motion on the normal to the flight path is to be modified, in the sense that the weight is to be replaced by the so-called *apparent weight*, that is, the difference between the actual weight and the centrifugal force which is due to the curvature of the Earth. Because of these reasons, the aerodynamic heating of a hypervelocity glider operating over a spherical Earth shall be considered in Volume 3. However, it can be anticipated that, while the conclusions relative to the heating rates are subject to considerable change, those relative to the over-all heat transfer are the same, since the equation of motion on the tangent to the flight path is, to a first approximation, unaffected by the consideration of the sphericity of the Earth.

6. REENTRY OF A SKIP VEHICLE

In the previous chapter, the motion of a skip vehicle was investigated under the assumptions that the gravitational forces are negligible with respect to the aerodynamic forces, that the angle of attack is constant, and that the atmosphere is exponential. Here, the thermal problem is investigated in a manner parallel to that of the ballistic missile and the glide vehicle. Both the over-all heat transfer and the distribution of heating rates are considered.

6.1 Over-all heat transfer. For the skip vehicle, the expressions for the heating rate to the wetted area (11) and the instantaneous acceleration (12) are identical with those of the ballistic missile and the glide vehicle. For this reason, the differential equation (13) is still valid. Furthermore, if the subscript k denotes quantities associated with the generic skip and if the end-conditions

$$Q_{ik} = 0, \qquad Q_{fk} = Q_k \tag{45}$$

are employed, the following result is obtained:

$$Q_k = \frac{W}{4g} \frac{K_{DF}}{K_D} (V_{ik}^2 - V_{fk}^2) \tag{46}$$

If the vehicle performs n skips with the same angle of attack, the total heat input over the entire trajectory is given by

$$Q = \frac{W}{4g} \frac{K_{DF}}{K_D} \sum_{k=1}^{n} (V_{ik}^2 - V_{fk}^2) \tag{47}$$

The evaluation of the summation appearing on the right-hand side of this equation requires the knowledge of the ballistic phase intermediate between any two skips. If the rotation of the Earth is neglected, the velocity at the beginning of each skip is equal to the velocity at the end of the previous skip (Volume 3); thus, if the recurrence relationship

$$V_{i(k+1)} = V_{fk} \tag{48}$$

is employed in combination with the assumptions

$$V_{i1} = V_i, \qquad V_{fn} = V_f \tag{49}$$

the series appearing in Eq. (47) has the sum

$$\sum_{k=1}^{n} (V_{ik}^2 - V_{fk}^2) = V_i^2 - V_f^2 \tag{50}$$

In particular, if the final kinetic energy is negligible with respect to the initial kinetic energy (this is necessary in order to achieve range), Eqs. (47) and (50) yield the following expression for the fraction of the initial kinetic energy transferred to the skip vehicle along the entire trajectory:

$$\frac{Q}{Q_R} = \frac{1}{2} \frac{K_{DF}}{K_D} \tag{51}$$

which is identical with that developed for the relatively light ballistic missile and the glide vehicle.

Because of range considerations, the bluntness ratio K_{DF}/K_D of the skip vehicle is generally higher than the bluntness ratio of the ballistic missile; hence, the skip vehicle absorbs more convective heating than the ballistic missile. In addition, comparison of the first skipping phase with a glide phase of equal decrease in kinetic energy shows that, owing to the difference in the flight times, the rate at which heat is convected to the skip vehicle is considerably larger than the rate at which heat is convected to the glide vehicle. Thus, while the glide vehicle is able to radiate thermal energy back to the atmosphere at a rate comparable to the convective rate, this is not true for the skip vehicle. In conclusion, the skip vehicle is thermally inferior to both the ballistic missile and the glide vehicle. Because of these reasons and because of the high accelerations experienced in the skipping phase, the skip vehicle is, from an engineering point of view, the least promising of the three types of hypervelocity vehicles considered here. This seems to be a generally accepted conclusion, even though, for some values of the lift-to-drag ratio, the skip vehicle is able to convert kinetic energy into range more efficiently than either the ballistic missile or the glide vehicle (Volume 3).

6.2 Heating rates. The next step is to determine the distribution of heating rates along the skipping path. Attention is focused on the first skip only, since this is the phase where the highest velocities occur and, hence, where the thermal problem is the most critical. Since the rate of heat transfer to the wetted area is proportional to ρV^3 and since the velocity decreases continuously along the path, peak heating can only occur in a region where the density is increasing, that is, in the descending branch of the trajectory. Concerning the ascending branch, the simultaneous decrease in the density and the velocity causes a sharp decrease in the heating rate.

Because of Eqs. (13–65) and (13–71), the distributions of density and velocity along the path can be written in the form

$$\frac{\rho}{\rho_o} = \frac{\cos \gamma - \cos \gamma_i}{K_L}$$

$$\frac{V}{V_i} = \exp\left(\frac{\gamma_i - \gamma}{E}\right) \tag{52}$$

where γ denotes the path inclination, E the lift-to-drag ratio, and

$$K_L = \frac{C_L \rho_o S \lambda g}{2W} \tag{53}$$

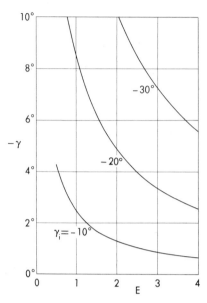

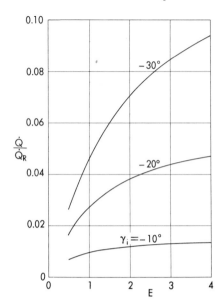

FIG. 6. Path inclination for peak over-all heating rate.

FIG. 7. Peak over-all heating rate.

the *lift factor*. Thus, after the reference heating rate

$$\dot{Q}_R = \frac{W}{2\lambda g} \frac{K_{DF}}{K_L} V_i^3 \tag{54}$$

is introduced, the over-all heating rate becomes

$$\frac{\dot{Q}}{\dot{Q}_R} = (\cos \gamma - \cos \gamma_i) \exp\left(3 \frac{\gamma_i - \gamma}{E}\right) \tag{55}$$

and attains a stationary value at that point of the descending branch of the trajectory where the relationship

$$\sin \gamma + \frac{3}{E} (\cos \gamma - \cos \gamma_i) = 0 \tag{56}$$

is satisfied. The solution of this equation is represented by

$$\sin \gamma = \frac{3}{9 + E^2} [E \cos \gamma_i - \sqrt{E^2 + 9 \sin^2 \gamma_i}] \tag{57}$$

and is plotted in Fig. 6 versus the aerodynamic efficiency for several values of the entrance angle. The corresponding values for the peak over-all heating rate are given in Fig. 7.

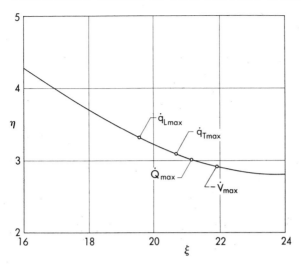

FIG. 8. Critical points in a skipping path.

By proceeding in much the same way, the distribution of heat inputs per unit area and unit time at the nose can be investigated. After the reference rate of heat transfer

$$\dot{q}_R = C \left(\frac{\rho_o}{K_L} \right)^x \frac{V_i^y}{r^z} \tag{58}$$

is introduced, the heating rate (4) can be written as

$$\frac{\dot{q}}{\dot{q}_R} = (\cos \gamma - \cos \gamma_i)^x \exp \left(y \frac{\gamma_i - \gamma}{E} \right) \tag{59}$$

and attains a stationary value when the condition

$$\sin \gamma + \frac{n}{E} (\cos \gamma - \cos \gamma_i) = 0 \tag{60}$$

is satisfied, where $n = y/x$. The solution of this equation is represented by

$$\sin \gamma = \frac{n}{n^2 + E^2} [E \cos \gamma_i - \sqrt{E^2 + n^2 \sin^2 \gamma_i}] \tag{61}$$

where $n = 6$ for the laminar stagnation point and $n = 15/4$ for the turbulent sonic point.

From the discussion of this chapter and that of the previous chapter, it appears that several *critical points* exist in a skipping path. They are the points where the peak values of the heating rates and the deceleration occur. Although their position on the skipping path depends on the lift-to-drag ratio and the initial path inclination, their sequence is independent of these parameters. More specifically, the peak heating rate at the stagnation point occurs first, while the peak heating rate at the turbulent sonic point, the peak heating rate to the wetted area, and the peak deceleration follow in sequence. In this connection, a particular example is shown in Fig. 8; it refers to a skip vehicle whose drag and lift factors are equal to one and whose initial conditions are

$$\xi_i = 0, \qquad \eta_i = 10, \qquad \gamma_i = -20°$$

EXERCISES

1. Consider the reentry of a ballistic missile, and retain all the hypotheses of Section 4.3. After defining the reference heat transfer per unit area at the stagnation point as

$$q_R = \frac{C\lambda V_i^2}{\sin(-\gamma_i)} \sqrt{\frac{\pi_* \rho_o}{2rK_B}} \qquad (62)$$

where $\pi_* = 3.14$, show that the time integral of the heat transfer per unit area at the stagnation point is given by

$$\frac{q}{q_R} = Erf(\sqrt{\pi_f}) - Erf(\sqrt{\pi_i}) \qquad (63)$$

where the error function is defined as

$$Erf(\sqrt{\pi}) = \frac{2}{\sqrt{\pi_*}} \int_0^{\sqrt{\pi}} \exp(-\pi) \, d(\sqrt{\pi}) \qquad (64)$$

Making use of convenient expansions for the error function, show that the proportionality relationship

$$q \sim \frac{1}{\sqrt{rK_B}} \qquad (65)$$

holds for the relatively light missile, while the proportionality relation

$$q \sim \frac{1}{\sqrt{r}} \qquad (66)$$

holds for the relatively heavy missile.

2. Consider the reentry of a ballistic missile in an isothermal atmosphere, and retain the hypotheses of Section 4. Show that the Reynolds number achieves the following maximum value:

$$R_e = \frac{\rho_o V_i l}{\mu e K_B} \qquad (67)$$

3. Consider the reentry of a ballistic missile, and employ the hypotheses of Section 4.2. Define the equilibrium temperature as the ideal

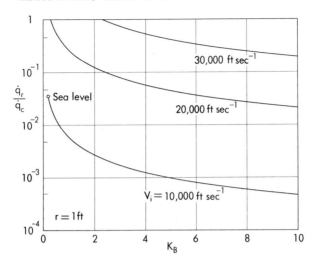

FIG. 9. Maximum ratio of the radiant heating to the convective heating for a ballistic missile.

temperature which the surface should achieve in order to radiate heat back to the atmosphere at a rate equal to the convective heating rate. Show that the distribution of the equilibrium temperature along the flight path is given by

$$\theta_w = \sqrt[4]{\frac{C_F}{4\epsilon\sigma} \rho V^3} \tag{68}$$

and achieves the following maximum value:

$$\theta_w = \sqrt[4]{\frac{C_F \rho_o V_i^3}{12\epsilon\sigma e K_B}} \tag{69}$$

4. Consider the stagnation point of the hemispheric nose of a missile, and define the *total rate of heat transfer* as the sum of the convective and radiant heating rates. Show that, for given values of the velocity and the altitude, this total rate of heat transfer has a minimum with respect to the nose radius. Prove that this minimum occurs when the radiant heating rate is one-half the convective heating rate.

5. Consider the stagnation point of the hemispheric nose of a reentering ballistic missile, and calculate the ratio of the radiant heating rate (subscript r) to the convective heating rate (subscript c). Retaining every hypothesis of Section 4.3, show that this ratio achieves the following maximum value (Fig. 9):

$$\frac{\dot{q}_r}{\dot{q}_c} = C \frac{r^{1.5} V_i^{5.5}}{K_B^{1.1}} \tag{70}$$

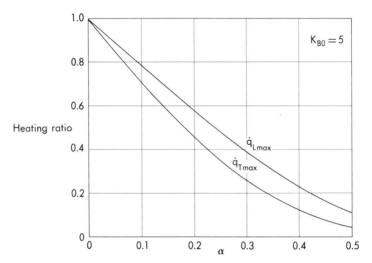

Fig. 10. Effect of the size of the spoilers on the peak heating rates to the nose of a variable-geometry missile.

where $C = 5.8 \times 10^{-25}$. Thus, for the velocities characteristic of intermediate range ballistic missiles, the radiant heating is negligible with respect to the convective heating. On the other hand, for an intercontinental ballistic missile, the radiant heating is negligible with respect to the convective heating only if the ballistic factor is larger than 2.

6. Consider the reentry of a variable-geometry missile excluding the effects of gravity. Retain the hypotheses of Section 3.1.1 of the previous chapter, that is, assume that the ballistic factor varies with the altitude according to the law

$$K_B = K_{BO}\left(\frac{\rho_o}{\rho}\right)^\alpha \tag{71}$$

where K_{BO} is the ballistic factor at sea level and α is a constant. Show that the peak heating rates at the laminar stagnation point and at the turbulent sonic point are reduced according to the ratios

$$\frac{\dot{q}(\alpha)}{\dot{q}(0)} = \left(\frac{x}{yeK_{BO}}\right)^{\alpha x/(1-\alpha)} \tag{72}$$

which are plotted in Fig. 10 for a missile whose ballistic factor at sea level is 5.

7. Consider the reentry of a constant-geometry missile, and retain the hypotheses of Section 4, but include the effects of gravity. Show that the peak heating rate to the wetted area, the peak heating rate at the laminar stagnation point, and the peak heating rate at the turbulent

sonic point occur when the following conditions are, respectively, satisfied:

$$C = \frac{3 \exp (\pi)}{3\pi - 2x} - Ei(\pi) \tag{73}$$

where C is the constant appearing in Eq. (13–45) and where $x = 1$ for the wetted area, $x = 1/2$ for the laminar stagnation point, and $x = 4/5$ for the turbulent sonic point.

8. Consider the reentry of a glide vehicle, and retain the hypotheses of Section 6. Show that the equilibrium temperature defined in Exercise 3 is given by

$$\theta_w = \sqrt[4]{\frac{V}{2\epsilon\sigma} \frac{C_F}{C_L} \frac{W}{S}} \tag{74}$$

Hence, for a given velocity, a decrease in the wing loading leads to a decrease in the equilibrium temperature.

ACKNOWLEDGMENT

The authors are indebted to Dr. Carl Gazley (The Rand Corporation), Dr. Dean R. Chapman (NASA), as well as Professors Paul S. Lykoudis and Robert J. Goulard (Purdue University) for constructive criticism.

REFERENCES

1. ALLEN, H. J. and EGGERS, A. J., *A Study of the Motion and Aerodynamic Heating of Missiles Entering the Earth's Atmosphere at High Supersonic Speeds*, NACA TN No. 4047, 1957.
2. EGGERS, A. J., ALLEN, H. J., and NEICE, S. E., *A Comparative Analysis of the Performance of Long-Range Hypervelocity Vehicles*, NACA TN No. 4046, 1957.
3. CHAPMAN, D. R., *An Approximate Analytical Method for Studying Entry into Planetary Atmospheres*, NACA TN No. 4276, 1958.
4. CHAPMAN, D. R., *An Analysis of the Corridor and Guidance Requirements for Supercircular Entry into Planetary Atmospheres*, NASA TR No. R-55, 1960.
5. DETRA, R. W. and HIDALGO, H., *Generalized Heat Transfer Formulae and Graphs*, AVCO Research Laboratory, Report No. 72, 1960.
6. ECKERT, E. R. G., *Survey of Boundary Layer Heat Transfer at High Velocities and High Temperatures*, WADC TR No. 59–624, 1960.
7. ENKENHUS, K. R., *The Flight Environment of Long-Range Ballistic Missiles and Glide Vehicles*, US Naval Ordnance Laboratory, NAVORD Report No. 6745, 1959.
8. FAY, J. A. and RIDDELL, F. R., *Theory of Stagnation Point Heat Transfer in Dissociated Air*, Journal of the Aerospace Sciences, Vol. 25, No. 2, 1958.

9. GAZLEY, C., *Heat Transfer Aspects of the Atmospheric Reentry of Long-Range Ballistic Missiles*, The Rand Corporation, Report No. R-273, 1954.
10. GAZLEY, C., *Deceleration and Heating of a Body Entering a Planetary Atmosphere from Space*, The Rand Corporation, Report No. P-955, 1957.
11. KIVEL, B. and BAILEY, K., *Tables of Radiation from High Temperature Air*, AVCO Research Laboratory, Report No. 21, 1957.
12. LEES, L., *Ablation in Hypersonic Flows*, IAS Preprint No. 59–146, 1959.
13. SCALA, S. M., *A Study of Hypersonic Ablation*, General Electric Missile and Space Vehicle Department, Report No. R59SD438, 1959.
14. SIBULKIN, M., *Estimation of Turbulent Heat Transfer at the Sonic Point of a Blunt-Nosed Body*, ARS Journal, Vol. 28, No. 8, 1958.
15. YOSHIKAWA, K. K. and WICK, B. H., *Radiative Heat Transfer during Atmosphere Entry at Parabolic Velocity*, NASA TN No. D-1074, 1961.
16. BLOOM, M., *Thermal Conditions Associated with Aircraft in Flight*, WADC TR No. 55–169, 1956.
17. BLOOM, M., *External Sources of Heat*, High Temperature Effects in Aircraft Structure, Pergamon Press, London, 1958.

CHAPTER 15

ROCKET PERFORMANCE
IN A VACUUM

1. INTRODUCTION

The fundamental characteristic of a rocket vehicle is that it carries both the fuel and the oxidizing agent necessary to create thrust. Consequently, powered flight in a vacuum is physically possible and is investigated here because of its great interest and mathematical simplicity.

In the analysis of rocket performance, several facts must be considered. First, because of the high rate of propellant consumption, the variation of the mass with the time must be taken into account. Second, the inertia terms are important everywhere along the flight path; thus, the quasi-steady state, which is characteristic of vehicles powered by air-breathing powerplants, is practically nonexistent as far as rocket operations are concerned. Third, for the particular case of flight in a vacuum, both the drag and the lift are zero. Fourth, since the control surfaces are useless in a vacuum, maneuvering can be accomplished only by varying the thrust modulus and/or the thrust direction. For these reasons, Eqs. (4–42) are rewritten as

$$\dot{X} - V \cos \gamma = 0$$
$$\dot{h} - V \sin \gamma = 0$$
$$T \cos \epsilon - m(g \sin \gamma + \dot{V}) = 0 \qquad (1)$$
$$T \sin \epsilon - m(g \cos \gamma + V\dot{\gamma}) = 0$$
$$\dot{m} + \beta = 0$$

where X denotes the horizontal distance, h the altitude, V the velocity, γ the path inclination, m the mass, T the thrust, β the propellant mass flow, ϵ the inclination of the thrust with respect to the velocity, g the acceleration of gravity, and the dot sign a derivative with respect to time.

1.1 Engine performance. According to Chapter 7, the thrust of a rocket engine operating in a vacuum is given by

$$T = \beta V_e + S_e p_e \qquad (2)$$

where V_e is the exit velocity, S_e the exit area, and p_e the exit pressure. Furthermore, if the *equivalent exit velocity*

$$V_E = V_e + \frac{S_e p_e}{\beta} \tag{3}$$

is introduced, the thrust can be rewritten in the form

$$T = \beta V_E \tag{4}$$

whose significance is now illustrated. Consider a constant geometry chemical rocket, and assume that the combustion chamber pressure (the control parameter of the engine) can be regulated in flight but that, by doing so, the combustion chamber temperature is unaffected. From one-dimensional aerodynamics of a perfect gas, it is known that, while the exit pressure and the propellant mass flow are linear functions of the combustion pressure, the exit velocity is independent of it. Hence, the equivalent exit velocity is independent of the combustion pressure and, in conclusion, is a characteristic of the engine, since it acts as a proportionality constant between the thrust and the mass flow.

1.2 Integration problem. In the light of Eq. (4), the equations of motion involve one independent variable, the time, and seven dependent variables $(X, h, V, \gamma, m, \beta, \epsilon)$. Therefore, there are two degrees of freedom, which is logical since the trajectory can be changed by controlling the thrust modulus and the thrust direction. Hence, for a given set of initial conditions for X, h, V, γ, m, infinite trajectories exist, more specifically, one trajectory for each arbitrarily prescribed pair of functions $\beta(t), \epsilon(t)$ or equivalent conditions. In this connection, the following sections consider the cases where (a) the thrust modulus is either constant or proportional to the instantaneous mass of the vehicle and (b) the thrust direction is either constant with respect to the horizon or tangent to the flight path (Refs. 1 through 6).

2. VERTICALLY ASCENDING PATHS

The performance along a vertically ascending path is now investigated. After the condition $\gamma = \pi/2$ is imposed, the kinematic relationship in the horizontal direction can be integrated to give $X = $ Const. Furthermore, the equation of motion on the normal to the flight path leads to $\epsilon = 0$, which means that the thrust is tangent to the flight path and, therefore, is always vertical. If the relationship between the thrust and the mass flow rate is considered, the remaining Eqs. (1) can be rewritten as

$$\dot{h} - V = 0$$

$$\dot{V} + g - \frac{\beta V_E}{m} = 0 \tag{5}$$

$$\dot{m} + \beta = 0$$

2.1 First integral. A mathematical consequence of the previous equations is the differential expression

$$dV + g\,dt + V_E \frac{dm}{m} = 0 \tag{6}$$

whose general integral is given by

$$V + gt + V_E \log m = \text{Const} \tag{7}$$

and holds independently of the rate at which propellant is being consumed, that is, regardless of the function $\beta(t)$. Incidentally, if the gravitational forces are negligible with respect to the thrust, this first integral simplifies to

$$V + V_E \log m = \text{Const} \tag{8}$$

2.2 Integration process. In order to integrate the equations of powered flight, it is convenient to select the instantaneous mass as the new independent variable and rewrite Eqs. (5) in the form

$$\frac{dh}{dm} + \frac{V}{\beta} = 0$$

$$\frac{dV}{dm} + \frac{V_E}{m} - \frac{g}{\beta} = 0 \tag{9}$$

$$\frac{dt}{dm} + \frac{1}{\beta} = 0$$

Consequently, if the thrust program is specified, that is, if the function $\beta(m)$ is prescribed, the integration of the third of Eqs. (9) yields the time distribution; subsequently, by using the first integral (7), one can calculate the velocity distribution; finally, by integrating the first of Eqs. (9), one can determine the altitude distribution.

The formal integration of these equations can be simplified considerably, if the dimensionless parameters

$$\theta = \frac{tg}{V_E}, \quad \eta = \frac{hg}{V_E^2}, \quad u = \frac{V}{V_E}, \quad \mu = \frac{m}{m_i}, \quad \tau = \frac{\beta V_E}{mg} \tag{10}$$

are introduced, where m_i is the initial mass and τ is the instantaneous thrust-to-weight ratio. Consequently, Eqs. (9) can be rewritten as

$$\frac{d\eta}{d\mu} + \frac{u}{\tau\mu} = 0$$

$$\frac{du}{d\mu} + \frac{1}{\mu}\left(1 - \frac{1}{\tau}\right) = 0 \tag{11}$$

$$\frac{d\theta}{d\mu} + \frac{1}{\tau\mu} = 0$$

while the first integral (7) becomes

$$u + \theta + \log\mu = \text{Const} \tag{12}$$

and simplifies to

$$u + \log\mu = \text{Const} \tag{13}$$

if the gravitational forces are neglected.

2.3 Simple thrust programs. In connection with the previous discussion, three particular thrust programs are now investigated, that is, constant thrust, thrust proportional to the instantaneous weight, and zero thrust.

If the thrust is held constant along the trajectory, the instantaneous thrust-to-weight ratio is given by

$$\tau = \frac{\tau_i}{\mu} \tag{14}$$

where τ_i is the initial thrust-to-weight ratio. Hence, after Eqs. (11) are integrated, the following results are obtained:

$$\mu + \tau_i\theta = C_1$$

$$u + \frac{C_1 - \mu}{\tau_i} + \log\mu = C_2 \tag{15}$$

$$\eta + \frac{C_2}{\tau_i}\mu + \frac{1}{2}\left(\frac{C_1 - \mu}{\tau_i}\right)^2 + \frac{\mu}{\tau_i}(1 - \log\mu) = C_3$$

where C_1 through C_3 are constants. A characteristic of the constant thrust trajectory is that the acceleration continuously increases with the time; since this acceleration may become physiologically intolerable, a definite limit exists to the applicability of the constant thrust program to manned vehicles.

If the thrust per unit weight is held constant, the thrust program is represented by

$$\tau = \tau_i \tag{16}$$

so that the integration of Eqs. (11) leads to the solutions

$$\log \mu + \tau_i \theta = C_4$$

$$u + \frac{\tau_i - 1}{\tau_i} \log \mu = C_5 \tag{17}$$

$$\eta + \frac{C_5}{\tau_i} \log \mu - \frac{\tau_i - 1}{2\tau_i^2} \log^2 \mu = C_6$$

where C_4 through C_6 are constants. A characteristic of this program, especially desirable for manned vehicles, is that the acceleration is constant at all points of the flight path. Hence, this program can also be called the *constant acceleration program*.

If the engine is shut off, the integration of the equations of motion is to be performed subject to the condition

$$\tau = 0 \tag{18}$$

Owing to the fact that Eqs. (11) become undetermined, it is necessary to employ Eqs. (5) which, after the dimensionless variables (10) are introduced, yield the results

$$\mu = C_7$$

$$u + \theta = C_8 \tag{19}$$

$$\eta + \frac{u^2}{2} = C_9$$

The last of these equations expresses the conservative nature of coasting flight in a vacuum, since the sum of the kinetic and potential energies is constant.

2.4 Composite thrust programs. In the previous section, a number of simple thrust programs were investigated, and the general integrals for the equations of motion were found. Here, some composite trajectories *ICF* are investigated, more specifically, those composed of a burning phase *IC* followed by a coasting phase *CF*. Two particular cases are considered: one in which a constant thrust program is followed by a zero thrust program and one in which a constant acceleration program is

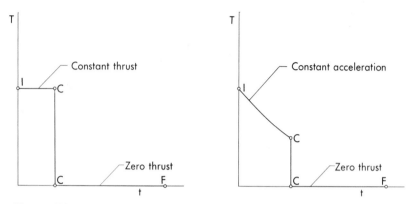

FIG. 1. The constant thrust-zero thrust program and the constant acceleration-zero thrust program.

followed by a zero thrust program (Fig. 1). In both cases, the following end-conditions are assumed:

$$\theta_i = u_i = \eta_i = 0, \qquad \mu_i = 1$$
$$u_f = 0, \qquad \mu_f = 1 - \zeta \tag{20}$$

where the subscript i denotes the initial point, the subscript f the final point, and ζ the ratio of the propellant mass to the initial mass. It is desired to determine the conditions at the end of the burning phase (subscript c) as well as those at the end of the coasting phase (subscript f) and, in particular, the peak altitude attained by the rocket.

If the constant thrust program is followed by a zero thrust program, the evaluation of the integration constants in terms of the initial and the final conditions leads to

$$C_1 = 1, \qquad C_2 = 0, \qquad C_3 = \frac{1}{\tau_i}$$
$$C_7 = 1 - \zeta, \qquad C_8 = \theta_f, \qquad C_9 = \eta_f \tag{21}$$

Furthermore, since Eqs. (15) and (19) are simultaneously valid at the burnout point C, the following results are obtained for the conditions at the end of the burning phase:

$$\theta_c = \frac{\zeta}{\tau_i}$$
$$u_c = -\frac{\zeta}{\tau_i} - \log (1 - \zeta) \tag{22}$$
$$\eta_c = -\frac{1}{2}\left(\frac{\zeta}{\tau_i}\right)^2 + \frac{1}{\tau_i}[\zeta + (1 - \zeta) \log (1 - \zeta)]$$

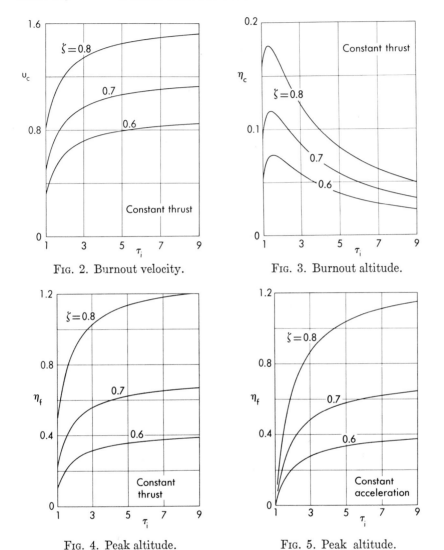

FIG. 2. Burnout velocity.

FIG. 3. Burnout altitude.

FIG. 4. Peak altitude.

FIG. 5. Peak altitude.

and for those at the end of the coasting phase:

$$\eta_f = \frac{1}{2} \log^2 (1 - \zeta) + \frac{\zeta + \log (1 - \zeta)}{\tau_i}$$

$$\theta_f = -\log (1 - \zeta)$$

(23)

As Fig. 2 indicates, the burnout velocity increases with the propellant mass ratio and the initial thrust-to-weight ratio. Furthermore, Fig. 3 supplies the burnout altitude, and Fig. 4, the peak altitude. While the burnout altitude has a maximum with respect to the initial thrust-to-weight ratio, the peak altitude increases monotonically with it. Hence, the highest value for η_f is obtained for $\tau_i = \infty$, that is, when all the propellant is consumed instantaneously (pulse burning).

If the constant acceleration program is followed by a zero thrust program, the integration constants have the values

$$C_4 = C_5 = C_6 = 0$$

$$C_7 = 1 - \zeta$$

$$C_8 = \theta_f \tag{24}$$

$$C_9 = \eta_f$$

Consequently, the following conditions are obtained at the end of the powered phase:

$$\theta_c = -\frac{1}{\tau_i} \log (1 - \zeta)$$

$$u_c = -\frac{\tau_i - 1}{\tau_i} \log (1 - \zeta) \tag{25}$$

$$\eta_c = \frac{\tau_i - 1}{2\tau_i^2} \log^2 (1 - \zeta)$$

and at the end of the coasting phase:

$$\eta_f = \frac{\tau_i - 1}{2\tau_i} \log^2 (1 - \zeta)$$

$$\theta_f = -\log (1 - \zeta) \tag{26}$$

In this connection, the peak altitude is plotted in Fig. 5 for several values of the propellant mass ratio and the initial thrust-to-weight ratio. Comparison of the constant thrust program and the constant acceleration program leads to the following conclusion: For the same propellant mass ratio and initial thrust-to-weight ratio, the peak altitude of the constant thrust program is higher than that of the constant acceleration program.* On the other hand, the flight time is independent of the mode of propellant consumption, as is logical, owing to the first integral (12).

---

* The constant thrust program is not only superior to the constant acceleration program but also to every other arbitrary program. The demonstration of this important property is not possible with the present limited approach and will be developed in Volume 2.

3. GRAVITY TURN TRAJECTORIES

A class of flight paths of particular interest for the launching of long-range missiles and satellites is the category known as gravity turn trajectories. The curvature of these trajectories is obtained by exploiting the attraction due to the Earth's gravitational field, while the thrust is held parallel to the velocity. Thus, after the condition $\epsilon = 0$ is imposed and the thrust function (4) is considered, Eqs. (1) are rewritten as

$$\dot{X} - V \cos \gamma = 0$$

$$\dot{h} - V \sin \gamma = 0$$

$$\dot{V} + g \sin \gamma - \frac{\beta V_E}{m} = 0 \tag{27}$$

$$\dot{\gamma} + \frac{g \cos \gamma}{V} = 0$$

$$\dot{m} + \beta = 0$$

Furthermore, if the variables (10) are considered and the dimensionless abscissa

$$\xi = \frac{Xg}{V_E^2} \tag{28}$$

is introduced, Eqs. (27) lead to the differential set

$$\frac{d\xi}{d\theta} - u \cos \gamma = 0$$

$$\frac{d\eta}{d\theta} - u \sin \gamma = 0$$

$$\frac{du}{d\theta} + \sin \gamma - \tau = 0 \tag{29}$$

$$\frac{d\gamma}{d\theta} + \frac{\cos \gamma}{u} = 0$$

$$\frac{d\mu}{d\theta} + \mu\tau = 0$$

whose integration is now discussed for three particular cases: constant thrust, constant thrust per unit weight, and zero thrust (Refs. 2, 3, and 5).

If the thrust is constant, it is convenient to use the mass ratio as the independent variable instead of the time. Consequently, after the thrust program (14) is accounted for, the previous equations can be rewritten in the form

$$\frac{d\xi}{d\mu} = -\frac{u \cos \gamma}{\tau_i}$$

$$\frac{d\eta}{d\mu} = -\frac{u \sin \gamma}{\tau_i}$$

$$\frac{du}{d\mu} = \frac{\sin \gamma}{\tau_i} - \frac{1}{\mu} \qquad (30)$$

$$\frac{d\gamma}{d\mu} = \frac{\cos \gamma}{\tau_i u}$$

$$\frac{d\theta}{d\mu} = -\frac{1}{\tau_i}$$

The fifth of these equations can be integrated in a closed form and yields the time distribution

$$\mu + \tau_i \theta = \text{Const} \qquad (31)$$

On the other hand, after the third and the fourth of Eqs. (30) are solved by means of approximate procedures, the velocity and the path inclination can be obtained. Finally, the geometry of the trajectory is calculated a posteriori by integrating the first and the second of Eqs. (30).

If the thrust is proportional to the instantaneous weight,* it is convenient to use the path inclination as the independent variable instead of the time. Consequently, after the thrust program (16) is accounted for, Eqs. (29) are transformed into

$$\frac{d\xi}{d\gamma} = -u^2$$

$$\frac{d\eta}{d\gamma} = -u^2 \tan \gamma$$

$$\frac{du}{d\gamma} = u \left(\tan \gamma - \frac{\tau_i}{\cos \gamma} \right) \qquad (32)$$

$$\frac{d\theta}{d\gamma} = -\frac{u}{\cos \gamma}$$

$$\frac{d\mu}{d\gamma} = \tau_i \frac{\mu u}{\cos \gamma}$$

---

* While this program yields constant acceleration in vertical flight, the same is not true for a gravity turn, owing to the continuous change in the path inclination.

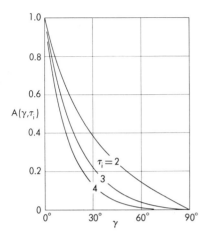

FIG. 6. The function $A(\gamma, \tau_i)$.

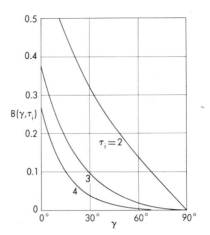

FIG. 7. The function $B(\gamma, \tau_i)$.

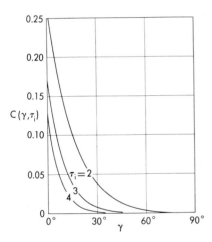

FIG. 8. The function $C(\gamma, \tau_i)$.

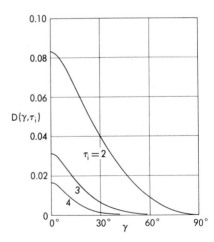

FIG. 9. The function $D(\gamma, \tau_i)$.

Notice that the differential equation governing the velocity distribution can be integrated independently of those remaining. Once the velocity is known, the determination of the time, the abscissa, and the ordinate is reduced to a process of simple quadratures. In this connection, if u_o denotes the dimensionless velocity of the rocket at $\gamma = 0$ and if the function

$$y(\gamma) = \cot\left(\frac{\pi}{4} + \frac{\gamma}{2}\right) \tag{33}$$

is defined, the following results are readily derived (Ref. 2):

$$\frac{u}{u_o} = A(\gamma, \tau_i), \qquad \frac{\theta}{u_o} = B(\gamma, \tau_i) + \text{Const}$$

$$\frac{\xi}{u_o^2} = C(\gamma, \tau_i) + \text{Const}, \qquad \frac{\eta}{u_o^2} = D(\gamma, \tau_i) + \text{Const} \tag{34}$$

where the functions A, B, C, D are given by

$$A(\gamma, \tau_i) = \tfrac{1}{2}(y^{\tau_i - 1} + y^{\tau_i + 1})$$

$$B(\gamma, \tau_i) = \frac{1}{2}\left(\frac{y^{\tau_i - 1}}{\tau_i - 1} + \frac{y^{\tau_i + 1}}{\tau_i + 1}\right)$$

$$C(\gamma, \tau_i) = \frac{1}{2}\left(\frac{y^{2\tau_i - 1}}{2\tau_i - 1} + \frac{y^{2\tau_i + 1}}{2\tau_i + 1}\right) \tag{35}$$

$$D(\gamma, \tau_i) = \frac{1}{4}\left(\frac{y^{2\tau_i - 2}}{2\tau_i - 2} - \frac{y^{2\tau_i + 2}}{2\tau_i + 2}\right)$$

and are plotted in Figs. 6 through 9 versus the path inclination for several values of the initial thrust-to-weight ratio. After the time distribution is known, the mass can be determined from the relationship

$$\log \mu + \tau_i \theta = \text{Const} \tag{36}$$

If the engine is shut off, the integration of Eqs. (29) must be performed subject to the constraint (18). After the dimensionless variables (10) and (28) are introduced, the following results are readily obtained:

$$\mu = C_1$$

$$u \cos \gamma = C_2$$

$$\theta + u \sin \gamma = C_3 \tag{37}$$

$$\xi - C_2 \theta = C_4$$

$$\eta - C_3 \theta + \frac{\theta^2}{2} = C_5$$

where C_1 through C_5 are constants.

3.1 Numerical example. In connection with the previous results, the powered portion of a gravity turn trajectory has been calculated for the initial conditions

$$\theta_i = \xi_i = \eta_i = 0$$

$$\mu_i = 1, \qquad u_i = 0.1, \qquad \gamma_i = 80° \tag{38}$$

It is assumed that the initial thrust-to-weight ratio is $\tau_i = 2$ and that the

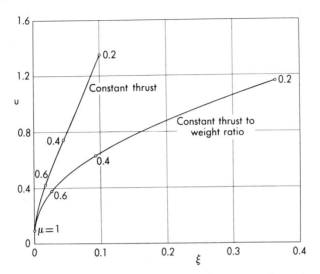

FIG. 10. Velocity distribution for gravity turn trajectories.

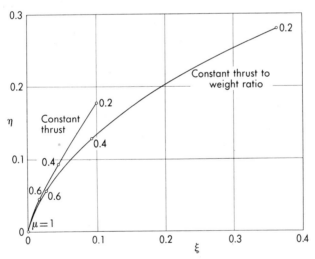

FIG. 11. Geometry of gravity turn trajectories.

propellant mass ratio is $\zeta = 0.8$. The results relative to both a constant thrust trajectory and a trajectory flown with constant thrust-to-weight ratio are plotted in Figs. 10 and 11. More specifically, Fig. 10 yields the velocity distribution, and Fig. 11, the geometry of the trajectory. Notice that, although the constant thrust trajectory is characterized by a lower increase in altitude, it has a comparatively higher increase in kinetic energy and, therefore, a higher increase in total energy.

4. TRAJECTORIES FLOWN WITH CONSTANT THRUST INCLINATION WITH RESPECT TO THE HORIZON

In the previous section, trajectories flown with constant inclination of the thrust with respect to the velocity were considered. Here, trajectories flown with constant inclination of the thrust with respect to the horizon are investigated. For convenience, the dynamical equations are projected on the horizontal and vertical directions rather than on the tangent and the normal to the flight path; furthermore, the velocity vector is described in terms of its horizontal and vertical components rather than in terms of its modulus and path inclination. Thus, after the variables

$$V_x = V \cos \gamma, \qquad V_h = V \sin \gamma, \qquad \omega = \epsilon + \gamma \qquad (39)$$

are defined, where ω is the inclination of the thrust with respect to the horizon, Eqs. (1) are rewritten as

$$\dot{X} - V_x = 0$$

$$\dot{h} - V_h = 0$$

$$T \cos \omega - m\dot{V}_x = 0 \qquad (40)$$

$$T \sin \omega - m(g + \dot{V}_h) = 0$$

$$\dot{m} + \beta = 0$$

4.1 First integrals. The following differential expressions are a mathematical consequence of the dynamic relationships and the definition of propellant mass flow:

$$dV_x + V_E \cos \omega \, \frac{dm}{m} = 0$$
$$dV_h + g \, dt + V_E \sin \omega \, \frac{dm}{m} = 0 \qquad (41)$$

Consequently, integration of these equations leads to the first integrals

$$V_x + V_E \cos \omega \log m = \text{Const}$$
$$V_h + gt + V_E \sin \omega \log m = \text{Const} \qquad (42)$$

which hold regardless of the rate at which propellant is being consumed, that is, regardless of the function $\beta(t)$. Incidentally, for the particular case of vertical flight, the first integral relative to the horizontal velocity component degenerates into a trivial expression, while the first integral relative to the vertical velocity component leads once more to Eq. (7).

4.2 Integration process. In order to integrate the equations of powered flight, the instantaneous mass is selected as the new independent variable, and Eqs. (40) are rewritten in the form

$$\frac{dX}{dm} + \frac{V_x}{\beta} = 0$$

$$\frac{dh}{dm} + \frac{V_h}{\beta} = 0$$

$$\frac{dV_x}{dm} + \frac{V_E \cos \omega}{m} = 0 \qquad (43)$$

$$\frac{dV_h}{dm} + \frac{V_E \sin \omega}{m} - \frac{g}{\beta} = 0$$

$$\frac{dt}{dm} + \frac{1}{\beta} = 0$$

Consequently, if the function $\beta(m)$ is prescribed, the fifth of these equations supplies the time distribution; subsequently, the first integrals (42) yield the velocity components; finally, the geometry of the trajectory can be determined by means of the first and second of Eqs. (43).

The formal integration of these equations can be simplified somewhat if the dimensionless variables (10), (28), and

$$\varphi = \frac{V_x}{V_E}, \qquad \psi = \frac{V_h}{V_E} \qquad (44)$$

are introduced. If this is done, Eqs. (43) become

$$\frac{d\xi}{d\mu} = -\frac{\varphi}{\tau\mu}$$

$$\frac{d\eta}{d\mu} = -\frac{\psi}{\tau\mu}$$

$$\frac{d\varphi}{d\mu} = -\frac{\cos \omega}{\mu} \qquad (45)$$

$$\frac{d\psi}{d\mu} = \frac{1}{\mu}\left(\frac{1}{\tau} - \sin \omega\right)$$

$$\frac{d\theta}{d\mu} = -\frac{1}{\tau\mu}$$

while the first integrals (42) are rewritten in the form

$$\varphi + \cos \omega \log \mu = \text{Const}$$
$$\psi + \theta + \sin \omega \log \mu = \text{Const} \qquad (46)$$

4.3 Simple thrust programs. In connection with the previous discussion, three particular cases are now investigated, that is, constant thrust, thrust proportional to the instantaneous weight, and zero thrust. If the modulus of the thrust is constant, the integration of Eqs. (45) leads to

$$\tau_i \theta + \mu = C_1$$

$$\varphi + \cos \omega \log \mu = C_2$$

$$\psi + \frac{C_1 - \mu}{\tau_i} + \sin \omega \log \mu = C_3 \qquad (47)$$

$$\xi + \frac{C_2}{\tau_i} \mu + \frac{\cos \omega}{\tau_i} \mu (1 - \log \mu) = C_4$$

$$\eta + \frac{C_3}{\tau_i} \mu + \frac{1}{2} \left(\frac{C_1 - \mu}{\tau_i} \right)^2 + \frac{\sin \omega}{\tau_i} \mu (1 - \log \mu) = C_5$$

where C_1 through C_5 are constants. If the modulus of the thrust is proportional to the instantaneous weight,* the following results are derived:

$$\tau_i \theta + \log \mu = C_6$$

$$\varphi + \cos \omega \log \mu = C_7$$

$$\psi + \left(\sin \omega - \frac{1}{\tau_i} \right) \log \mu = C_8$$

$$\xi + \frac{C_7}{\tau_i} \log \mu - \frac{\cos \omega}{2\tau_i} \log^2 \mu = C_9 \qquad (48)$$

$$\eta + \frac{C_8}{\tau_i} \log \mu - \frac{1}{2\tau_i} \left(\sin \omega - \frac{1}{\tau_i} \right) \log^2 \mu = C_{10}$$

where C_6 through C_{10} are constants. Finally, if the engine is shut off, the integration of Eqs. (40) leads to

$$\mu = C_{11}$$

$$\varphi = C_{12}$$

$$\psi + \theta = C_{13} \qquad (49)$$

$$\xi - \varphi\theta = C_{14}$$

$$\eta + \frac{\psi^2}{2} = C_{15}$$

where C_{11} through C_{15} are constants.

---

* This thrust program is characterized by constant acceleration components and, therefore, by constant total acceleration. For this reason, this program is again referred to as a constant acceleration program.

4.4 Composite thrust programs. In the previous sections, a number of simple thrust programs were investigated, and the general integrals for the equations of motion were found. Here, some composite trajectories *ICF* are investigated, more specifically, those composed of a burning phase *IC* followed by a coasting phase *CF*. Two particular cases are considered: one in which the burning phase is characterized by constant thrust and one in which the burning phase is characterized by constant acceleration. In both cases, the end-conditions

$$\theta_i = \xi_i = \eta_i = \varphi_i = \psi_i = 0, \qquad \mu_i = 1 \tag{50}$$
$$\eta_f = 0, \qquad \mu_f = 1 - \zeta$$

are specified. It is desired to determine the conditions at the end of the burning phase as well as those at the end of the coasting phase and, in particular, the over-all range flown by the rocket.

If the constant thrust program is followed by a zero thrust program, the integration constants have the values

$$C_1 = 1, \qquad C_2 = C_3 = 0$$
$$C_4 = \frac{\cos \omega}{\tau_i}, \qquad C_5 = \frac{\sin \omega}{\tau_i} \tag{51}$$
$$C_{11} = 1 - \zeta, \qquad C_{12} = \varphi_f, \qquad C_{13} = \psi_f + \theta_f$$
$$C_{14} = \xi_f - \varphi_f \theta_f, \qquad C_{15} = \frac{\psi_f^2}{2}$$

Since Eqs. (47) and (49) are simultaneously valid at point C, the following burnout conditions are obtained:

$$\theta_c = \frac{\zeta}{\tau_i}$$
$$\varphi_c = -\cos \omega \log (1 - \zeta)$$
$$\psi_c = -\frac{\zeta}{\tau_i} - \sin \omega \log (1 - \zeta)$$
$$\xi_c = \frac{\cos \omega}{\tau_i} [\zeta + (1 - \zeta) \log (1 - \zeta)] \tag{52}$$
$$\eta_c = -\frac{1}{2}\left(\frac{\zeta}{\tau_i}\right)^2 + \frac{\sin \omega}{\tau_i} [\zeta + (1 - \zeta) \log (1 - \zeta)]$$

and are related to the range flown with engine shut off by the expression

$$\xi_f - \xi_c = \varphi_c(\psi_c + \sqrt{2\eta_c + \psi_c^2}) \tag{53}$$

which is a consequence of the coasting equations (49). Hence, if Eqs.

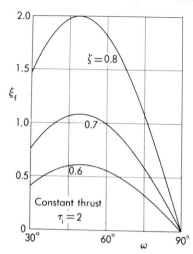

FIG. 12. Effect of the thrust inclination on the range.

(52) and (53) are combined, the over-all range becomes

$$\xi_f = \cos \omega \log^2 (1 - \zeta) \left[\sin \omega - \frac{1}{K} + \sqrt{\sin \omega \left(\sin \omega - \frac{2}{K} \right)} \right] \quad (54)$$

where

$$K = - \frac{\tau_i \log^2 (1 - \zeta)}{\zeta + \log (1 - \zeta)} \quad (55)$$

This equation is plotted in Fig. 12 for $\tau_i = 2$ and shows that, for each propellant mass ratio, there exists a thrust inclination such that the range is a maximum. This maximum occurs for

$$K = \frac{2 \sin^3 \omega}{2 \sin^2 \omega - 1} \quad (56)$$

and can be calculated by substituting the value of ω which satisfies Eq. (56) into either Eq. (54) or

$$\xi_f = \frac{\cos \omega}{2 \sin^3 \omega} \log^2 (1 - \zeta) \quad (57)$$

In connection with these results, the optimum thrust inclination is plotted in Fig. 13 versus the initial thrust-to-weight ratio for several values of the propellant mass ratio; as the graph indicates, ω decreases as the initial thrust-to-weight ratio increases and reaches its lowest value of 45° for the limiting case where $\tau_i = \infty$ (pulse burning). The associated maximum range is plotted in Fig. 14 and increases with both the propellant mass ratio and the initial thrust-to-weight ratio.

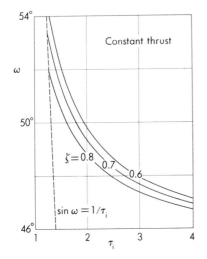

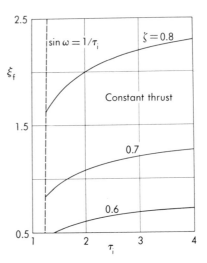

FIG. 13. Inclination of the thrust for maximum range.

FIG. 14. Maximum range.

If the constant acceleration program is followed by a zero thrust program, the integration constants have the values

$$C_6 = C_7 = C_8 = C_9 = C_{10} = 0$$

$$C_{11} = 1 - \zeta$$

$$C_{12} = \varphi_f$$

$$C_{13} = \psi_f + \theta_f \tag{58}$$

$$C_{14} = \xi_f - \varphi_f \theta_f$$

$$C_{15} = \frac{\psi_f^2}{2}$$

so that the following burnout conditions are obtained:

$$\theta_c = -\frac{1}{\tau_i} \log (1 - \zeta)$$

$$\varphi_c = -\cos \omega \log (1 - \zeta)$$

$$\psi_c = \frac{1 - \tau_i \sin \omega}{\tau_i} \log (1 - \zeta) \tag{59}$$

$$\xi_c = \frac{\cos \omega}{2\tau_i} \log^2 (1 - \zeta)$$

$$\eta_c = \frac{\tau_i \sin \omega - 1}{2\tau_i^2} \log^2 (1 - \zeta)$$

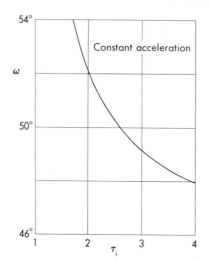

FIG. 15. Inclination of the thrust for maximum range.

FIG. 16. Maximum range.

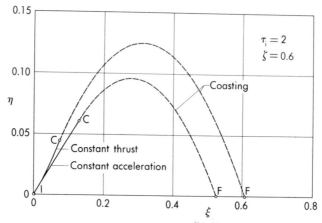

FIG. 17. Comparison of constant thrust and constant acceleration trajectories.

Since the coasting range is still represented by Eq. (53), the over-all range becomes

$$\xi_f = \cos \omega \log^2 (1 - \zeta) \left[\sin \omega - \frac{1}{2\tau_i} + \sqrt{\sin \omega \left(\sin \omega - \frac{1}{\tau_i} \right)} \right] \quad (60)$$

and admits a maximum for the value of ω which satisfies the equation (Fig. 15)

$$\tau_i = \frac{\sin^3 \omega}{2 \sin^2 \omega - 1} \quad (61)$$

Once the optimum thrust inclination is known, the associated **range** can be computed from either Eq. (60) or Eq. (57) and is plotted in Fig. 16. Comparison of Figs. 14 and 16 shows that, for the same propellant mass ratio and initial thrust-to-weight ratio, the constant thrust program is more efficient than the constant acceleration program. This effect is clearly shown in Fig. 17 for $\tau_i = 2$ and $\zeta = 0.6$; more specifically, the range associated with the constant thrust program is about 16% greater than that of the constant acceleration program. At any rate, it is emphasized that the constant thrust program is superior not only to the constant acceleration program but also to every other arbitrary program; this important property cannot be shown with the present limited approach and will be proved in Volume 2.

EXERCISES

1. Denote by h_e the total energy or energy height, that is, the sum of the potential and kinetic energies per unit weight. Show that the following relationship is a mathematical consequence of Eqs. (1):

$$\frac{dh_e}{dt} = \tau V \cos \epsilon \qquad (62)$$

where τ is the thrust-to-weight ratio. Hence, for given values of the velocity and the thrust-to-weight ratio, the time rate of increase of the energy height is a maximum when the thrust is tangent to the flight path.

2. Consider a gravity turn trajectory flown with constant thrust-to-weight ratio. Denoting by s a curvilinear abscissa measured along the flight path, show that

$$h_e - \tau_i s = \text{Const} \qquad (63)$$

Hence, the total increase in energy height is proportional to the length of the flight path.

3. Consider a vertical path flown with constant thrust-to-weight ratio, and assume that the initial velocity is zero. Show that the burnout altitude is a maximum for $\tau_i = 2$.

4. Consider vertical flight, and compare the constant thrust-zero thrust program (subscript 1) with the constant acceleration-zero thrust program (subscript 2). Show that the peak altitude is the same for both programs if the initial thrust-to-weight ratios satisfy the relationship

$$\frac{\tau_{i2}}{\tau_{i1}} = -\frac{1}{2} \frac{\log^2 (1 - \zeta)}{\zeta + \log (1 - \zeta)} \qquad (64)$$

This means that, if the propellant mass ratio is 0.8, the initial thrust-to-weight ratio of the constant acceleration program is to be 60% greater than that of the constant thrust program.

5. Consider a trajectory flown with constant thrust inclination with respect to the horizon. Show that, if the thrust-to-weight ratio is constant, the components of the acceleration and, hence, the total acceleration are constant.

6. In connection with the previous exercise, show that, if the rocket is initially at rest, its powered flight trajectory is a straight line.

7. Consider a constant thrust-zero thrust trajectory flown with constant thrust inclination with respect to the horizon. Retaining the end-conditions (50), show that maximum range is obtained when the thrust is perpendicular to the final velocity, that is, when

$$\tan \omega = -\frac{\varphi_f}{\psi_f} \tag{65}$$

Prove that this property also holds for a constant acceleration-zero thrust trajectory.

8. Consider a trajectory flown with constant thrust inclination with respect to the horizon, and compare the constant thrust-zero thrust program (subscript 1) and the constant acceleration-zero thrust program (subscript 2). Show that the range is the same for both programs provided ω is the same and the initial thrust-to-weight ratios satisfy relationship (64).

9. Consider a trajectory flown with constant thrust inclination with respect to the horizon, and focus attention on the following two burning programs: (a) constant thrust followed by coasting and (b) constant acceleration followed by coasting. Retaining the initial conditions (50), show that the coordinates of the highest point of the trajectory are given by

$$\xi = \cos \omega \left[\frac{\zeta}{\tau_i} + \log (1 - \zeta) \left\{ \frac{1}{\tau_i} + \sin \omega \log (1 - \zeta) \right\} \right]$$

$$\eta = \sin \omega \left[\frac{\zeta}{\tau_i} + \log (1 - \zeta) \left\{ \frac{1}{\tau_i} + \frac{1}{2} \sin \omega \log (1 - \zeta) \right\} \right] \tag{66}$$

for program (a) and by

$$\xi = \cos \omega \left(\frac{2\tau_i \sin \omega - 1}{2\tau_i} \right) \log^2 (1 - \zeta)$$

$$\eta = \sin \omega \left(\frac{\tau_i \sin \omega - 1}{2\tau_i} \right) \log^2 (1 - \zeta) \tag{67}$$

for program (b).

10. In connection with Exercise 9, show that, for the particular case of vertical flight, the peak altitude supplied by Eqs. (66) and (67) reduces to that given by Eqs. (23) and (26).

REFERENCES

1. IVEY, H. R., BOWEN, E. N., and OBORNY, L. F., *Introduction to the Problem of Rocket-Powered Aircraft Performance*, NACA TN No. 1401, 1947.
2. MOYAL, J. E., *Rocket Motion in a Gravitational Field*, Journal of the British Interplanetary Society, Vol. 7, No. 3, 1948.
3. LAWDEN, D. F., *Initial Arc of the Trajectory of Departure*, Journal of the British Interplanetary Society, Vol. 7, No. 3, 1948.
4. NEWTON, R. R., *On the Optimum Trajectory of a Rocket*, Journal of the Franklin Institute, Vol. 266, No. 3, 1958.
5. CULLER, G. J. and FRIED, B. D., *Universal Gravity Turn Trajectories*, Journal of Applied Physics, Vol. 28, No. 6, 1957.
6. MIELE, A. and CAPPELLARI, J. O., *Topics in Dynamic Programming for Rockets*, ZFW, Vol. 7, No. 1, 1959.

CHAPTER 16

MULTISTAGE ROCKETS
IN A VACUUM

---

1. INTRODUCTION

A considerable limitation to the performance of single-stage rockets arises from the fact that a large fraction of the energy developed by the powerplant is employed to accelerate masses which cease to be useful for propulsion purposes. This limitation can be overcome by dividing the rocket into a number of stages, each having its own powerplant and propellant mass. When the propellant mass of a given stage is exhausted, the tanks and the engine of that stage are separated from the remaining part of the rocket. The resulting discontinuities in the distribution of mass versus time are essentially responsible for the superior performance which multistage rockets exhibit with respect to single-stage rockets (Refs. 1 through 6).

While the conceptual difficulties associated with multistage rocket analyses are not staggering, the mathematics is rather cumbersome; hence, only a few simplified cases of flight in a vacuum are investigated here. More specifically, after the performance limitations of single-stage rockets are discussed, the analysis of multistage rockets is developed in the light of the contribution of Malina and Summerfield (Ref. 1). Furthermore, for the sake of clarity, the discussion is divided into two parts: in the first part, gravitational effects are neglected; in the second part, gravitational effects in vertical flight are considered. Particular attention is devoted to configurations in which the parameters characterizing each stage (e.g., the equivalent exit velocity, the payload ratio, the propellant mass ratio, the structural factor, and the initial or final thrust-to-weight ratios) are identical. Although some of these configurations represent optimum designs, no attempt is made to prove any special property. Thus, the analytical treatment of the problem of optimum staging is delayed to Volume 2, where some more advanced mathematical techniques will be employed.

2. DEFINITIONS PERTINENT TO SINGLE-STAGE ROCKETS

In order to analyze the performance limitations of single-stage rockets, certain definitions must be introduced. Denote by m_i the initial mass, m_f the final mass, m_p the propellant mass, m_s the structural mass (tanks,

TABLE 1

DIMENSIONLESS GROUPS CHARACTERIZING A SINGLE-STAGE ROCKET

$\dfrac{m_p}{m_i}$	ζ	$(1-\epsilon)(1-\pi)$
$\dfrac{m_f}{m_i}$	$1-\zeta$	$\epsilon + (1-\epsilon)\pi$
$\dfrac{m_s}{m_i}$	$\dfrac{\epsilon\zeta}{1-\epsilon}$	$\epsilon(1-\pi)$
$\dfrac{m_*}{m_i}$	$\dfrac{1-\epsilon-\zeta}{1-\epsilon}$	π

engines, pipes, etc.), and m_* the payload mass; and observe that, by definition,

$$m_i = m_p + m_f, \qquad m_f = m_s + m_* \qquad (1)$$

Furthermore, introduce the dimensionless ratios

$$\pi = \frac{m_*}{m_i}, \qquad \zeta = \frac{m_p}{m_i}, \qquad \epsilon = \frac{m_s}{m_s + m_p} \qquad (2)$$

which are called the *payload ratio*, the *propellant mass ratio*, and the *structural factor*,* respectively. Because of Eqs. (1) and (2), several relationships can be derived between the dimensionless groups characterizing a single-stage rocket. The calculation of these relationships is only a matter of algebraic manipulations and is omitted for the sake of brevity. The results are presented in Table 1 in terms of either the propellant mass ratio and the structural factor or the payload ratio and the structural factor.

3. PERFORMANCE LIMITATIONS OF SINGLE–STAGE ROCKETS

Consider a single-stage rocket, and assume that the thrust is tangent to the flight path and that both the aerodynamic and gravitational forces are negligible. Under these hypotheses, the following indefinite integral holds (see Chapter 15):

$$V + V_E \log m = \text{Const} \qquad (3)$$

---

* The structural factor is a measure of the structural efficiency of a rocket. In practice, the lowest values obtained with present-day designs are in the neighborhood of $\epsilon = 0.05$–0.10.

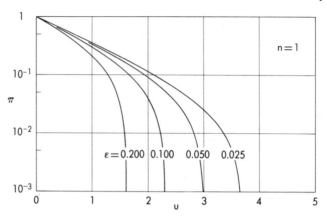

FIG. 1. Payload ratio.

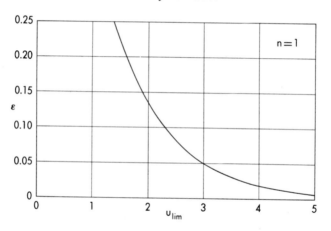

FIG. 2. Limiting velocity.

where V is the velocity, V_E the equivalent exit velocity, and m the mass. The corresponding definite form is represented by

$$V_f - V_i + V_E \log \frac{m_f}{m_i} = 0 \tag{4}$$

where the subscript i denotes initial conditions and the subscript f, final conditions. Now, consider the end-conditions

$$V_i = 0, \qquad V_f = V_* \tag{5}$$

where V_* denotes the burnout or payload velocity, and indicate by

$$u = \frac{V_*}{V_E} \tag{6}$$

the *dimensionless burnout or payload velocity*. If Eqs. (4) through (6) are combined and the final-to-initial mass ratio given in Table 1 is employed, the following result is obtained:

$$u = \log \frac{1}{\epsilon + (1 - \epsilon)\pi} \tag{7}$$

Consequently, the payload ratio is given by

$$\pi = \frac{\exp(-u) - \epsilon}{1 - \epsilon} \tag{8}$$

and is plotted in Fig. 1 as a function of the dimensionless burnout speed for several values of the structural factor. As the graph indicates, the payload ratio decreases so rapidly with the desired final velocity that single-stage rockets become economically prohibitive for high payload velocities. Furthermore, there is an upper limit to the velocity which can be achieved by a single-stage rocket; this limiting velocity occurs when the payload mass is zero and is given by (Fig. 2)

$$u_{\lim} = \log \frac{1}{\epsilon} \tag{9}$$

For example, consider a single-stage chemical rocket having a structural factor of 0.1 and an equivalent exit velocity of 10,000 ft sec^{-1}; assume that the desired burnout velocity is 15,000 ft sec^{-1}, as is the case with intermediate range ballistic missiles. Since the required dimensionless speed ($u = 1.5$) is smaller than the limiting speed associated with the given structural factor ($u = 2.3$), this mission is physically possible; furthermore, the payload ratio is $\pi = 0.14$. As another example, assume that the desired burnout velocity is 26,000 ft sec^{-1}, which is required for satellite vehicles; since the required dimensionless speed ($u = 2.6$) is greater than the limiting speed, this mission is not physically possible with a single-stage rocket whose structural factor is 0.1. This circumstance stresses the importance of the multistage rocket which is analyzed in the following sections.

4. DEFINITIONS PERTINENT TO MULTISTAGE ROCKETS

In order to analyze the performance of multistage rockets, it is necessary to introduce several definitions (Fig. 3). Denote by n the total number of stages, k the generic stage, m_{pk} and m_{sk} the propellant and structural masses of the kth stage, and by m_{ik} and m_{fk} the initial and final masses of the kth stage plus all the subsequent stages; observe that the following relations hold for each stage:

$$m_{ik} = m_{pk} + m_{fk}, \qquad m_{fk} = m_{sk} + m_{i(k+1)} \tag{10}$$

TABLE 2

DIMENSIONLESS GROUPS CHARACTERIZING A MULTISTAGE ROCKET

$\dfrac{m_{pk}}{m_{ik}}$	ζ_k	$(1 - \epsilon_k)(1 - \pi_k)$
$\dfrac{m_{fk}}{m_{ik}}$	$1 - \zeta_k$	$\epsilon_k + (1 - \epsilon_k)\pi_k$
$\dfrac{m_{sk}}{m_{ik}}$	$\dfrac{\epsilon_k \zeta_k}{1 - \epsilon_k}$	$\epsilon_k(1 - \pi_k)$
$\dfrac{m_{i(k+1)}}{m_{ik}}$	$\dfrac{1 - \epsilon_k - \zeta_k}{1 - \epsilon_k}$	π_k

where the subscript k can take any value between 1 and n. Indicate by

$$\pi_k = \frac{m_{i(k+1)}}{m_{ik}}, \qquad \zeta_k = \frac{m_{pk}}{m_{ik}}, \qquad \epsilon_k = \frac{m_{sk}}{m_{sk} + m_{pk}} \qquad (11)$$

the *payload ratio*, the *propellant mass ratio*, and the *structural factor* of the kth stage. Since these definitions are formally identical with those of the single-stage rocket, the data of Table 2 can be readily established by analogy with those of Table 1. Denote, now, by

$$m_o = m_{i1}, \qquad m_* = m_{i(n+1)}, \qquad m_{po} = \sum_{k=1}^{n} m_{pk} \qquad (12)$$

the over-all mass, payload mass, and propel-lant mass of the rocket, and define the *over-all payload ratio* and the *over-all propellant mass ratio* as

$$\pi_o = \frac{m_*}{m_o}, \qquad \zeta_o = \frac{m_{po}}{m_o} \qquad (13)$$

Simple algebraic manipulations lead to the following relationships between the over-all ratios and the partial ratios:

$$\pi_o = \prod_{k=1}^{n} \pi_k$$

$$\zeta_o = \sum_{k=1}^{n} \zeta_k \prod_{j=1}^{k-1} \pi_j \qquad (14)$$

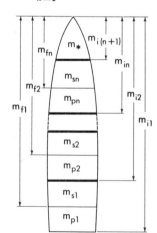

FIG. 3. Multistage rocket nomenclature.

4.1 Particular case. An interesting particular case occurs when the rocket is designed in such a way that the dimensionless groups characterizing each stage are identical. Therefore, under the hypotheses[*]

$$\pi_k = \pi$$

$$\zeta_k = \zeta$$

(15)

the over-all payload and propellant mass ratios become

$$\pi_o = \pi^n$$

$$\zeta_o = \zeta \sum_{k=1}^{n} \pi^{k-1}$$

(16)

Notice that the summation appearing on the right-hand side of the second of Eqs. (16) is a geometric progression of common ratio π and that a well-known property of this progression is that the sum of the first n terms satisfies the relationship

$$\sum_{k=1}^{n} \pi^{k-1} = \frac{1 - \pi^n}{1 - \pi}$$

(17)

Therefore, after Eqs. (16) and (17) are combined and the data of Table 2 are employed, the following result is obtained:

$$\zeta_o = (1 - \epsilon)(1 - \pi_o)$$

(18)

Hence, for a given structural factor, there exists a one-to-one correspondence between the over-all propellant mass ratio and the over-all payload ratio, so that the following concepts can be inferred: (a) any two rockets with identical propellant mass ratios have identical payload ratios, even though the number of stages may not be the same; and (b) the relative advantages or disadvantages of multistage versus single-stage configurations can be discussed in terms of either the over-all propellant mass ratio or the over-all payload ratio. However, since the existing literature has been mainly developed in terms of payload ratios, this point of view is retained in the following analyses. In closing, it must be noted that several other relationships can be derived which link the over-all parameters and the partial parameters. While the calculation of these relationships is rather tedious, the results can be of considerable assistance in multistage rocket analyses and, therefore, are summarized in Table 3.

---

[*] A mathematical consequence of Eqs. (15) is that the structural factors of each stage are identical, that is, $\epsilon_k = \epsilon$.

Table 3

Relationships Between Over-all Parameters and Partial Parameters for a Multistage Rocket

π_o	$\pi_o^{1/n}$	π^n	$\dfrac{1-\epsilon-\zeta_o}{1-\epsilon}$	$\left(\dfrac{1-\epsilon-\zeta}{1-\epsilon}\right)^n$
π			$\left(\dfrac{1-\epsilon-\zeta_o}{1-\epsilon}\right)^{1/n}$	$\dfrac{1-\epsilon-\zeta}{1-\epsilon}$
ζ_o	$(1-\epsilon)(1-\pi_o)$	$(1-\epsilon)(1-\pi^n)$		$(1-\epsilon)\left[1-\left(\dfrac{1-\epsilon-\zeta}{1-\epsilon}\right)^n\right]$
ζ	$(1-\epsilon)(1-\pi_o^{1/n})$	$(1-\epsilon)(1-\pi)$	$(1-\epsilon)\left[1-\left(\dfrac{1-\epsilon-\zeta_o}{1-\epsilon}\right)^{1/n}\right]$	
$1-\zeta_o$	$\epsilon+(1-\epsilon)\pi_o$	$\epsilon+(1-\epsilon)\pi^n$		$\epsilon+(1-\epsilon)\left(\dfrac{1-\epsilon-\zeta}{1-\epsilon}\right)^n$
$1-\zeta$	$\epsilon+(1-\epsilon)\pi_o^{1/n}$	$\epsilon+(1-\epsilon)\pi$	$\epsilon+(1-\epsilon)\left(\dfrac{1-\epsilon-\zeta_o}{1-\epsilon}\right)^{1/n}$	

5. ANALYSIS OF MULTISTAGE ROCKETS NEGLECTING GRAVITY

The performance of a multistage rocket in a vacuum is now investigated with the assumption that the thrust is tangent to the flight path and that the gravitational forces are negligible. Consequently, in analogy with Eq. (3), the following indefinite integral holds for each stage:

$$V_k + V_{Ek} \log m_k = \text{Const} \tag{19}$$

while the corresponding definite form is represented by

$$V_{fk} - V_{ik} + V_{Ek} \log \frac{m_{fk}}{m_{ik}} = 0 \tag{20}$$

Hence, if the rocket is initially at rest and if the final velocity of each stage is equal to the initial velocity of the next, summation of the n equations (20) yields the following expression for the payload velocity:

$$V_* = \sum_{k=1}^{n} V_{Ek} \log \frac{m_{ik}}{m_{fk}} \tag{21}$$

which, in consideration of the data of Table 2, can be rewritten as

$$V_* = \sum_{k=1}^{n} V_{Ek} \log \frac{1}{\epsilon_k + (1 - \epsilon_k)\pi_k} \tag{22}$$

Now, consider a rocket which is designed in such a way that the characteristic parameters of each stage are identical. Thus, under the hypotheses

$$V_{Ek} = V_E, \qquad \pi_k = \pi, \qquad \epsilon_k = \epsilon \tag{23}$$

the dimensionless payload velocity is given by

$$u = n \log \frac{1}{\epsilon + (1 - \epsilon)\pi} \tag{24}$$

and implies that

$$\pi = \frac{\exp(-u/n) - \epsilon}{1 - \epsilon} \tag{25}$$

Consequently, the over-all payload ratio becomes

$$\pi_o = \left[\frac{\exp(-u/n) - \epsilon}{1 - \epsilon} \right]^n \tag{26}$$

and is plotted in Fig. 4 versus the dimensionless velocity for a structural factor of 0.1 and for several numbers of stages. The graph indicates that,

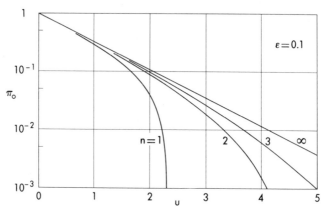

FIG. 4. Payload ratio.

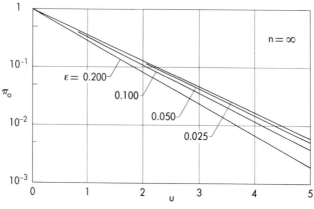

FIG. 5. Payload ratio.

if the required dimensionless velocity is ·2 (intercontinental missile powered by chemical rockets), the over-all payload ratio is 0.039 with a one-stage rocket and increases to 0.089 with a two-stage rocket. If the required dimensionless speed is 2.6 (satellite vehicle powered by chemical rockets), there exists no one-stage solution which is physically possible with a structural factor of 0.1; on the other hand, a two-stage rocket with a payload ratio of 0.037 can accomplish this mission. Finally, if the required dimensionless speed is 3.7 (space vehicle powered by chemical rockets), the over-all payload ratio is 0.004 with a two-stage rocket, 0.010 with a three-stage rocket, and 0.012 with a four-stage rocket.

While these results emphasize the beneficial effects which can be obtained by staging the rocket, it must be noted that the over-all payload ratio does not increase indefinitely but, for $n \to \infty$, tends to the upper limit

$$\pi_o = \exp\left(-\frac{u}{1-\epsilon}\right) \tag{27}$$

which is plotted in Fig. 5 for several values of the structural factor. Thus, in practice, it is not convenient to increase the number of stages beyond a certain value, because any subsequent gain in the payload mass is offset entirely by the increased mechanical complexity of the rocket and the associated decrease in reliability. In this connection, a practical upper limit to the number of stages for intercontinental ballistic missiles powered by chemical rockets is two, for satellite vehicles, three, and for vehicles designed for space missions, four or five.* Should nuclear rockets become a reality, that is, should equivalent exit velocities in the order of 25,000–30,000 ft sec^{-1} be obtained, then the number of stages required for intercontinental missiles and satellite vehicles would be reduced to one, while the number of stages required for space vehicles would become two or three, depending on the mission.*

While Eq. (27) yields an upper limit for the payload ratio, it is evident that there also exists a lower limit and that this lower limit is zero. When this situation occurs, the following relationship holds:

$$u_{\lim} = n \log \frac{1}{\epsilon} \tag{28}$$

and can be interpreted in either of two ways: (a) it yields the limiting velocity which can be achieved with a given number of stages and shows that this limiting velocity is proportional to the number of stages; or (b) it yields the lowest number of stages required for a given velocity. For example, if the required dimensionless speed is 3.7 (space vehicle powered by chemical rockets) and the structural factor is 0.1, the lowest number of stages is $n = 1.6$; hence, the mission in question is impossible with a one-stage rocket but is technically possible with a two-stage rocket.

5.1 Treatment of an infinite-stage rocket by a continuous process. In the previous section, the performance of an infinite-stage rocket was derived as a particular case of that relative to a rocket with a finite number of stages by means of the limiting process $n \to \infty$. The same results can be calculated by means of a continuous process, that is, by assuming that, in each infinitesimal time interval, an infinitesimal pro-

---

* It is emphasized that these conclusions are valid subject to the zero-gravity approximation. Should gravity be considered, the number of stages for each case would increase by one.

pellant mass is ejected with relative velocity V_E while an infinitesimal structural mass is ejected with zero relative velocity. If both the aerodynamic and gravitational forces are neglected and if the thrust is tangent to the flight path, the equation of motion on the tangent to the flight path is written in the form

$$\beta V_E - m\dot{V} = 0 \tag{29}$$

where β is the propellant mass flow. Notice that, if ϵ is the constant structural factor of the infinitesimal stage and $\dot{m}$ is the time rate of change of the rocket mass, the fraction $\epsilon\dot{m}$ is ejected in the form of structural mass and the fraction $(1 - \epsilon)\dot{m}$ in the form of propellant mass. Hence, the relationship between the propellant mass flow and the time rate of change of the rocket mass is given by

$$\beta + (1 - \epsilon)\dot{m} = 0 \tag{30}$$

If the previous relationships are combined, and the propellant mass flow is eliminated, the following differential expression is obtained:

$$dV + V_E(1 - \epsilon)\frac{dm}{m} = 0 \tag{31}$$

and its general integral is given by

$$V + V_E(1 - \epsilon)\log m = \text{Const} \tag{32}$$

The corresponding definite form is represented by

$$V_f - V_i + V_E(1 - \epsilon)\log\frac{m_f}{m_i} = 0 \tag{33}$$

and, for the end-conditions

$$V_i = 0, \qquad V_f = V_*, \qquad m_f = m_* \tag{34}$$

implies that

$$u = (1 - \epsilon)\log\frac{1}{\pi_o} \tag{35}$$

where π_o is the over-all payload ratio. It can be immediately verified that this equation is identical with Eq. (27).

6. ANALYSIS OF MULTISTAGE ROCKETS INCLUDING GRAVITY

In the previous section, the performance of a multistage rocket was analyzed under the assumption that the gravitational forces are negligible. Since the payload ratios calculated in this way are somewhat optimistic, a refinement of the preceding analysis is presented here, in that the effects of gravity are included. More specifically, vertical flight in a vacuum with the thrust tangent to the flight path is considered. If g denotes the acceleration of gravity and t the time, the following indefinite integral holds for each stage (see Chapter 15):

$$V_k + V_{Ek} \log m_k + g t_k = \text{Const} \qquad (36)$$

and its corresponding definite form is represented by

$$V_{fk} - V_{ik} + V_{Ek} \log \frac{m_{fk}}{m_{ik}} + g(t_{fk} - t_{ik}) = 0 \qquad (37)$$

If the rocket is initially at rest and if the final velocity of each stage is equal to the initial velocity of the next, summation of the n equations (37) yields the following expression for the payload velocity:

$$V_* = \sum_{k=1}^{n} V_{Ek} \log \frac{m_{ik}}{m_{fk}} - g t_* \qquad (38)$$

where t_* is the over-all burning time. After the final-to-initial mass ratios given in Table 2 are used, the payload velocity can be rewritten in the equivalent form

$$V_* = \sum_{k=1}^{n} V_{Ek} \log \frac{1}{\epsilon_k + (1 - \epsilon_k)\pi_k} - g t_* \qquad (39)$$

and, clearly, depends not only on the distribution of masses within the rocket but also on the over-all burning time, which in turn is related to the thrust program. Since the discussion of the thrust program is of paramount importance in understanding the behavior of a multistage rocket in a gravitational field, three particular classes of rockets are now analyzed: (a) configurations whose burning time is independent of the number of stages; (b) configurations in which the thrust of each stage is constant and the initial thrust-to-weight ratio of each stage is prescribed; and (c) configurations in which the thrust of each stage is constant and the final thrust-to-weight ratio of each stage is prescribed.

6.1 **Burning time independent of the number of stages.** In this section, attention is focused on the class of multistage rockets which are designed in such a way that the over-all burning time is the same for each member of the class. For these rockets, Eq. (39) can be rewritten in the form

$$V'_* = \sum_{k=1}^{n} V_{Ek} \log \frac{1}{\epsilon_k + (1 - \epsilon_k)\pi_k} \qquad (40)$$

where
$$V'_* = V_* + gt_*$$
(41)

After Eqs. (22) and (40) are compared, it is seen that the performance relevant to the gravity-included case can be obtained from that pertinent to the gravity-free case by simply replacing the payload velocity with the *augmented velocity*, that is, the sum of the payload velocity and the modulus of the velocity loss due to gravity.

If the rocket is designed in such a way that the characteristic parameters of each stage are identical, Eq. (40) can be rewritten as

$$\pi_o = \left[\frac{\exp\left(-u'/n\right) - \epsilon}{1 - \epsilon}\right]^n$$
(42)

where
$$u' = u + \theta$$
(43)

is the *dimensionless augmented velocity* and

$$\theta = \frac{t_* g}{V_E}$$
(44)

the *dimensionless burning time*. Consequently, Figs. 4 and 5, which were developed for the gravity-free case, are also valid for the gravity-included case provided that the burnout velocity u is replaced by the augmented velocity u'. Clearly, gravity causes a considerable decrease in the payload ratio attainable for a given burnout velocity as well as in the limiting velocity attainable when the payload ratio is zero. For example, consider a two-stage rocket whose structural factor is $\epsilon = 0.1$ and whose dimensionless burning time is $\theta = 0.4$. If the desired burnout velocity is $u = 1.5$, the payload ratio calculated neglecting gravity is 0.17 and reduces to 0.10 when gravity is included. For the same two-stage rocket, the limiting velocity calculated by neglecting gravity is 4.6 and reduces to 4.2 when gravity is included.

6.2 Constant thrust; given initial thrust-to-weight ratios. In this section, attention is focused on the class of multistage rockets which are designed in such a way that the thrust of each stage is constant and that the initial thrust-to-weight ratio of each stage is prescribed. For these rockets, the over-all burning time is a function of the number of stages and can be calculated by summing the partial burning times, each of which equals the ratio of the propellant mass to the mass flow of each stage, that is,

$$t_* = \sum_{k=1}^{n} \frac{m_{pk}}{\beta_k}$$
(45)

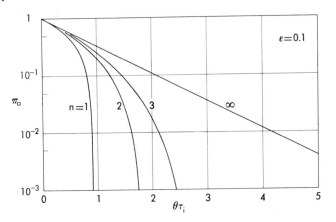

FIG. 6. Dimensionless burning time.

After the *initial thrust-to-weight ratio* of each stage is defined as

$$\tau_{ik} = \frac{\beta_k V_{Ek}}{m_{ik} g} \tag{46}$$

and the data of Table 2 are considered, the following relationship is readily derived:

$$t_* = \frac{1}{g} \sum_{k=1}^{n} \frac{V_{Ek}}{\tau_{ik}} \frac{m_{pk}}{m_{ik}} = \frac{1}{g} \sum_{k=1}^{n} \frac{V_{Ek}}{\tau_{ik}} (1 - \epsilon_k)(1 - \pi_k) \tag{47}$$

and simplifies to

$$\theta = \frac{1 - \epsilon}{\tau_i} n (1 - \pi_o^{1/n}) \tag{48}$$

if the characteristic parameters of each stage are identical, that is, if

$$V_{Ek} = V_E, \qquad \pi_k = \pi, \qquad \epsilon_k = \epsilon, \qquad \tau_{ik} = \tau_i \tag{49}$$

With reference to the dimensionless burning time-payload ratio domain, Eq. (48) is plotted in Fig. 6 for $\epsilon = 0.1$ and for several numbers of stages. For a given payload ratio, the dimensionless burning time (and, hence, the velocity loss due to gravity) increases with the number of stages; furthermore, it decreases with the initial thrust-to-weight ratio, becoming zero for $\tau_i = \infty$: this is precisely the case of negligible gravity already analyzed in Section 5.

If the velocity corresponding to the gravity-free case and the velocity loss due to gravity are superimposed, the payload velocity becomes

$$V_* = \sum_{k=1}^{n} V_{Ek} \log \frac{1}{\epsilon_k + (1 - \epsilon_k)\pi_k} - \sum_{k=1}^{n} \frac{V_{Ek}}{\tau_{ik}} (1 - \epsilon_k)(1 - \pi_k) \tag{50}$$

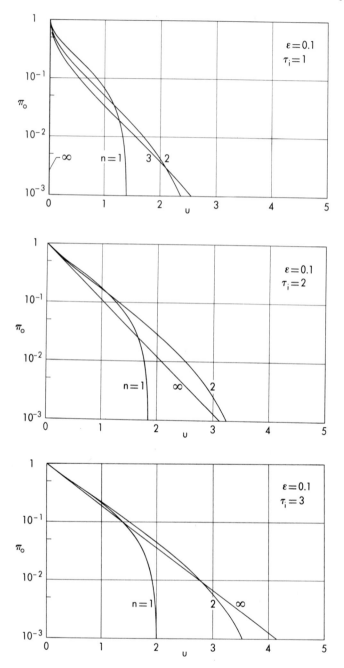

Fig. 7. Velocity-payload ratio relationship for several numbers of stages.

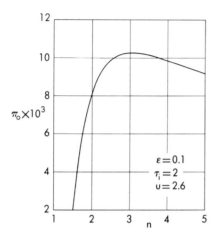

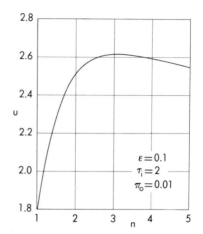

FIG. 8. Effect of the number of stages on the payload ratio (constant burnout velocity).

FIG. 9. Effect of the number of stages on the burnout velocity (constant payload ratio).

and reduces to

$$u = n \log \frac{1}{\epsilon + (1 - \epsilon)\pi_o^{1/n}} - n \frac{(1 - \epsilon)(1 - \pi_o^{1/n})}{\tau_i} \qquad (51)$$

if the characteristic parameters of each stage are identical. If u_o denotes the dimensionless velocity corresponding to the gravity-free case, Eq. (51) has the form

$$u = u_o(\pi_o, n, \epsilon) - \theta(\pi_o, n, \epsilon, \tau_i) \qquad (52)$$

and is plotted in Fig. 7 by combining the results of Figs. 4 and 6 linearly. While, in the gravity-free case, the payload ratio increases monotonically with the number of stages, this is not true when gravity is included. More specifically, the fact that the $n = \text{Const}$ curves cross each other indicates that, for each given burnout velocity, there exists a number of stages such that the payload ratio is a maximum (Fig. 8). Conversely, for each given payload ratio, there exists a number of stages such that the burnout velocity is a maximum (Fig. 9). This interesting behavior is amenable to a simple physical interpretation if one observes that (a) the burnout velocity of the gravity-included case is equal to the burnout velocity of the gravity-free case minus the corrective term due to gravity and (b) both the burnout velocity of the gravity-free case and the corrective term due to gravity increase with the number of stages. Consequently, the beneficial effect associated with the ejection of useless mass is partially counterbalanced by the fact that, as n increases, a less effective thrust program is employed.

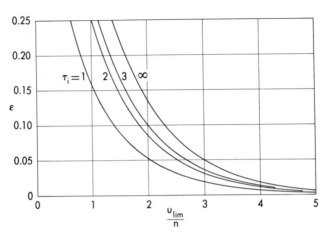

FIG. 10. Limiting velocity.

In closing, it is worth noting that, as the burnout velocity increases, the payload ratio associated with given values of the structural factor, the initial thrust-to-weight ratio, and the number of stages decreases, becoming zero when the velocity attains the limiting value

$$\frac{u_{\lim}}{n} = \log\frac{1}{\epsilon} - \frac{1-\epsilon}{\tau_i} \tag{53}$$

which is plotted in Fig. 10 versus the structural factor for several values of the initial thrust-to-weight ratio. As an example, for a two-stage rocket whose structural factor is 0.1 and whose initial thrust-to-weight ratio is 2, the limiting velocity calculated by neglecting gravity is 4.6 and reduces to 3.7 if gravity is included.

6.3 Constant thrust; given final thrust-to-weight ratios. In this section, attention is focused on the class of multistage rockets which are designed in such a way that the thrust of each stage is constant and that the final thrust-to-weight ratio of each stage is prescribed.* After the *final thrust-to-weight ratio* of each stage is defined as

$$\tau_{fk} = \frac{\beta_k V_{Ek}}{m_{fk}g} \tag{54}$$

---

* This is equivalent to prescribing the final acceleration of each stage, since this acceleration and the final thrust-to-weight ratio are related by the expression

$$\frac{\dot{V}_{fk}}{g} = \tau_{fk} - 1$$

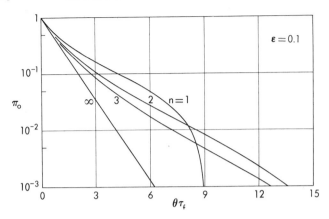

FIG. 11. Dimensionless burning time.

and the data of Table 2 are considered, the over-all burning time can be rewritten in the form

$$t_* = \frac{1}{g} \sum_{k=1}^{n} \frac{V_{Ek}}{\tau_{fk}} \frac{m_{pk}}{m_{fk}}$$

$$= \frac{1}{g} \sum_{k=1}^{n} \frac{V_{Ek}}{\tau_{fk}} \frac{(1 - \epsilon_k)(1 - \pi_k)}{\epsilon_k + (1 - \epsilon_k)\pi_k} \tag{55}$$

which simplifies to

$$\theta = \frac{n(1 - \epsilon)}{\tau_f} \frac{1 - \pi_o^{1/n}}{\epsilon + (1 - \epsilon)\pi_o^{1/n}} \tag{56}$$

if the characteristic parameters of each stage are identical. With reference to the dimensionless burning time-payload ratio domain, this function is plotted in Fig. 11 for $\epsilon = 0.1$ and for several numbers of stages. Notice that, for every payload ratio satisfying the inequality $0.012 < \pi_o < 1$, the dimensionless burning time (and, hence, the velocity loss due to gravity) decreases monotonically with the number of stages. On the other hand, for every payload ratio such that $0.001 < \pi_o < 0.012$, the dimensionless burning time achieves its highest value for the two-stage rocket.

If the velocity corresponding to the gravity-free case and the velocity loss due to gravity are superimposed, the payload velocity becomes

$$V_* = \sum_{k=1}^{n} V_{Ek} \log \frac{1}{\epsilon_k + (1 - \epsilon_k)\pi_k} - \sum_{k=1}^{n} \frac{V_{Ek}}{\tau_{fk}} \frac{(1 - \epsilon_k)(1 - \pi_k)}{\epsilon_k + (1 - \epsilon_k)\pi_k} \tag{57}$$

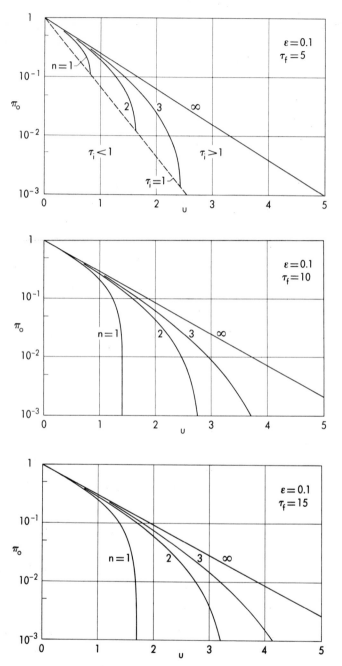

FIG. 12. Velocity-payload ratio relationship for several numbers of stages.

and reduces to

$$u = n \log \frac{1}{\epsilon + (1 - \epsilon)\pi_o^{1/n}} - \frac{n}{\tau_f} \frac{(1 - \epsilon)(1 - \pi_o^{1/n})}{\epsilon + (1 - \epsilon)\pi_o^{1/n}} \qquad (58)$$

if the characteristic parameters of each stage are identical. This equation has the form

$$u = u_o(\pi_o, n, \epsilon) - \theta(\pi_o, n, \epsilon, \tau_f) \qquad (59)$$

and is plotted in Fig. 12 by combining the results of Figs. 4 and 11 linearly. Since the curves $n = $ Const never cross each other, it becomes apparent that (a) for each given velocity, the payload ratio increases with the number of stages and (b) for each given payload ratio, the burnout velocity increases with the number of stages. This behavior is quite different from that shown in Fig. 7 for the case where the initial thrust-to-weight ratio is given and, with reference to the payload ratio interval $0.012 < \pi_o < 1$, can be explained as follows. While the burnout velocity of the gravity-free case increases with the number of stages, the corrective term due to the gravity decreases. Consequently, the burnout velocity of the gravity-included case increases with n, since the beneficial effect associated with the ejection of useless mass is coupled with the fact that a more effective thrust program is employed. An analogous explanation holds for the payload ratio interval $0.001 < \pi_o < 0.012$ as long as $n > 2$. For $n < 2$, a complication arises in that the velocity loss of the two-stage rocket is greater than that of the one-stage rocket; in spite of this, the burnout velocity of the two-stage rocket is higher than that of the one-stage rocket, since the beneficial effects associated with the ejection of useless mass are more important than the detrimental effects caused by a less effective thrust program.

Since the initial and final thrust-to-weight ratios of each stage are related by

$$\frac{\tau_i}{\tau_f} = \epsilon + (1 - \epsilon)\pi_o^{1/n} \qquad (60)$$

each point of Fig. 12 corresponds to a different initial thrust-to-weight ratio. In particular, the geometrical locus of multistage solutions such that $\tau_i = 1$ is represented by the parametric equations

$$u = n \left(\log \tau_f + \frac{1 - \tau_f}{\tau_f} \right)$$

$$\pi_o = \left[\frac{1 - \epsilon \tau_f}{(1 - \epsilon)\tau_f} \right]^n \qquad (61)$$

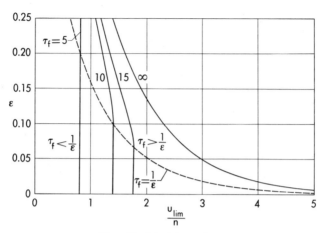

FIG. 13. Limiting velocity.

which are valid subject to the condition that

$$\tau_f < \frac{1}{\epsilon} \tag{62}$$

Elimination of the parameter n from Eqs. (61) leads to the relationship

$$\pi_o = \left[\frac{1 - \epsilon\tau_f}{(1 - \epsilon)\tau_f} \right]^{\frac{u\,\tau_f}{1 + \tau_f(\log \tau_f - 1)}} \tag{63}$$

which is represented by the dashed line in Fig. 12. This line divides the velocity-payload ratio domain into two regions: The region above the line corresponds to multistage solutions such that $\tau_i > 1$; the region below corresponds to solutions such that $\tau_i < 1$ and has, therefore, no interest for rocket operations.

Another interesting quantity is the limiting velocity which a multistage rocket can achieve for given values of the structural factor, the final thrust-to-weight ratio, and the number of stages. If the configuration is such that inequality (62) is satisfied, the limiting velocity is achieved when $\tau_i = 1$ and is given by

$$\frac{u_{\lim}}{n} = \log \tau_f + \frac{1 - \tau_f}{\tau_f} \tag{64}$$

Otherwise, the limiting velocity is obtained when the payload ratio is zero and is written as (Fig. 13)

$$\frac{u_{\lim}}{n} = \log \frac{1}{\epsilon} - \frac{1 - \epsilon}{\epsilon\tau_f} \tag{65}$$

As an example, for a two-stage rocket such that $\epsilon = 0.1$ and $\tau_f = 10$, the limiting velocity calculated by neglecting gravity is 4.6 and reduces to 2.8 if gravity is included.

6.4 Remark. It is emphasized that the results of this chapter can be subjected to considerable qualitative and quantitative variations if any or all of the following additional factors are considered: (a) the presence of aerodynamic forces, (b) the fact that only a part of the trajectory of satellite or space vehicles is rectilinear, and (c) the influence of the design parameters on the distribution of structural factors within the rocket. For example, if the final thrust-to-weight ratio is given, the initial thrust-to-weight ratio increases with the number of stages. Hence, for the same initial mass, the thrust of the first stage increases as n increases. In turn, this circumstance influences the weight of the engine and, hence, the structural factor.

EXERCISES

1. For a single-stage rocket, derive the relationships indicated in Table 1. Retaining the hypotheses of Section 3, show that the propellant mass ratio necessary to attain a given burnout velocity is given by $\zeta = 1 - \exp(-u)$.

2. For a multistage rocket, derive the relationships indicated in Table 2. Furthermore, assuming that the parameters characteristic of each stage are identical, prove the relationships of Table 3.

3. Consider a multistage rocket, and assume that the parameters characteristic of each stage are identical. Retaining the hypotheses of Section 5, show that the propellant mass ratio of each stage is given by $\zeta = 1 - \exp(-u/n)$, while the over-all propellant mass ratio is written as

$$\zeta_o = (1 - \epsilon)\left\{1 - \left[\frac{\exp(-u/n) - \epsilon}{1 - \epsilon}\right]^n\right\} \tag{66}$$

For given values of the structural factor and the burnout velocity, prove that this function decreases monotonically with the number of stages and, for $n \to \infty$, tends to the lower limit

$$\zeta_o = (1 - \epsilon)\left[1 - \exp\left(-\frac{u}{1 - \epsilon}\right)\right] \tag{67}$$

4. Consider the vertical flight of a multistage rocket in a vacuum, and assume that the thrust of each stage is constant and tangent to the flight path and that the parameters characteristic of each stage are identical. Denoting by h_* the burnout altitude, by h_{e*} the total energy at burnout

(sum of the potential and kinetic energies per unit weight), and defining the dimensionless groups

$$\eta = \frac{h_* g}{V_E^2}$$

$$\eta_e = \frac{h_{e*} g}{V_E^2}$$

(68)

show that the following relationships hold:

$$\eta = \frac{n}{\tau_i}\left[-\frac{n \zeta^2}{2\tau_i} + \zeta + \left(1 - \frac{n+1}{2}\zeta\right)\log\,(1 - \zeta)\right]$$

$$\eta_e = \frac{n}{\tau_i}\left[\zeta + \left(1 + \frac{n-1}{2}\zeta\right)\log\,(1 - \zeta)\right] + \frac{n^2}{2}\log^2\,(1 - \zeta)$$

(69)

For the limiting case where $n = \infty$, prove that the burnout altitude and the burnout total energy associated with given values of τ, ϵ, π_o become

$$\eta = \frac{1}{2\tau}\left(1 - \frac{1}{\tau}\right)(1 - \epsilon)^2 \log^2 \pi_o$$

$$\eta_e = \frac{1}{2}\left(1 - \frac{1}{\tau}\right)(1 - \epsilon)^2 \log^2 \pi_o$$

(70)

5. Analyze the performance of an infinite-stage rocket by means of a continuous process; that is, assume that in each infinitesimal time interval an infinitesimal propellant mass is ejected with relative velocity V_E while an infinitesimal structural mass is ejected with zero relative velocity. Retaining the hypotheses of Exercise 4, show that the following result holds:

$$V + V_E(1 - \epsilon)\left(1 - \frac{1}{\tau}\right)\log m = \text{Const} \tag{71}$$

where ϵ denotes the constant structural factor of the infinitesimal stage and τ the constant thrust-to-weight ratio. Notice that, for the infinite-stage rocket, the final mass equals the payload mass. Hence, by applying the previous equation at the endpoints and assuming that the initial velocity is zero, show that the dimensionless velocity at burnout is given by

$$u = (1 - \epsilon)\left(1 - \frac{1}{\tau}\right)\log \frac{1}{\pi_o} \tag{72}$$

6. Consider a multistage rocket in vertical flight in a vacuum. Retain every hypothesis used in Exercise 4, but replace the constant thrust program with a constant thrust per unit weight program. Assuming that the

physical characteristics of each stage are the same, show that the dimensionless burnout velocity, altitude, and total energy are given by

$$u = -n \left(1 - \frac{1}{\tau_i}\right) \log (1 - \zeta)$$

$$\eta = \frac{n^2}{2\tau_i} \left(1 - \frac{1}{\tau_i}\right) \log^2 (1 - \zeta) \tag{73}$$

$$\eta_e = \frac{n^2}{2} \left(1 - \frac{1}{\tau_i}\right) \log^2 (1 - \zeta)$$

and reduce to

$$u = - \left(1 - \frac{1}{\tau}\right) (1 - \epsilon) \log \pi_o$$

$$\eta = \frac{1}{2\tau} \left(1 - \frac{1}{\tau}\right) (1 - \epsilon)^2 \log^2 \pi_o \tag{74}$$

$$\eta_e = \frac{1}{2} \left(1 - \frac{1}{\tau}\right) (1 - \epsilon)^2 \log^2 \pi_o$$

for the limiting case of an infinite-stage rocket.

REFERENCES

1. MALINA, F. J. and SUMMERFIELD, M., *The Problem of Escape from the Earth by Rocket*, Journal of the Aerospace Sciences, Vol. 14, No. 8, 1947.
2. FROELICH, J. E., *Capabilities of Multistaged Chemical Rocket Systems*, Astronautica Acta, Vol. 6, No. 6, 1960.
3. HALL, H. H. and ZAMBELLI, E. D., *On the Optimization of Multistage Rockets*, ARS Journal, Vol. 28, No. 7, 1958.
4. VERTREGT, M., *A Method for Calculating the Mass Ratios of Step-Rockets*, Journal of the British Interplanetary Society, Vol. 15, No. 2, 1956.
5. VERTREGT, M., *Calculation of Step-Rockets*, Journal of the British Interplanetary Society, Vol. 14, No. 1, 1955.
6. SCHURMANN, E. E. H., *Optimum Staging Technique for Multistaged Rocket Vehicles*, ARS Journal, Vol. 27, No. 8, 1957.

CHAPTER 17

ROCKET PERFORMANCE WITH AERODYNAMIC FORCES INCLUDED

1. INTRODUCTION

In Chapter 15, an introduction to rocket performance was presented under the assumption of flight in a vacuum. In this chapter, the previous analysis is extended to cover the case where aerodynamic forces are present. If it is assumed that the thrust is tangent to the flight path, Eqs. (4–42) are written as

$$\dot{X} - V \cos \gamma = 0$$

$$\dot{h} - V \sin \gamma = 0$$

$$T - D - m(g \sin \gamma + \dot{V}) = 0 \qquad (1)$$

$$L - m(g \cos \gamma + V\dot{\gamma}) = 0$$

$$\dot{m} + \beta = 0$$

where X denotes the horizontal distance, h the altitude, V the velocity, γ the path inclination, m the mass, g the acceleration of gravity, D the drag, L the lift, T the thrust, β the propellant mass flow, and the dot sign a derivative with respect to time.

1.1 Engine performance. According to Chapter 7, the thrust of a rocket engine operating in the atmosphere is given by

$$T = \beta V_e + S_e(p_e - p) \qquad (2)$$

where V_e is the exit velocity, S_e the exit area, p_e the exit pressure, and p the atmospheric pressure. Furthermore, if the *equivalent exit velocity*

$$V_E = V_e + \frac{S_e(p_e - p)}{\beta} \qquad (3)$$

is introduced, the thrust can be rewritten in the form

$$T = \beta V_E \qquad (4)$$

While the equivalent exit velocity of a rocket engine operating in a vacuum ($p = 0$) is constant, this is not true for flight in a resisting medium owing to the atmospheric pressure term. In fact, inspection of Eq. (3) shows that, for a constant geometry chemical rocket, the equivalent exit velocity depends on both the altitude and the propellant mass flow (the control parameter of the engine). It must be noted, however, that there are many rocket designs in which the relative increase of the equivalent exit velocity with the altitude is less than 20%. In this case, it is permissible to approximate V_E with a constant average value, at least as far as preliminary design computations are concerned. Since this point of view yields a considerable simplification in the analysis, it is retained throughout the entire chapter.

1.2 Integration problem. After a drag function of the form $D = D(h, V, L)$ is assumed and it is considered that, for a constant equivalent exit velocity, the thrust function has the form $T = T(\beta)$, the equations of motion involve one independent variable, the time, and seven dependent variables $(X, h, V, \gamma, m\ L, \beta)$. Consequently, there are two degrees of freedom, which is logical since the trajectory can be changed by controlling the elevator position and the engine power setting. Thus, for a given set of initial conditions for $X, h, V, \gamma, m,$ infinite trajectories exist, more specifically, one trajectory for each arbitrarily prescribed pair of functions $L(t)$, $\beta(t)$ or equivalent conditions. In this connection, the following sections consider the integration of the equations of motion for several types of lift and mass flow programs having particular interest in the flight of air-to-air missiles, sounding rockets, and rocket-powered aircraft.

2. SHORT RANGE NONLIFTING MISSILES

A category of flight paths of interest for air-to-air missiles is that flown with zero lift and constant mass flow. These trajectories are now investigated with the aid of the simplifying assumptions

$$\cos \gamma \cong 1, \qquad \sin \gamma \cong \gamma, \qquad mg \sin \gamma \ll T \tag{5}$$

the last of which means that the weight component on the tangent to the flight path is negligible with respect to the thrust. Consequently, the equations of motion are rewritten in the form

$$\dot{X} - V = 0$$

$$\dot{h} - V\gamma = 0$$

$$\dot{V} - \frac{\beta V_E - D}{m} = 0 \tag{6}$$

$$\dot{\gamma} + \frac{g}{V} = 0$$

$$\dot{m} + \beta = 0$$

and, after the time is eliminated and the velocity is selected as the new independent variable, lead to the differential system

$$\frac{dX}{dV} = \frac{mV}{\beta V_E - D}$$

$$\frac{dh}{dV} = \frac{mV\gamma}{\beta V_E - D}$$

$$\frac{d\gamma}{dV} = -\frac{mg}{V(\beta V_E - D)}$$

$$\frac{dm}{dV} = -\frac{m\beta}{\beta V_E - D}$$

(7)

whose integration must usually be performed by approximate methods. However, if the drag coefficient is assumed to be constant and if the variations in the flight altitude are so small that the air density can be regarded as constant, an analytical solution is possible for the mass-velocity relationship; furthermore, the distributions of path inclination, distance, and altitude versus the velocity can be obtained by simple quadratures (Refs. 4 and 5).

In consideration of the previous hypotheses, it is convenient to introduce the dimensionless coordinates

$$u = \frac{V}{V_R}$$

$$\xi = \frac{Xg}{V_R^2}$$

$$\eta = \frac{hg}{V_R^2}$$

$$\mu = \frac{m}{m_i}$$

(8)

where m_i is the initial mass and where the reference velocity

$$V_R = \sqrt{\frac{2\beta V_E}{C_D \rho S}}$$

(9)

is the limiting velocity which the missile can achieve with the prescribed thrust. If the ratio of the limiting velocity to the equivalent exit velocity and the initial thrust-to-weight ratio are denoted by

$$\alpha = \frac{V_R}{V_E}, \qquad \tau_i = \frac{\beta V_E}{m_i g}$$

(10)

Eqs. (7) can be transformed into the dimensionless set

$$\frac{d\xi}{du} = \frac{\mu u}{\tau_i(1 - u^2)}$$

$$\frac{d\eta}{du} = \frac{\mu u \gamma}{\tau_i(1 - u^2)}$$

$$\frac{d\gamma}{du} = -\frac{\mu}{\tau_i u(1 - u^2)}$$

$$\frac{d\mu}{du} = -\frac{\mu \alpha}{1 - u^2}$$

(11)

whose general integral is given by

$$\frac{\mu}{C_1} = A(\alpha, u)$$

$$\frac{\xi \tau_i}{C_1} = B(\alpha, u) + C_2$$

$$\frac{\gamma \tau_i}{C_1} = -C(\alpha, u) + C_3$$

$$\frac{\eta \tau_i^2}{C_1^2} = C_3 B(\alpha, u) - D(\alpha, u) + C_4$$

(12)

where C_1 through C_4 are constants. The functions A, B, C, D are defined as

$$A(\alpha, u) = \left(\frac{1 - u}{1 + u}\right)^{\alpha/2}$$

$$B(\alpha, u) = \int_{u_o}^{u} \frac{A(\alpha, u)u}{1 - u^2} \, du$$

$$C(\alpha, u) = \int_{u_o}^{u} \frac{A(\alpha, u)}{1 - u^2} \frac{du}{u}$$

$$D(\alpha, u) = \int_{u_o}^{u} \frac{A(\alpha, u)C(\alpha, u)}{1 - u^2} u \, du$$

(13)

where $u_o = 0.01$ is an arbitrary lower limit of integration. These functions are plotted in Figs. 1 through 4 for several values of the parameter α; typical values of this important parameter range between zero and two, depending on the thrust per unit frontal area and the altitude at which the air-to-air missile is launched.

An important problem concerning an air-to-air missile is that of the optimum burning program, that is, the problem of obtaining the maximum

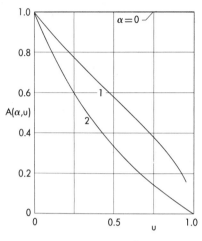

FIG. 1. The function $A(\alpha, u)$.

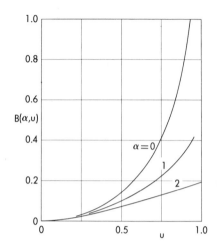

FIG. 2. The function $B(\alpha, u)$.

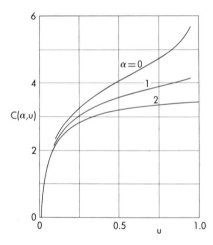

FIG. 3. The function $C(\alpha, u)$.

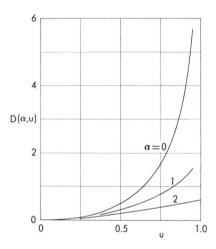

FIG. 4. The function $D(\alpha, u)$.

range while transferring the missile from one combination of mass and velocity to another. Since this problem cannot be solved with the present limited approach, it is reconsidered in those sections of Volume 2 which deal with variational methods. However, it can be anticipated that the particular burning program investigated here has more than a passing interest, since the optimum flight path generally includes parts flown with maximum thrust, parts flown with constant velocity, and parts flown with zero thrust, depending on the end-conditions which are prescribed.

Furthermore, after combining the second and the third of Eqs. (25) and eliminating the path inclination, one obtains the differential relationship

$$\frac{dm}{m} = -(\varphi\, dV + \psi\, dh) \tag{26}$$

The functions φ and ψ are defined as

$$\varphi = \frac{\beta}{\beta V_E - D}, \qquad \psi = \frac{\beta g}{V(\beta V_E - D)} \tag{27}$$

and, owing to the neglect of the induced drag, depend on the velocity and the altitude only. If Eq. (26) is integrated between the endpoints of the trajectory and if ζ denotes the propellant mass ratio, the following result is obtained (Ref. 6):

$$\zeta = 1 - \exp(-I) \tag{28}$$

where

$$I = \int_i^f (\varphi\, dV + \psi\, dh) \tag{29}$$

Thus, the determination of the propellant mass ratio requires that the line integral (29) be calculated; in turn, the calculation of this integral requires that the velocity-altitude distribution $V(h)$ be specified. In this connection, two typical maneuvers are now investigated, that is, climbing flight with constant velocity and climbing flight with constant dynamic pressure.

4.1 Climbing flight with constant velocity. For a climbing trajectory flown with constant velocity, the line integral (29) reduces to the form

$$I = \int_i^f \psi\, dh \tag{30}$$

where the function ψ is supplied by Eq. (27). Generally speaking, this integral must be evaluated by approximate methods; however, an analytical solution is possible if an exponential atmosphere is assumed. In fact, after the coordinates (17) are introduced and the dimensionless variable

$$\epsilon = \sqrt{\frac{2\beta V_E}{C_D \rho S \lambda g}} \tag{31}$$

is defined, the following expression is derived:

$$I = \frac{1}{u u_E} \int_i^f \frac{d\epsilon^2}{\epsilon^2 - u^2} \tag{32}$$

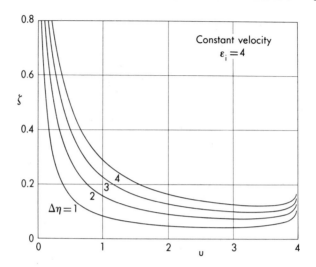

FIG. 9. Propellant mass ratio required for constant velocity climb.

which implies that

$$I = \log \left(\frac{\epsilon_f^2 - u^2}{\epsilon_i^2 - u^2} \right)^{1/u u_E} \tag{33}$$

Consequently, the propellant mass ratio necessary to transfer the rocket-powered aircraft from the initial point to the final point is given by

$$\zeta = 1 - \left(\frac{\epsilon_i^2 - u^2}{\epsilon_f^2 - u^2} \right)^{1/u u_E} \tag{34}$$

Notice that the end-values of the parameter ϵ satisfy the relationship*

$$\frac{\epsilon_f}{\epsilon_i} = \exp \left(\frac{\Delta \eta}{2} \right) \tag{35}$$

where $\Delta \eta$ denotes the altitude increment between the endpoints. Hence, Eq. (34) can be rewritten in the functional form

$$\zeta = \zeta(u, \Delta \eta, \epsilon_i, u_E) \tag{36}$$

which is plotted in Fig. 9 versus the dimensionless climbing speed for several values of the altitude increment. For each altitude increment,

---

* Typical values of the parameter ϵ_i range between 1 and 10, depending on the *superficial thrust* $\beta V_E/S$ and the altitude at which the climbing maneuver is initiated.

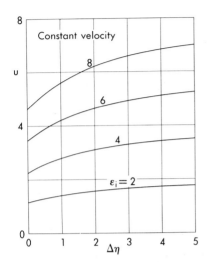

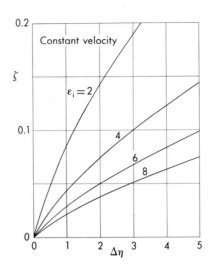

FIG. 10. Optimum speed for constant velocity climb.

FIG. 11. Minimum propellant mass ratio for constant velocity climb.

there exists a climbing speed which minimizes the propellant consumption. This optimum speed must satisfy the transcendental equation

$$\log \frac{\epsilon_i^2 - u^2}{\epsilon_f^2 - u^2} + \frac{2u^2(\epsilon_f^2 - \epsilon_i^2)}{(\epsilon_i^2 - u^2)(\epsilon_f^2 - u^2)} = 0 \qquad (37)$$

and, in consideration of Eq. (35), has the form

$$u = u\,(\Delta\eta,\,\epsilon_i) \qquad (38)$$

which is plotted in Fig. 10. The corresponding propellant mass ratio is indicated in Fig. 11.

The main conclusion of the previous analysis is that the optimum climbing speed increases with the altitude increment and the superficial thrust but is independent of the equivalent exit velocity (and hence, independent of the specific propellant consumption). On the other hand, the propellant mass ratio decreases with the superficial thrust; hence, the use of high thrusts has a beneficial effect on the constant velocity climb.

4.2 Climbing flight with constant dynamic pressure. The case of a climbing trajectory flown with constant dynamic pressure is now investigated. This means that the line integral (29) is to be calculated subject to the constraint

$$\tfrac{1}{2}\rho V^2 = \text{Const} \qquad (39)$$

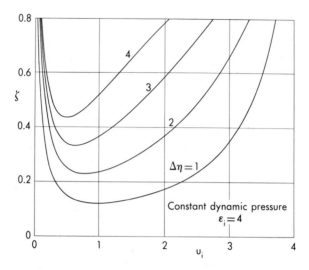

FIG. 12. Propellant mass ratio required for constant dynamic pressure climb.

After assuming an exponential atmosphere, introducing the dimensionless coordinates of the previous section, and observing that the ratio ϵ/u is constant, one can rewrite this line integral in the form

$$I = \frac{1}{u_E} \frac{\epsilon^2}{\epsilon^2 - u^2} \int_i^f \left(1 + \frac{2}{u^2}\right) du \qquad (40)$$

which implies that

$$I = F(\epsilon_f, u_f, u_E) - F(\epsilon_i, u_i, u_E) \qquad (41)$$

where

$$F(\epsilon, u, u_E) = \frac{1}{u_E} \frac{\epsilon^2}{\epsilon^2 - u^2}\left(u - \frac{2}{u}\right) \qquad (42)$$

Consequently, the propellant mass ratio necessary to transfer the vehicle from the initial condition to the final condition is given by

$$\zeta = 1 - \exp\left[F(\epsilon_i, u_i, u_E) - F(\epsilon_f, u_f, u_E)\right] \qquad (43)$$

and, after the relationship

$$\frac{\epsilon_f}{\epsilon_i} = \frac{u_f}{u_i} = \exp\left(\frac{\Delta\eta}{2}\right) \qquad (44)$$

is considered, can be written in functional form as

$$\zeta = \zeta(u_i, \Delta\eta, \epsilon_i, u_E) \qquad (45)$$

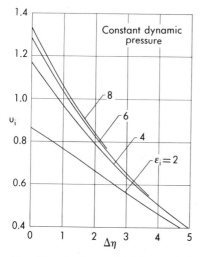

FIG. 13. Optimum initial speed for constant dynamic pressure climb.

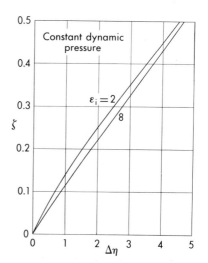

FIG. 14. Minimum propellant mass ratio for constant dynamic pressure climb.

This function is plotted in Fig. 12 versus the dimensionless initial velocity for several values of the altitude increment. For each altitude increment, there exists an initial climbing speed which minimizes the propellant consumption. This optimum speed must be a solution of the biquadratic equation

$$u_i^4 + \epsilon_i \left(\epsilon_i + \frac{6}{\epsilon_f} \right) u_i^2 - 2 \frac{\epsilon_i^3}{\epsilon_f} = 0 \qquad (46)$$

and, in consideration of Eqs. (44), can be written in the form

$$u_i = u_i \left(\Delta\eta, \epsilon_i \right) \qquad (47)$$

which is plotted in Fig. 13. The corresponding propellant mass ratio is indicated in Fig. 14.

The main conclusion of the previous analysis is that the optimum initial velocity (and, hence, the optimum dynamic pressure) decreases with the altitude increment, increases with the superficial thrust, and is independent of the equivalent exit velocity (and, hence, independent of the specific propellant consumption). On the other hand, the propellant mass ratio decreases with the superficial thrust, although not as sharply as in the constant velocity case.

Comparison of the constant velocity climb and the constant dynamic pressure climb shows that, for the same increase in potential energy, the constant velocity climb requires less propellant. However, the reader

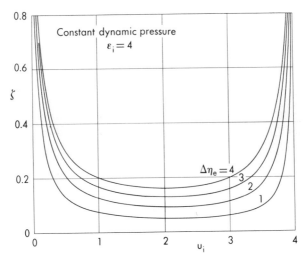

Fig. 15. Propellant mass ratio required for constant dynamic pressure climb.

should not be misled by this result, since the constant dynamic pressure climb is accompanied by an increase in kinetic energy. Consequently, a more interesting comparison of these climbing techniques is that based on the change in energy height, where the energy height is defined as

$$h_e = h + \frac{V^2}{2g} \tag{48}$$

in a dimensional form and

$$\eta_e = \eta + \frac{u^2}{2} \tag{49}$$

in a dimensionless form. When this new variable is introduced, the propellant mass ratio required for a constant dynamic pressure climb takes the form

$$\zeta = \zeta(u_i, \Delta\eta_e, \epsilon_i, u_E) \tag{50}$$

and is plotted in Fig. 15 as a function of the initial velocity for several values of the energy height increment. Comparison of Figs. 9 and 15 shows that, for the same energy height increment, the best constant velocity climb is still slightly better than the best constant dynamic pressure climb. At any rate, owing to the arbitrariness of these climbing programs, neither of them yields a truly optimum path. The exact determination of the velocity-altitude distribution $V(h)$ which minimizes the propellant expenditure belongs to the realm of the Calculus of Variations; consequently, it will be considered in Volume 2.

4.3 Remark. After the command program has been specified (e.g., constant velocity or constant dynamic pressure), the equation of motion on the tangent to the flight path supplies the sine of the path inclination. It is obvious that the climbing path is physically possible if, and only if, $\sin \gamma \leq 1$ everywhere. Should this inequality be violated along some portion of the trajectory (this is possible for relatively high values of the initial thrust-to-weight ratio), then, for that portion, the prescribed velocity-altitude distribution must be replaced by that corresponding to a vertically ascending path.

Exercises

1. Consider an air-to-air missile flying in a homogeneous atmosphere in such a way that hypotheses (5) are satisfied. Assuming that the thrust is equal to the drag at all time instants, show that the equations of motion can be integrated to yield

$$V = C_1$$
$$X = Vt + C_2$$
$$\gamma = -\frac{gt}{V} + C_3 \tag{51}$$
$$h = -\frac{gt^2}{2} + C_3 Vt + C_4$$

where C_1 through C_4 are constants. Furthermore, if the atmosphere is homogeneous and the drag coefficient is constant, prove that the required mass flow is constant, so that $m = C_5 - \beta t$, where C_5 is a constant.

2. Consider a rocket-powered aircraft in level flight with constant propellant mass flow. Assume that the induced drag is negligible with respect to the zero-lift drag and that the zero-lift drag coefficient is constant. Starting from the line integral (29) and using definitions (8) through (10), show that the propellant mass ratio which is required to accelerate the aircraft from a given initial condition to a given final condition is given by

$$\zeta = 1 - \frac{A(\alpha, u_f)}{A(\alpha, u_i)} \tag{52}$$

where

$$A(\alpha, u) = \left(\frac{1 - u}{1 + u}\right)^{\alpha/2} \tag{53}$$

3. Consider a rocket-powered aircraft which climbs with constant propellant mass flow and constant tangential acceleration, so that both the mass and the velocity are linear functions of the time. Neglect the induced drag with respect to the zero-lift drag; furthermore, assume that

the zero-lift drag coefficient is constant and that the atmosphere is exponential. Using the dimensionless coordinates (16) and (17) and denoting by τ the thrust-to-weight ratio, show that the reciprocal of the relative density and the dimensionless time $\theta = t\sqrt{g/\lambda}$ satisfy the linear differential equation

$$\frac{d(1/\sigma)}{d\theta} + \frac{A(\theta)}{\sigma} + B(\theta) = 0 \tag{54}$$

where

$$A(\theta) = u\left(\frac{\dot{V}}{g} - \tau\right), \qquad B(\theta) = \frac{C_D \rho_o S \lambda}{2m} u^3 \tag{55}$$

REFERENCES

1. IVEY, H. R., BOWEN, E. N., and OBORNY, L. F., *Introduction to the Problem of Rocket-Powered Aircraft Performance*, NACA TN No. 1401, 1947.
2. MALINA, F. J. and SMITH, A. M. O., *Flight Analysis of the Sounding Rocket*, Journal of the Aerospace Sciences, Vol. 5, No. 5, 1938.
3. LIPPISCH, A., *Performance Theory of Airplanes with Jet Propulsion*, Headquarters, Air Matériel Command, Translation Report No. F-TS-685-RE, 1946.
4. STRUBLE, R. E., STEWART, C. E., and GRANTON, J., *The Trajectory of a Rocket with Thrust*, ARS Journal, Vol. 28, No. 7, 1958.
5. PUCKETT, A. E. and EDWARDS, R. H., *The Optimum Performance of Short-Range Rocket-Powered Missiles*, IAS Preprint No. 279, 1950.
6. MIELE, A., *Optimum Climbing Technique for a Rocket-Powered Aircraft*, ARS Journal, Vol. 25, No. 8, 1955.

PROPERTIES OF THE ATMOSPHERE

1. INTRODUCTION

The description and comparison of the performance of all types of vehicles become meaningful only if all the data are referred to an established set of conditions. Thus, it is important that a standard atmosphere be defined, even though the vertical distribution of the physical properties of the atmosphere depends on the latitude, the longitude, and the time.

For the altitude region between sea level and $h = 6.5 \times 10^4$ ft, several attempts have been made to define a standard atmosphere. Early analyses (see, for example, Ref. 1) were based on the simplifying assumptions of constant acceleration of gravity and constant molecular weight. These hypotheses are not valid at the altitudes which are of interest today because of recent developments in aeronautics and astronautics. At these altitudes, a more sophisticated approach to the computation of the atmospheric properties is required, in the sense that the variation of both the acceleration of gravity and the molecular weight with the altitude must be taken into account (Refs. 2 through 4). With this point of view in mind, general equations, applicable to an arbitrary atmosphere, are introduced; a model atmosphere is then defined; and, finally, some useful engineering approximations, valid for particular cases, are presented.

2. FUNDAMENTAL EQUATIONS

There are two basic equations which must be satisfied by the gas composing any atmosphere. One is the *aerostatic equation*

$$dp = -\rho g \, dh \tag{1}$$

which, if it is assumed that the air is at rest with respect to the Earth, links the pressure differential dp, the density ρ, the acceleration of gravity g, and the altitude differential dh. The other is the *equation of state*

$$p = \rho R \theta \tag{2}$$

which sets forth a relationship between the pressure, the density, and the temperature θ of a gas whose characteristic constant is R.

If quantities evaluated at sea level are denoted by the subscript o and the *geopotential altitude* is defined as

$$H = \frac{1}{g_o} \int_0^h g \, dh \qquad (3)$$

the aerostatic equation can be rewritten in the form

$$dp = -\rho g_o \, dH \qquad (4)$$

On the other hand, if it is observed that the characteristic constant R is inversely proportional to the molecular weight m and if the *molecular temperature* is defined as

$$\tau = \theta \frac{m_o}{m} = \theta \frac{R}{R_o} \qquad (5)$$

the equation of state becomes

$$p = \rho R_o \tau \qquad (6)$$

A mathematical consequence of Eqs. (4) and (6) is the set of differential equations

$$\frac{dp}{p} = -\frac{g_o}{R_o \tau} dH, \qquad \frac{d\rho}{\rho} = -\left(\frac{g_o}{R_o} + \alpha\right)\frac{dH}{\tau} \qquad (7)$$

where

$$\alpha = \frac{d\tau}{dH} \qquad (8)$$

is the gradient of the molecular temperature with respect to the geopotential altitude. From these equations, it appears that the concept of molecular temperature combines usefully the concepts of temperature and molecular weight. In fact, by specifying the distribution of the molecular temperature versus the geopotential altitude $\tau(H)$, the pressure and the density can be determined; this means that it is not necessary to prescribe the individual functional variations of the temperature and the molecular weight. However, the molecular weight-geopotential height relationship is necessary in order to determine the static temperature with Eq. (5). Furthermore, the distribution of the acceleration of gravity versus the geometric altitude is necessary in order to determine the relationship between the geopotential and geometric altitudes by means of Eq. (3).

3. MODEL ATMOSPHERE

In connection with the previous discussion, the most complete set of empirical data available today is known as the ARDC Model Atmosphere,* and its basic assumptions are the following (Ref. 4):

---

* The symbol ARDC stands for Air Research and Development Command of the United States Air Force.

(a) The space immediately surrounding the Earth is divided into eleven concentric layers, in each of which the gradient of the molecular temperature with respect to the geopotential altitude is constant.

(b) For the six layers belonging to the lower atmosphere (region between sea level and 3×10^5 ft), the composition of the air is constant, so that the molecular weight is constant.

(c) For the five layers belonging to the upper atmosphere (region between 3×10^5 ft and 2.3×10^6 ft), the composition of the air is variable, and the molecular weight is represented by inverse trigonometric functions of the geopotential altitude.

(d) The acceleration of gravity varies with the altitude according to the inverse square law

$$g = g_0 \left(\frac{r_0}{r_0 + h} \right)^2 \tag{9}$$

where $r_0 = 20.9 \times 10^6$ ft is the radius of the Earth.

In the light of hypothesis (a), the integration of Eqs. (7) and (8) leads to the following solutions for the molecular temperature, the static pressure, and the density:

$$\alpha \neq 0 \begin{cases} \tau = \alpha H + C_1 \\ p = C_2 \tau^{-(g_0/\alpha R_0)} \\ \rho = C_3 \tau^{-[1+(g_0/\alpha R_0)]} \end{cases} \tag{10}$$

$$\alpha = 0 \begin{cases} \tau = C_4 \\ p = C_5 \exp \left(-\frac{g_0}{R_0 \tau} H \right) \\ \rho = C_6 \exp \left(-\frac{g_0}{R_0 \tau} H \right) \end{cases} \tag{11}$$

where C_1 through C_6 are integration constants. These solutions, in combination with hypotheses (b) and (c), determine how the static temperature θ (and, hence, the speed of sound a and the dynamic viscosity μ) varies with the geopotential altitude. Finally, if Eqs. (3) and (9) are employed, the relationship between the geopotential and geometric altitudes* is given by

$$H = \frac{r_0}{r_0 + h} h \tag{12}$$

---

* The geopotential altitude of the model atmosphere is always smaller than the geometric altitude. However, these altitudes become identical in the flat Earth model, in which $r_0 = \infty$.

3.1 Description of tables. Since the data relative to the upper atmosphere are still uncertain and probably subject to modification, the tables of this appendix are limited to the lower atmosphere, where the composition of the air is constant. Concerning the upper atmosphere, the reader is referred to Ref. 4.

Table 1 lists the properties of the atmosphere at sea level, including the speed of sound and the dynamic viscosity. Table 2 contains a definition of layers I through VI, with the subscript 1 denoting the lower boundary of each layer and the subscript 2, the upper boundary. Incidentally, the geopotential altitudes bounding each layer are expressed by rather unusual numbers only because they were originally defined in the metric system; in this system, the limiting geopotential altitudes are 0, 11, 25, 47, 53, 79, and 90 km. Finally, Table 3 gives the distributions of temperature, speed of sound, dynamic viscosity, density, and pressure as functions of the geopotential altitude.

3.2 Remark. Although this appendix stems directly from Ref. 4, an important conceptual difference is to be stressed. In Ref. 4, the independent variable is the *geopotential*

$$G = \int_0^h g \, dh \tag{13}$$

which is dimensionally an energy per unit mass and, with reference to the British Engineering System, is measured in standard geopotential feet.* However, in the interest of simplicity and in order to streamline the discussion of the model atmosphere, the independent variable considered here is the *geopotential altitude*, which is dimensionally a length and is measured in feet. Since the numerical value of H in feet equals the numerical value of G in standard geopotential feet, the tables of Ref. 4 are readily converted into those of the present appendix by means of the simple substitution of H for G and ft for ft$'$.

4. ENGINEERING APPROXIMATIONS

There are numerous problems in which the distributions of density and pressure of the ARDC Model Atmosphere can be replaced by a somewhat simplified model. In this connection, a few important approximations are now indicated.

4.1 Exponential atmosphere. For the preliminary design of rocket-powered vehicles, it is frequently useful to approximate the pressure and

---

* The standard geopotential foot is defined as 1 ft$'$ = 32.174 ft^2 sec^{-2}.

the density by either of the following sets of exponen

$$\frac{\rho}{\rho_o} = \exp\left(-\frac{H}{\lambda_1}\right), \qquad \frac{p}{p_o} = \exp\left(-\frac{?}{?}\right)$$

or

$$\frac{\rho}{\rho_o} = \exp\left(-\frac{h}{\lambda_3}\right), \qquad \frac{p}{p_o} = \exp\left(-\frac{h}{\lambda_4}\right)$$

In the altitude interval between sea level and 2.5×10^5 ft, the suggested values for the constants are

$$\lambda_1 = 23,600 \text{ ft}, \qquad \lambda_2 = 23,000 \text{ ft}$$

$$\lambda_3 = 23,800 \text{ ft}, \qquad \lambda_4 = 23,200 \text{ ft}$$

and lead to a maximum relative error of about 25%.

4.2 Isothermal atmosphere. If the static temperature is assumed to be ideally constant, Eqs. (14) are still valid, providing that the numerical constants for the density and the pressure are identical. If the following values are employed:

$$\lambda_1 = \lambda_2 = 23,300 \text{ ft}, \qquad \lambda_3 = \lambda_4 = 23,500 \text{ ft}$$

the upper limit to the relative error is about 30% in the altitude interval between sea level and 2.5×10^5 ft.

4.3 Constant gravity atmosphere. The performance analysis of aircraft powered by air-breathing jet engines is mainly concerned with the atmospheric region below 10^5 ft. For this region, the hypotheses $g/g_o = 1$ is acceptable and implies that

$$H = h \tag{15}$$

The relative error involved in the computation of the density and the pressure increases as the altitude increases, becoming approximately 2% at the upper boundary of the region under consideration.

REFERENCES

1. DIEHL, W. S., *Standard Atmosphere. Tables and Data*, NACA TR No. 218, 1925.
2. WARFIELD, C. N., *Tentative Tables for the Properties of the Upper Atmosphere*, NACA TN No. 1200, 1947.
3. GRIMMINGER, G., *Analysis of Temperature, Pressure, and Density of the Atmosphere Extending to Extreme Altitudes*, The RAND Corporation, Report No. R-105, 1948.
4. MINZNER, R. A., CHAMPION, K. S. W., and POND, H. L., *The ARDC Model Atmosphere, 1959*, Air Force Cambridge Research Center, TR No. 59-267, 1959.

TABLE 1

PROPERTIES OF THE MODEL ATMOSPHERE AT SEA LEVEL

Quantity	Symbol	Numerical value	Units
Ratio of specific heats	k_o	1.4	
Molecular weight	m_o	2.8966×10^1	
Acceleration of gravity	g_o	3.2174×10^1	ft sec^{-2}
Air constant	R_o	1.7165×10^3	ft^2 sec^{-2} °R^{-1}
Temperature	θ_o	5.1869×10^2	°R
Molecular temperature	τ_o	5.1869×10^2	°R
Speed of sound	a_o	1.1164×10^3	ft sec^{-1}
Dynamic viscosity	μ_o	3.7373×10^{-7}	lb sec ft^{-2}
Density	ρ_o	2.3769×10^{-3}	lb sec^2 ft^{-4}
Pressure	p_o	2.1162×10^3	lb ft^{-2}

TABLE 2

LAYERS COMPOSING THE MODEL ATMOSPHERE

Layer	H_1 (ft)	H_2 (ft)	$\tau_1 = \theta_1$ (°R)	$\tau_2 = \theta_2$ (°R)	$\alpha \times 10^3$ (°R ft^{-1})
I	0	36,089	518.69	389.99	−3.566
II	36,089	82,021	389.99	389.99	0
III	82,021	154,199	389.99	508.79	1.646
IV	154,199	173,885	508.79	508.79	0
V	173,885	259,186	508.79	298.19	−2.469
VI	259,186	295,276	298.19	298.19	0

TABLE 3

DISTRIBUTION OF TEMPERATURE, SPEED OF SOUND, DYNAMIC VISCOSITY, DENSITY, AND PRESSURE IN THE MODEL ATMOSPHERE

$H \times 10^{-3}$ (ft)	$\dfrac{\tau}{\tau_o} = \dfrac{\theta}{\theta_o}$	$\dfrac{a}{a_o}$	$\dfrac{\mu}{\mu_o}$	$\sigma = \dfrac{\rho}{\rho_o}$	$\dfrac{p}{p_o}$
0	1	1	1	1	1
5	0.9656	0.9827	0.9731	8.617×10^{-1}	8.320×10^{-1}
10	0.9312	0.9650	0.9457	7.385	6.877
15	0.8969	0.9470	0.9178	6.292	5.643
20	0.8625	0.9287	0.8894	5.328	4.595
25	0.8281	0.9100	0.8605	4.481	3.711
30	0.7937	0.8909	0.8311	3.741	2.970
35	0.7594	0.8714	0.8011	3.099	2.353
36.089	0.7519	0.8671	0.7945	2.971	2.234
40	0.7519	0.8671	0.7945	2.462	1.851
45	0.7519	0.8671	0.7945	1.936	1.455
50	0.7519	0.8671	0.7945	1.522	1.145
55	0.7519	0.8671	0.7945	1.197	9.000×10^{-2}
60	0.7519	0.8671	0.7945	9.414×10^{-2}	7.078
65	0.7519	0.8671	0.7945	7.403	5.566
70	0.7519	0.8671	0.7945	5.821	4.377
75	0.7519	0.8671	0.7945	4.578	3.442
80	0.7519	0.8671	0.7945	3.600	2.707
82.021	0.7519	0.8671	0.7945	3.267	2.456
85	0.7613	0.8725	0.8028	2.798	2.130
90	0.7772	0.8816	0.8167	2.167	1.684
95	0.7931	0.8905	0.8305	1.687	1.338
100	0.8089	0.8994	0.8442	1.320	1.068
110	0.8407	0.9169	0.8711	8.196×10^{-3}	6.890×10^{-3}
120	0.8724	0.9340	0.8977	5.179	4.518

(Continued)

PROPERTIES OF THE ATMOSPHERE

Table 3 (Continued)

$H \times 10^{-3}$ (ft)	$\dfrac{\tau}{\tau_o} = \dfrac{\theta}{\theta_o}$	$\dfrac{a}{a_o}$	$\dfrac{\mu}{\mu_o}$	$\sigma = \dfrac{\rho}{\rho_o}$	$\dfrac{p}{p_o}$
130	0.9041	0.9509	0.9237	3.327×10^{-3}	3.008×10^{-3}
140	0.9359	0.9674	0.9494	2.170	2.031
150	0.9676	0.9837	0.9746	1.436	1.389
154.199	0.9809	0.9904	0.9851	1.212	1.189
160	0.9809	0.9904	0.9851	9.786×10^{-4}	9.600×10^{-4}
170	0.9809	0.9904	0.9851	6.771	6.641
173.885	0.9809	0.9904	0.9851	5.868	5.756
180	0.9518	0.9756	0.9621	4.811	4.579
190	0.9042	0.9509	0.9238	3.430	3.102
200	0.8566	0.9255	0.8845	2.402	2.058
210	0.8090	0.8995	0.8442	1.648	1.333
220	0.7614	0.8726	0.8029	1.105	8.412×10^{-5}
230	0.7138	0.8449	0.7604	7.219×10^{-5}	5.153
240	0.6662	0.8162	0.7167	4.580	3.052
250	0.6186	0.7865	0.6718	2.810	1.738
259.186	0.5749	0.7582	0.6293	1.733	9.964×10^{-6}
260	0.5749	0.7582	0.6293	1.647	9.467
270	0.5749	0.7582	0.6293	8.783×10^{-6}	5.050
280	0.5749	0.7582	0.6293	4.684	2.693
290	0.5749	0.7582	0.6293	2.498	1.436
295.276	0.5749	0.7582	0.6293	1.793	1.031

AUTHOR INDEX

Abzug, M. J., 57, 68
Allen, H. J., 94, 307 (2), 333(2)
Amaldi, U., 17, 26
Ashkenas, I. L., 189, 212

Bailey, K., 334
Bloom, M., 334 (2)
Blum, R., 307
Bowen, E. N., 357, 398
Brand, L., 57
Bredt, J., 307
Brigham, G., 283
Buckingham, W. R., 283
Bussard, R. W., 112

Cappellari, J. O., 307, 357
Chambré, P. L., 94
Champion, K. S. W., 403
Chapman, D. R., 333 (2)
Collar, A. R., 57
Crocco, G. A., 283
Culler, G. J., 357

De Lauer, R. D., 112
Detra, R. W., 333
Diehl, W. S., 403
Donovan, A. F., 94
Douwes Dekker, F. E., 283
Duncan, W. J., 57

Eckert, E. R. G., 333
Edelbaum, T., 251
Edwards, A. D., 189
Edwards, R. H., 398
Eggers, A. J., 94, 307 (2), 333 (2)
Ehlers, F. E., 283
Enkenhus, K. R., 307, 333

Fay, J. A., 333
Frazer, R. A., 57
Freeman, H. B., 189
Fried, B. D., 357

Froelich, J. E., 381

Gantmacher, F. R., 41
Garbell, M. A., 283
Gazley, C., 307, 334 (2)
Goldstein, H., 17, 26, 68
Granton, J., 398
Griffith, B. A., 17, 26
Grimminger, G., 403
Gross, G. L., 26, 41

Hall, H. H., 381
Hartnett, J. P., 307
Hayes, W. D., 94, 251
Hidalgo, H., 333
Hildebrand, F. B., 17
Hodge, J., 112
Hoerner, S., 94

Ivey, H. R., 357, 398

Katzen, E. D., 307
Kelber, C. C., 283
Kettle, D. J., 283
Kivel, B., 334
Klein, H., 41
Kuethe, A. M., 41

Lanchester, F. W., 271
Langley Research Center, Staff of, 251
Lass, H., 17
Lausetti, A., 189, 212
Lawden, D. F., 357
Lawrence, H. R., 94
Lean, D., 283
Lebedev, V. B., 251
Lees, L., 334
Levi-Civita, T., 17, 26
Levin, L. M., 41
Linnell, R. D., 307
Lippisch, A., 189, 212, 398
Ludwig, R., 57, 68

Lusty, A. H., 252

Malina, F. J., 307, 358, 381, 398
Mattioli, E., 41
Meyerhoff, L., 283
Meyerhoff, S., 283
Miele, A., 41, 57, 68, 148 (2), 189 (3),
    212, 252 (3), 283, 307 (2), 357,
    398
Minzner, R. A., 403
Moe, M. M., 307
Moyal, J. E., 357

National Bureau of Standards, 307
Neice, S. E., 94, 307, 333
Newton, R. R., 26, 41, 357
Nielsen, J. N., 94

Oborny, L. F., 357, 398
Oswald, W. B., 80

Page, R. K., 189
Perlis, S., 57
Phillips, F. C., 148
Phillips, H. B., 17
Pond, H. L., 403
Prandtl, L., 41
Probstein, R. F., 94
Puckett, A. E., 398

Riddell, F. R., 333
Rogerson, G. E., 283
Rosser, J. B., 26, 41

Sänger, E., 307

Santangelo, G., 189 (3), 212
Scala, S. M., 334
Schaaf, S. A., 94
Schetzer, J. D., 41
Schulz, W., 57, 68
Schurmann, E. E. H., 381
Sibulkin, M., 334
Smith, A. M. O., 307, 398
Staff of the Langley Research Center,
    251
Stewart, C. E., 398
Struble, R. E., 398
Summerfield, M., 358, 381
Sutton, G. P., 41, 112
Synge, J. L., 17, 26

Tietjens, O. G., 41
Turnacliff, R. D., 307

Van Every, K. E., 94
Vertregt, M., 381 (2)
Von Kármán, T., 94

Warden, R. V., 307
Warfield, C. N., 403
Weatherston, R. C., 41
Whitcomb, R. T., 83
Wick, B. H., 334
Wyatt, D. M. D., 41

Yoshikawa, K. K., 334
Young, W. M., 283

Zambelli, E. D., 381
Zucrow, M. J., 112

SUBJECT INDEX

Ablative system, 314
Absolute, acceleration, 14
  motion, 14
  reference frame, 18
  velocity, 14
Acceleration, 9
  absolute, 14
  Coriolis, 15
  relative, 15
  transport, 15, 36
Acceleration components, 9, 16
  normal or centripetal, 9
  radial, 16
  tangential, 9
  transversal, 16
Acceleration factor, 138, 177, 247
Aerodynamic characteristics, 69
  ballistic missile, 87
  hypervelocity glider, 90
  sphere in free molecular flow, 92
  subsonic aircraft, 78
  supersonic aircraft, 83
  transonic aircraft, 80
Aerodynamic efficiency, 73
  ratio, 152, 217
Aerodynamic force, jet-powered
  vehicle, 38, 40
  rocket vehicle, 33, 37
Aerodynamic force components, drag,
  49, 69
  lift, 49, 69
  side force, 49, 69
Aerodynamic heating, 308
  ballistic missile, 315
  glide vehicle, 323
  skip vehicle, 325
Aerodynamic heating limit, 145
Aerodynamic moment, 33
Aerostatic equation, 399
Air-breathing propulsion systems, 100
  ramjet, 100
  ramrocket, 109

  turbofan, 107
  turbojet, 103
  turbojet with afterburner, 105
  turboramjet, 108
Aircraft performance (nonsteady), 257
  gliding flight, 258, 262
  powered flight, 264, 268
  rocket flight, 390
  take-off and landing, 274
Aircraft performance (quasi-steady),
  117
  arbitrary polar, 190
  compressibility effects, 213
  constant power, 184, 207
  constant thrust, 149, 190
  flight in a horizontal plane, 139,
    179, 202, 238
  flight in a vertical plane, 118, 149,
    190, 215
  parabolic polar, 149
  subsonic, 149, 190, 213
  supersonic, 213, 245
Air-to-air missile, 383
Angle of, attack (aircraft), 46
  attack (thrust), 49
  bank, 139, 180, 203, 239
  latitude, 60
  longitude, 60
  sideslip (aircraft), 46
  sideslip (thrust), 49
  velocity pitch, 45
  velocity roll, 45
  velocity yaw, 45
Angular, momentum, 21
  relationships between coordinate
    systems, 44, 60
  velocity, 11, 16
Area rule, 83
Ascent of a sounding rocket, 285, 387
Aspect ratio, 79
Atmosphere, 399
  constant gravity, 403

exponential, 402
isothermal, 403
standard or model, 400

Ballistic factor, 289
Ballistic missile, aerodynamic
    characteristics, 87
aerodynamic heating, 315
reentry, 288
Base drag, 88
Best endurance, level flight, 127, 160,
    198, 227
quasi-level flight, 129, 168, 199, 229
Best range, level flight, 127, 160, 198,
    227
quasi-level flight, 129, 168, 199, 229
Binormal vector, 8
Bluntness ratio, 317, 324, 327
Body axes system, 21, 28, 43, 58
Boundary layer, 72, 309
Buffet, limit, 144
lift coefficient, 76
Burnout velocity, 340, 360

Ceiling, 125, 158, 196, 224
Center of mass, 22
Centripetal acceleration, 9
Climb economy factor, 233
Climbing flight, 132
arbitrary polar, 200
compressibility effects, 233, 247
nonsteady, 391
parabolic polar, 171
Coefficient of, drag, 70
friction, 275
friction drag, 74
induced drag, 75
lift, 70
lift at buffeting, 76
lift at lift-off, 274
lift at stall, 73, 194, 274
lift at touchdown, 274
peak drag, 83
pressure, 70
pressure drag, 74
side force, 70
skin friction, 70

skin friction (equivalent), 312
specific fuel consumption, 100
specific propellant consumption, 97
thrust, 97, 100
thrust (modified), 219
wave drag, 84
zero-lift drag, 75
Conservative paths, 268
constant lift coefficient, 271
constant load factor, 269
Continuum flow, 71, 72
Control variables, 51
Convective heating, 309
laminar stagnation point, 311
turbulent sonic point, 311
wetted area, 312
Cooling systems, 313
ablative system, 314
heat exchanger, 313
heat sink, 313
mass transfer system, 314
radiant shield, 314
Coordinate systems, 42, 58
body axes, 43, 58
curvilinear ground system, 59
Earth axes, 59
for flight over a flat Earth, 42
for flight over a spherical Earth, 58
ground axes, 43
local horizon, 43, 60
wind axes, 43, 58
Coriolis, acceleration, 15, 36, 64
force, 31, 68
moment, 32
Corrected, fuel-to-air ratio, 102
rotor speed, 104
Critical Mach numbers, 80, 84
Critical points, ballistic reentry, 321
skipping path, 329
Cruise-climb, 131, 169, 199, 233, 246
Curvature, 7
Curvilinear ground system, 59

Degrees of freedom, 51
Derivative, local, 30
logarithmic, 193, 218
substantial, 23, 29

Drag, 49, 69
  coefficient, 70
  factor, 299
  function, 93, 118, 132, 150, 216
  polar, 72, 75, 77
  ratio, 152, 217
Drag components, 74
  base drag, 88
  form drag, 78
  friction drag, 74
  induced drag, 74
  pressure drag, 74
  vortex drag, 74
  wave drag, 81
  zero-lift drag, 74
Dynamic pressure, 70
Dynamic relationships, flat Earth, 49
  spherical Earth, 64
Dynamics, 18
  constant mass system, 19
  jet-powered vehicle, 37
  material point, 18
  rigid body, 21
  rocket vehicle, 23, 27
  rotor mounted on a rigid body, 22
  variable mass system, 23

Earth axes system, 59
Endurance, climbing flight, 136
  gliding flight, 123, 154, 194, 222,
    261, 263, 297
  level flight, 126, 159, 197, 225, 261,
    266
  quasi-level flight, 129, 167, 199, 228
Endurance factor, 229
Engine, control parameter, 50, 110
  limits, 145
  performance (see Propulsion
    systems)
Equation of forces, 19, 21
  rigid body, 22
  rocket vehicle, 24, 31, 33, 35, 36
  rotor mounted on a rigid body, 22
Equation of moments, 20, 21
  rigid body, 22
  rocket vehicle, 31, 33
  rotor mounted on a rigid body, 23

Equations of motion over a flat
    Earth, 42, 48–50
  climbing flight, 132, 171, 200, 233
  flight in a horizontal plane, 54, 139,
    179, 202, 238
  flight in a vertical plane, 52, 118,
    149, 190, 215
  gliding flight, 120, 152, 192, 219
  level flight, 124, 157, 195, 222
  quasi-level flight, 128, 167, 198, 227
Equations of motion over a spherical
    Earth, 36, 58, 64–65
  flight in a great-circle plane, 66
Equation of state, 399
Equivalent, exit velocity, 336, 382
  skin-friction coefficient, 312
Euler, constant, 286
  force equations, 25
  moment equations, 25
Evolutory velocity, 46, 63
  turning flight, 139, 180, 203, 239
Excess, power, 133
  thrust, 133
Exponential atmosphere, 402
Exponential-integral function, 286, 293

Fastest climb, 135, 173, 200, 235
Fixed Stars, 18
Flattest glide, 121, 153, 192, 221
Flight in a horizontal plane, 139
  arbitrary polar, 202
  compressibility effects, 238
  parabolic polar, 179
Flight in a vertical plane (nonsteady),
    aircraft, 257, 390
  hypervelocity vehicles, 284, 308
  rocket vehicles, 335, 358, 382
Flight in a vertical plane (quasi-
    steady), 118, 149, 190, 215
  climbing flight, 132, 171, 200, 233
  gliding flight, 120, 152, 192, 219
  level flight, 124, 157, 195, 222
  quasi-level flight, 128, 167, 198, 227
Flight limitations, 143
  aerodynamic heating limit, 145
  buffet limit, 144
  engine limits, 145

gust load limit, 144
sonic boom limit, 144
stalling limit, 144
Flight over a flat Earth, 42
coordinate systems, 42
dynamic relationships, 49
kinematic relationships, 48
motion in a horizontal plane, 54
motion in a vertical plane, 52
Flight over a spherical Earth, 58
coordinate systems, 58
dynamic relationships, 64
kinematic relationships, 64
motion in a great-circle plane, 66
Flow regimes, continuum, 71, 72
free molecular, 71, 90
hypersonic, 72, 87
Newtonian, 87, 90
subsonic, 72, 78
supersonic, 72, 84
transition, 71
transonic, 72, 81, 83
Force, acting on a rocket in flight, 32
aerodynamic, 33, 37, 38, 40
Coriolis, 31, 68
due to the unsteadiness of the
relative motion, 31
friction, 275
reactive, 25, 31
Form drag, 78
Free molecular flow, 71, 90
Friction, coefficient, 275
drag, 74
drag coefficient, 74
force, 275
Fuel consumed per unit, increase of
altitude, 133
time, 118
Fuel-to-air ratio, 100
corrected, 102
Fuel-to-weight ratio, 161, 198, 232
Fundamental, meridian, 59
parallel, 59

Geopotential, 402
altitude, 400
Glide angle, 120, 153, 192, 220

Glide vehicle, aerodynamic
characteristics, 90
aerodynamic heating, 323
reentry, 296
Glide with minimum sinking speed,
122, 153, 192, 221
Gliding flight (nonsteady), constant
altitude, 258
constant angle of attack, 262, 296
Gliding flight (quasi-steady), 120
arbitrary polar, 192
compressibility effects, 219
parabolic polar, 152
Gravity turn, 343
Ground, axes system, 43
interference effects, 277
Gust load limit, 144
Gyroscopic moment, 23

Heat exchanger, 313
Heat-sink system, 313
Heat transfer, 308
convection, 309
protection and cooling, 313
radiation, 312
Hybrid propulsion systems, 95
ramrocket, 109
turboramjet, 108
Hypersonic flow, 72, 87
Hypervelocity vehicles, 87, 284, 308
ballistic missile, 87, 288, 315
glide vehicle, 90, 296, 323
skip vehicle, 297, 325
sounding rocket, 285, 387

Induced drag, 74
coefficient, 75
Infinite-stage rocket, 367
Integral performance, 117, 119, 142
Interference effects, 78, 83, 277
Isothermal atmosphere, 403

Jet engine (*see* Propulsion systems)
Jet-powered vehicle, aerodynamic
force, 38, 40
performance, 117, 149, 190, 213, 257
thrust, 38, 100

Kinematic relationships, flat Earth, 48
    spherical Earth, 64
Kinematics, 5
    angular motion, 9
    motion of a point, 8
    relative motion, 14
    rigid body, 12
Kinetic energy correction, 137, 177, 247
Knudsen number, 71

Laminar stagnation point, 311
Landing, 274
Latitude, 60
Level flight, 124
    arbitrary polar, 195
    compressibility effects, 222, 246
    nonsteady, 258, 264
    parabolic polar, 157
Lewis number, 310
Lift, 49, 69
    coefficient, 70
    factor, 299
Lift-off velocity, 224
Lift-to-drag ratio, 73
Limiting velocity (rocket vehicle), 361, 367, 374, 378
Linear momentum, 20, 21
Liquid propellant rocket, 27, 96
Load factor, flight in a horizontal plane, 140, 180, 203, 239
    flight in a vertical plane, 150, 216, 268
Local derivative, 30
Local horizon system, 43, 60
Logarithmic derivative, 193, 218
Longitude, 60

Mach number, 71
    for drag divergence, 81
    for peak drag, 83
    lower critical, 80
    upper critical, 84
Mass flow, 50, 65
    of fuel, 100
    of propellant, 96
Mass-transfer system, 314

Material point, constant mass, 18
    variable mass, 24, 35
Material system, constant mass, 19, 21
    variable mass, 23
Mean free path, 71
Meridian, 59
Missile performance (see Ballistic missile)
Model atmosphere, 400
Modified, drag factor, 289
    thrust coefficient, 219
Molecular temperature, 400
Moment, acting on a rocket in flight, 32
    aerodynamic, 33
    Coriolis, 32
    due to the thrust, 33
    due to the unsteadiness of the relative motion, 32
    gyroscopic, 23
    reactive, 32
Momentum, angular, 21
    linear, 20, 21
Most economic climb, 135, 173, 235
Motion, absolute, 14
    relative, 14
    transport, 14
Multiflow propulsion systems, 95
    turbofan, 107
Multistage rockets, 358
    analysis including gravity, 368
    analysis neglecting gravity, 365

Newton's law, 18
Newtonian flow, 87, 90
Normal acceleration, 9
Nuclear rocket, 96
Number of, degrees of freedom, 51
    Knudsen, 71
    Lewis, 310
    Mach, 71
    Nusselt, 310
    Prandtl, 310
    Reynolds, 71
    Stanton, 310
Nusselt number, 310

Osculating plane, 6
Oswald's efficiency factor, 80
Over-all, payload ratio, 362
    propellant mass ratio, 362

Parabolic polar, 75
Parallel, 59
Particle, constant mass, 18
    variable mass, 24, 35
Path inclination, 133, 172, 200, 233
Payload ratio, 359
    over-all, 362
Payload velocity, 360, 365, 371
Peak drag coefficient, 83
Phugoid trajectories, 271
Point performance, 117, 119, 139
Poisson's formulas, 11
Position vector, 6
Power setting, 50, 110
Prandtl number, 310
Pressure, coefficient, 70
    drag, 74
    drag coefficient, 74
Principal normal vector, 7
Principle of action and reaction, 19
Principal trihedral, 8, 53, 55
Propellant mass flow, 96
Propellant mass ratio, 340, 359
    over-all, 362
Propulsion systems, 95
    ramjet, 100
    ramrocket, 109
    rocket, 95
    turbofan, 107
    turbojet, 103
    turbojet with afterburner, 105
    turboramjet, 108

Quasi-level flight, 128
    arbitrary polar, 198
    compressibility effects, 227, 246
    parabolic polar, 167

Radial, acceleration, 16
    velocity, 16
Radiant, heating, 309, 312
    shield, 314

Radius of curvature, 7
    turning flight, 140, 180, 203, 239
Ramjet, 100
Ramrocket, 109
Range, climbing flight, 136
    gliding flight, 123, 154, 194, 222,
        261, 263, 297
    level flight, 126, 159, 197, 225, 261,
        266
    quasi-level flight, 129, 167, 199,
        228, 246
Range factor, 229
Rate of climb, 133, 172, 200, 233
Reactive force, 25, 31
Reactive moment, 32
Reentry, ballistic missile, 288
    glide vehicle, 296
    skip vehicle, 297
Reference frame, absolute, 18
    principal trihedral, 8, 53, 55
    rigidly associated with the Earth,
        35
Relative, acceleration, 15
    motion, 14
    velocity, 15
Reynolds, analogy, 312
    number, 71
Rigid body, 12, 21, 25
    acceleration distribution, 14
    equation of forces, 22, 25
    equation of moments, 22, 25
    velocity distribution, 13
Rocket engine, 95
    liquid propellant, 96
    nuclear, 96
    solid propellant, 96
Rocket performance (multistage, in
        vacuum), 358
    including gravity, 368
    neglecting gravity, 365
Rocket performance (single-stage, in
        air), 382
    air-to-air missile, 383
    rocket-powered aircraft, 390
    sounding rocket, 285, 387
Rocket performance (single-stage, in
        vacuum), 335

constant thrust inclination, 348
gravity turn, 343
performance limitations, 359
vertical flight, 336
Rocket-powered aircraft, 390
constant dynamic pressure climb, 393
constant velocity climb, 391
Rotor mounted on a rigid body, 22
Rotor speed, 104
corrected, 104

Short range nonlifting missile, 383
Side force, 49, 69
coefficient, 70
Sideslip angle, 46
Single-flow propulsion systems, 95
ramjet, 100
rocket, 95
turbojet, 103
turbojet with afterburner, 105
Single-stage rockets, 335, 382
air-to-air, 383
constant thrust inclination, 348
gravity turn, 343
performance limitations, 359
vertical flight, 285, 336, 387
Sinking speed, 120, 153, 192, 220
Skin friction coefficient, 70
Skip vehicle, aerodynamic heating, 325
reentry, 297
Solid propellant rocket, 96
Solidification principle, rocket
vehicles, 32
rotor mounted on a rigid body, 23
Sonic boom limit, 144
Sounding rocket, 285, 387
Specific, fuel consumption, 100
impulse, 97
propellant consumption, 97
Speed of sound, 71
Stalling, lift coefficient, 73, 194, 274
limit, 144
point, 73
speed, 123, 194, 274
Standard atmosphere, 400
Stanton number, 310
State variables, 51

Steepest climb, 133, 173, 200, 235
Stefan-Boltzmann constant, 314
Stress vector, 33
Structural factor, 359, 362
Subsonic aircraft, aerodynamic
characteristics, 78
performance, 149, 190, 213
Subsonic flow, 72, 78
Substantial derivative, 23, 29
Superficial thrust, 393
Supersonic aircraft, aerodynamic
characteristics, 83
performance, 213, 245
Supersonic flow, 72, 84

Take-off, 274
Tangent vector, 6
Tangential acceleration, 9
Theoretical ceiling, 125, 158, 196, 224
Theorem of, angular momentum, 21
composition of accelerations, 15
composition of velocities, 15
continuity, 30
divergence, 30
linear momentum, 20
Thermodynamic cycle (ideal), ramjet,
101
turbofan, 108
turbojet, 103
turbojet with afterburner, 105
Thickness ratio, 78
Thrust, angle of attack, 49
coefficient, 97, 100
control parameter, 50, 110
function, 110, 119
jet-powered vehicle, 38, 100
reversal, 278
rocket vehicle, 33, 37, 40, 96
sideslip angle, 49
Thrust-to-weight ratio, 172, 191, 337,
370, 374
Touchdown velocity, 224
Transition flow, 71
Transonic aircraft, aerodynamic
characteristics, 80
performance, 213
Transonic flow, 72, 81, 83

Transport, acceleration, 15, 36
  motion, 14
  velocity, 15
Transversal, acceleration, 16
  velocity, 16
Turbofan, 107
Turbojet, 103
  with afterburner, 105
Turboramjet, 108
Turbulent sonic point, 311
Turn rate, 139, 180, 203, 239
Turning flight, 139
  arbitrary polar, 202
  compressibility effects, 238
  parabolic polar, 179

Variable-geometry ballistic missile,
  292, 332
Variable mass system, 23
Velocity, 8
  absolute, 14

angular, 11, 16
pitch angle, 45
relative, 15
roll angle, 45
sound, 71
stall, 123, 194, 274
thermal agitation, 91
transport, 15
yaw angle, 45
Velocity component, radial, 16
  transversal, 16
Vortex drag, 74

Wave drag, 81
  coefficient, 84
Weight flow of fuel, 118
Wetted area method, 78
Wind axes system, 43, 58

Zero-lift drag, 74
  coefficient, 75

ABCDE698765432

COMPLETED